MASTERPIECES OF ART

CATALOGUE

OF EUROPEAN PAINTINGS AND

SCULPTURE FROM 1300-1800

Compiled by
GEORGE HENRY McCALL

Under the Editorship of
WILLIAM R. VALENTINER

MASTERPIECES OF ART

NEW YORK WORLD'S FAIR

May to October, 1939

PUBLISHERS PRINTING COMPANY
William Bradford Press
NEW YORK CITY

This catalogue has been set in Weiss type

MASTERPIECES OF ART

Exhibition at the New York World's Fair 1939

Organized by ART ASSOCIATES, INC.
(A Non-Profit Membership Corporation)

President: Alexander Hamilton Rice

Chairman of the Board: Louis S. Levy

Director-General: William R. Valentiner

Secretary: Francisco Borrell

Business Manager: Norman S. Mackie

Treasurer: J. Arthur Leve

EXHIBITION EXECUTIVE COMMITTEE

Chairman: Charles R. Henschel
Millard J. Bloomer, Jr.
Alfred M. Frankfurter
Louis S. Levy
Norman S. Mackie
Alexander Hamilton Rice
William R. Valentiner

Secretary: Perry T. Rathbone

CHAIRMEN OF COMMITTEES

Loan of Paintings and Sculpture: William R. Valentiner

Catalogue and Publicity: Alfred M. Frankfurter

Insurance and Transportation: H. Russell Farjeon

Consultation on Condition of Paintings: Stephen S. Pichetto
Restorer, Metropolitan Museum, N. Y.
William Suhr

Honorary Committee

Mr. George Harold Edgell, *Boston*
Mr. Jacob Epstein, *Baltimore, Md.*
Mr. Max Epstein, *Winnetka, Ill.*
Baroness d'Erlanger, *Paris, France*
Mr. Lyonel Feininger, *New York*
Mr. David Finley, *Washington, D. C.*
Mr. Alfred J. Fisher, *Detroit*
Mr. and Mrs. Charles T. Fisher, *Detroit*
Mr. and Mrs. Edward F. Fisher, *Detroit*
Mr. and Mrs. Fred J. Fisher, *Detroit*
Mr. Lawrence P. Fisher, *Detroit*
Mr. William A. Fisher, *Detroit*
Mr. Edward W. Forbes, *Cambridge, Mass.*
Mr. and Mrs. Edsel B. Ford, *Detroit*
Mr. J. Paul Getty, *New York*
Mrs. Henry Goldman, *New York*
Mr. G. W. Goman, *New York*
Mr. Chas. W. Goodyear, *Buffalo, N. Y.*
Jonkheer A. C. D. de Graeff, *The Hague, Holland*
Dr. G. D. Gratama, *Haarlem, Holland*
Miss Belle da Costa Greene, *New York*
Mr. Maitland F. Griggs, *New York*
Mrs. Daniel Guggenheim, *New York*
Mr. and Mrs. Murry Guggenheim, *New York*
Senator and Mrs. Simon Guggenheim, *New York*
Mr. and Mrs. Solomon R. Guggenheim, *New York*
Mrs. Lillian Henkel Haass, *Grosse Pointe Farms, Mich.*
Mr. D. Hannema, *Rotterdam, Holland*
Mr. Edward S. Harkness, *New York*
Mr. G. Huntington Hartford, *New York*
Mr. and Mrs. Horace Havemeyer, *New York*
Mr. Wm. Randolph Hearst, *San Simeon, Cal.*
Dr. Walter Heil, *San Francisco*
Dr. Rudolf Heinemann, *New York*
Mr. and Mrs. Chas. V. Hickox, *New York*
Dr. Jacob Hirsch, *New York*
Dr. Franz H. Hirschland, *New York*
Mr. Philip Hofer, *Cambridge, Mass.*
Mr. E. B. Hosmer, *Montreal, Canada*
Mr. Archer Huntington, *New York*
Mr. Richard M. Hurd, *New York*
Mrs. Louis F. Hyde, *Glens Falls, New York*
Mr. Albert Kahn, *Detroit*

Mrs. Otto H. Kahn, *New York*
Mr. and Mrs. Ernest Kanzler, *Grosse Pointe Farms, Mich.*
Mr. Nathan Katz, *Dieren, Holland*
Mr. Messmore Kendall, *New York*
Mr. Franz Koenigs, *Amsterdam, Holland*
Mr. Samuel H. Kress, *New York*
Mr. W. M. Fulton Kurtz, *Philadelphia*
Mr. Louis La Beaume, *St. Louis*
M. Paul Lambotte, *Brussels, Belgium*
Mr. Thomas W. Lamont, *New York*
Mrs. Arthur Lehman, *New York*
Governor Herbert H. Lehman, *Albany, N. Y.*
Mr. Philip Lehman, *New York*
Mr. Robert Lehman, *New York*
Mrs. Irma B. Levy, *New York*
Dr. C. J. K. van Aalst, *Hoevelaken, Holland*
Dr. Karl Lilienfeld, *New York*
His Excellency Sir Ronald Lindsay, *Washington, D. C.*
    The British Ambassador to the United States
Mrs. Frank Granger Logan, *Chicago*
His Excellency Dr. A. Loudon, *Washington, D. C.*
    The Dutch Minister to the United States
Mr. Henry McBride, *New York*
Mr. George Henry McCall, *New York*
Mr. John McCormick, *Chicago*
Mr. Henry P. McIlhenny, *Philadelphia*
Mrs. Audrey F. McMahon, *New York*
Dr. Gregorio Marañon, *Paris, France*
Mr. Henri Gabriel Marceau, *Philadelphia*
Dr. W. Martin, *The Hague, Holland*
Prof. Frank Jewett Mather, Jr., *Princeton, New Jersey*
Mr. William G. Mather, *Cleveland, Ohio*
Mr. Adolf Mayer, *New York*
Mr. Everett V. Meeks, *New Haven, Conn.*
Mr. Paul Mellon, *Washington, D. C.*
Mr. Robert B. Meyer, *New York*
Mrs. Clarence Millhiser, *New York*
Mr. William M. Milliken, *Cleveland, Ohio*
Mr. C. Powell Minnigerode, *Washington, D. C.*
Mrs. William H. Moore, *New York*
Signore Antonio Morassi, *Milan, Italy*
Professor Charles Rufus Morey, *Princeton, New Jersey*
Hon. Robert Moses, *New York*

Mrs. John S. Newberry, *Grosse Pointe Farms, Mich.*
Mr. Henry Ringling North, *Sarasota, Florida*
Sir Harry Oakes, Bart., *Nassau, Bahamas*
Mr. Robert Treat Paine, 2nd, *Chestnut Hill, Mass.*
Mr. and Mrs. Clarence Y. Palitz, *New York*
Mr. Parish-Watson, *New York*
Mr. Harold Woodbury Parsons, *New York*
Mr. and Mrs. Charles S. Payson, *Manhasset, Long Island*
Mr. Duncan Phillips, *Washington, D. C.*
Mr. Alfred F. Pillsbury, *Minneapolis*
Mrs. Dan Fellows Platt, *Englewood, New Jersey*
Mr. Russell A. Plimpton, *Minneapolis*
Mr. Reginald H. Poland, *San Diego, Cal.*
Mr. and Mrs. Harold I. Pratt, *New York*
M. L. van Puyvelde, *Brussels, Belgium*
Mr. and Mrs. Robert W. Reford, *Montreal, Canada*
Mrs. Ogden Reid, *New York*
Mr. E. P. Richardson, *Detroit*
Mr. Meyric R. Rogers, *St. Louis*
Mrs. Samuel P. Rotan, *Chestnut Hill, Pa.*
Mr. Arthur Sachs, *New York*
Mr. Paul J. Sachs, *Cambridge, Mass.*
Mr. Homer Saint-Gaudens, *Pittsburgh*
His Excellency Count René Doynel de Saint-Quentin, *Washington, D. C.*
    The French Ambassador to the United States
Mr. Mitchell Samuels, *New York*
Mr. Maurice Bower Saul, *Philadelphia*
Dr. Hans Schaeffer, *New York*
Mr. John M. Schiff, *New York*
Mrs. Leon Schinasi, *New York*
Dr. F. Schmidt-Degener, *Amsterdam, Holland*
Mr. Stevenson Scott, *New York*
Mr. Germain Seligmann, *New York*
M. José Sert, *Paris, France*
Mr. Donald G. Shepard, *Washington, D. C.*
Mr. Walter H. Siple, *Cincinnati*
Mr. Theodore Sizer, *New Haven, Conn.*
Mr. Frank C. Smith, Jr., *Worcester, Mass.*
Mr. James Speyer, *New York*
Mr. Chauncey D. Stillman, *New York*
His Excellency Count Robert van der Straten-Ponthoz, *Washington, D. C.*
    The Belgian Ambassador to the United States
Mrs. Herbert N. Straus, *New York*

Mr. and Mrs. Percy S. Straus, *New York*
Mr. Robert H. Tannahill, *Detroit*
Mr. Myron C. Taylor, *New York*
Mr. John S. Thacher, *Cambridge, Mass.*
Mr. and Mrs. William R. Timken, *New York*
Dr. Antonio Valenti-Mestre, *New York*
Dr. A. van Schendel, *Amsterdam, Holland*
Mr. and Mrs. Michael van Beuren, *Newport, R. J.*
Dr. Lionello Venturi, *Paris, France*
M. Henri Verne, *Paris, France*
Mr. John Walker, 3rd, *Washington, D. C.*
Mr. Edward M. M. Warburg, *New York*
Mrs. Felix M. Warburg, *New York*
Dr. W. Wartmann, *Zürich, Switzerland*
Mr. Gordon Washburn, *Buffalo*
Mr. and Mrs. Edgar B. Whitcomb, *Grosse Pointe Farms, Mich.*
Mr. Joseph E. Widener, *Elkins Park, Pa.*
Mr. Felix Wildenstein, *New York*
M. Georges Wildenstein, *Paris, France*
Mr. Charles F. Williams, *Cincinnati, Ohio*
Mrs. Van Wie Willys, *New York*
Mr. Herbert E. Winlock, *New York*
Mr. Frank P. Wood, *Toronto, Canada*
Mr. and Mrs. Charles H. Worcester, *Chicago*

List of Lenders

Dr. C. J. K. van Aalst Collection, *Hoevelaken, Holland*
Mr. and Mrs. John E. Aldred, *New York*
The Musée Royal, *Antwerp, Belgium*
The Jules S. Bache Collection, *New York*
Mr. LeRoy M. Backus, *San Francisco*
Mr. John Bass, *New York*
Mr. Frederick R. Bay, *New York*
Mrs. Sosthenes Behn, *New York*
Comtesse de la Béraudière, *Paris, France*
Miss Julia Berwind, *New York*
Mr. J. M. B. Beuker, *Heelsum, Holland*
The Ralph Harman Booth Collection, *Grosse Pointe, Mich.*
Mr. and Mrs. Walter O. Briggs, *Detroit*
Estate of Joseph L. Buttenwieser, *New York*
Mr. H. E. ten Cate, *Almelo, Holland*
The Art Institute of Chicago
Cincinnati Art Museum, *Cincinnati, Ohio*
Hon. Oscar B. Cintas, *Havana, Cuba*
Mr. Stephen C. Clark, *New York*
The Cleveland Museum of Art, *Cleveland, Ohio*
Dr. G. H. A. Clowes, *Indianapolis*
Mr. André de Coppet, *New York*
The Chester Dale Collection, *New York*
The Detroit Institute of Arts, *Detroit*
Mrs. Watson B. Dickermann, *Oyster Bay, L. I.*
The Dumbarton Oaks Collection, *Washington, D. C.*
Mr. Charles E. Dunlap, *New York*
Mr. Jacob Epstein, *Baltimore, Md.*
Mr. Alfred J. Fisher, *Detroit*
Mr. and Mrs. Charles T. Fisher, *Detroit*
Mr. and Mrs. Edward F. Fisher, *Detroit*
Mr. and Mrs. Fred J. Fisher, *Detroit*
Mr. Lawrence P. Fisher, *Detroit*
Mr. L. M. Flesh, *New York*
Fogg Art Museum, *Cambridge, Mass.*
Mr. and Mrs. Edsel B. Ford, *Detroit*
Mr. J. Paul Getty, *New York*
Mr. Richard Goetz, *Paris, France*
Mrs. Henry Goldman, *New York*
The William Goldman Collection, *New York*

Dr. Jakob Goldschmidt, *New York*
Mr. Maitland F. Griggs, *New York*
Mrs. Daniel Guggenheim, *New York*
Senator and Mrs. Simon Guggenheim, *New York*
Mr. and Mrs. Solomon R. Guggenheim, *New York*
The F. Gutmann Collection, *Holland*
Mrs. Lillian Henkel Haass, *Grosse Pointe Farms, Mich.*
Mr. Edward S. Harkness, *New York*
Mr. G. Huntington Hartford, *New York*
Mrs. J. C. Hartogs, *Arnhem, Holland*
Mr. Horace Havemeyer, *New York*
The William Randolph Hearst Collection, *New York*
Mrs. Charles R. Henschel, *New York*
Mr. and Mrs. Charles V. Hickox, *New York*
Dr. Franz H. Hirschland, *Harrison, N. Y.*
Mr. Phillip Hofer, *Cambridge, Mass.*
Mr. Richard M. Hurd, *New York*
Mrs. Louis F. Hyde, *Glens Falls, N. Y.*
The John G. Johnson Collection, *Philadelphia*
Kansas City Museum, The William Rockhill Nelson Gallery, *Kansas City*
Mr. and Mrs. Ernest Kanzler, *Grosse Pointe Farms, Mich.*
Mr. Albert Keller, *New York*
Mr. Allan P. Kirby, *New York*
Mr. and Mrs. Paul Klotz, *Pontresina, Switzerland*
Mr. Franz Koenigs, *Amsterdam, Holland*
Mr. Samuel H. Kress, *New York*
Governor Herbert H. Lehman, *Albany*
Mrs. Arthur Lehman, *New York*
Mr. Robert Lehman, *New York*
The Edwin D. Levinson Collection, *New York*
Mrs. I. D. Levy, *New York*
Mr. Louis S. Levy, *New York*
Mr. Carl M. Loeb, *New York*
Mrs. Frank Granger Logan, *Chicago*
The Louvre, *Paris, France*
Mr. Henry P. McIlhenny, *Germantown, Pa.*
Mr. Adolf Mayer, *New York*
The Mellon Collection, National Gallery of Art, *Washington, D. C.*
The Minneapolis Institute of Arts, *Minneapolis*
The Art Association of Montreal
Mrs. William H. Moore, *New York*
Mr. J. Pierpont Morgan, *New York*
Mrs. Stanley Mortimer, *New York*

The National Gallery, *London, England*
The National Gallery of Victoria, *Melbourne, Australia*
Mrs. John S. Newberry, *Grosse Pointe Farms, Mich.*
Mr. Henry Ringling North, *Sarasota, Fla.*
Sir Harry Oakes, Bart., *Nassau, Bahamas*
Mr. Clarence Y. Palitz, *New York*
Mrs. Charles S. Payson, *Manhasset, L. I.*
The Phillips Memorial Gallery, *Washington, D. C.*
Mr. Stephen S. Pichetto, *New York*
Mrs. Dan Fellows Platt, *Englewood, N. J.*
Mr. and Mrs. Harold I. Pratt, *New York*
Mrs. F. F. Prentiss, *Cleveland, Ohio*
Mr. and Mrs. J. Warner Prins, *New York*
Mrs. Johnston L. Redmond, *New York*
Mr. and Mrs. Robert W. Reford, *Montreal, Canada*
Mr. Henry Reichhold, *Birmingham, Mich.*
The Museum of Art, Rhode Island School of Design, *Providence, R. I.*
Dr. Alexander Hamilton Rice, *New York*
The Rijksmuseum, *Amsterdam, Holland*
The Rochester Memorial Art Gallery, *Rochester, N. Y.*
Mr. and Mrs. John D. Rockefeller, Jr., *New York*
President F. D. Roosevelt, *Washington, D. C.*
Mrs. Ernst Rosenfeld, *New York*
Mr. Lessing J. Rosenwald, *Philadelphia*
Mrs. Samuel P. Rotan, *Chestnut Hill, Pa.*
Mr. Arthur Sachs, *New York*
The Paul J. Sachs Collection, *Cambridge, Mass.*
Estate of Henry W. Sage, *New York*
The San Diego Fine Arts Gallery, *San Diego, Cal.*
Dr. Preston Pope Satterwhite, *New York*
Mr. John M. Schiff, *New York*
Mrs. Leon Schinasi, *New York*
Estate of John L. Severance, *Cleveland, Ohio*
Mrs. John W. Simpson, *New York*
Mr. Frank C. Smith, Jr., *Worcester, Mass.*
Mr. James Speyer, *New York*
Mr. Frederick L. Stephens, *New York*
Mr. Chauncey D. Stillman, *New York*
Estate of Edward T. Stotesbury, *Philadelphia*
Mrs. Herbert N. Straus, *New York*
Mrs. Jesse Isidor Straus, *New York*
Mr. and Mrs. Percy S. Straus, *New York*
Mrs. Roger W. Straus, *New York*

List of Lenders ... CONTINUED

Mrs. William R. Timken, *New York*
Mr. W. H. Thompson, *Indianapolis*
Mr. and Mrs. Michael Van Beuren, *Newport, R. J.*
The Wadsworth Atheneum, *Hartford, Conn.*
Mrs. Felix M. Warburg, *New York*
Mr. and Mrs. Edgar B. Whitcomb, *Grosse Pointe Farms, Mich.*
Mrs. Harry Payne Whitney, *New York*
Mr. Joseph E. Widener, *Elkins Park, Pa.*
Mrs. Van Wie Willys, *New York*
Mr. Charles F. Williams, *Cincinnati, Ohio*
Mr. C. Stillman-Mrs. Langbourne M. Williams, Jr., *New York*
Mr. Frank P. Wood, *Toronto, Canada*
Gallery of Fine Arts, Yale University, *New Haven, Conn.*

Architects:

Messrs. Harrison and Fouilhoux, *New York*

General Contractors:

Messrs. Chatfield Bros. and Seeley, *New York*

Executors of Murals:

The Rambush Decorating Co., *New York*

Wall Fabrics:

Mr. B. F. Ruskin, New York

Lighting:

Messrs. Richard Kelly and Chauncey Thompson, *New York*

Landscaping:

Messrs. Lewis and Valentine, *Roslyn, Long Island*

Typographical Designs:

Mr. W. von Eckardt, *New York*

PLAN OF GALLERIES

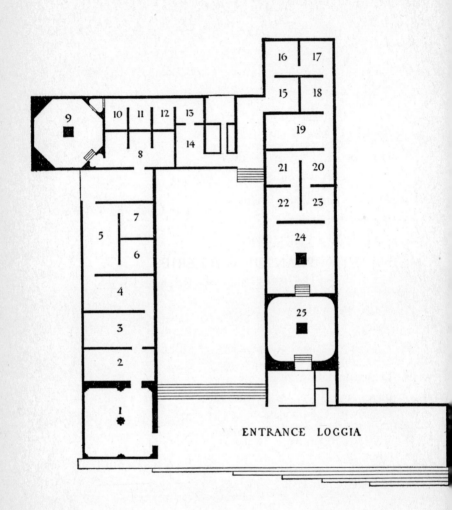

ENTRANCE LOGGIA

PLAN OF GALLERIES

1. Gothic Art, XIVth and XVth Centuries
2. Florentine Painting and Sculpture, XVth Century
3. Umbrian, and North Italian Painting, XVth Century
4. Flemish and Dutch Painting, XVth Century
5. Flemish and Dutch Painting, XVIth Century
6. German and French Painting, XVth and XVIth Centuries
7. Dürer Prints and Drawings
8. Leonardo and School, Raphael and Florentine Painting, XVIth Century
9. Venetian Painting, XVIth Century
10. El Greco
11. Velazquez and Murillo
12. Goya
13. French XVIIth Century
14. Tiepolo, Canaletto and Guardi
15. Rubens
16. Van Dyck and Rubens
17. Van Dyck
18. Frans Hals
19. Rembrandt
20. Van Goyen and Ostade
21. Vermeer, De Hooch and Hobbema
22. Terborch and Ruysdael
23. Jan Steen and Cuyp
24. British Painting, XVIIIth Century
25. French Painting, XVIIIth Century

INTRODUCTION

The present exhibition, arranged in chronological order, offers a panoramic survey of the greatest art epochs in Europe from 1300, at which time the practice of easel painting was established, until about 1800, when in the wake of the French Revolution the foundations of modern art were laid. The exhibition is divided into three sections. The first comprises the art of painting from the fourteenth to the early sixteenth century, beginning with Gothic art mainly in Italy and France, followed by the early Renaissance in the South from Fra Angelico to Botticelli and Giovanni Bellini, and the contemporary art of painting in the North, from Jan van Eyck to Dürer and Holbein. The second section contains paintings of the Italian High Renaissance, of Raphael, Leonardo, Giorgione and Titian and of their contemporaries, and of the Italian Baroque from Caravaggio to Tiepolo and Guardi. It includes the painters of these epochs in France, Claude Lorrain and Poussin, and in Spain from Greco to Velasquez and Goya. In the third section the paintings of the great Flemish and Dutch flowering of the seventeenth century are exhibited, the works of Rubens, and Van Dyck, of Frans Hals, Rembrandt, Vermeer and their contemporaries. This is followed by English and French painting of the eighteenth century, from Hogarth to Lawrence, from Watteau to David.

A selection of sculptures and tapestries is shown together with the paintings, especially in the earlier rooms, not with any intention of completeness in the representation of these arts, but so as to show how closely painting, sculpture and decorative arts were related in the epochs nearest to the Middle Ages.

The majority of the exhibited works of art are loans from American private collections for, most of all, the exhibition is designed to convey an idea of what private collectors in this country have accomplished toward the advancement of art within the short period of one generation. Thanks are due first of all to these collectors, mentioned in the list of lenders, who have so generously contributed to the good of all by the loan of their art treasures.

In addition to art from American collections a number of outstanding masterpieces have been secured from European countries. That this was possible is due to the efforts of the official representatives of these countries in Washington whose names are listed in our committee of honorary members, as well as to the directors of the museums in these different countries. Special acknowledgment must be given to M. Henri Verne, Director General of the Louvre, Sir Kenneth Clark, Director of the National Gallery in London, Mr. F. Schmidt-Degener, Director of the Rijksmuseum in Amsterdam, M. L. van Puyvelde, Director of the Brussels Museum, M. Arthur Cornette, Director of the Antwerp Museum, and Mr. James S. MacDonald, Director of the National Gallery in Melbourne.

Several foreign private collectors have wholeheartedly followed the splendid example of their governments by sending us some of their masterpieces so as to round out the exhibition in those fields less fully represented in American collections. This pertains especially to Dutch seventeenth century art which, because of these extraordinary contributions, is represented in a variety of masters, as never before shown in any exhibition or any museum in this country. In this connection we extend our thanks to such well-known collectors in Holland as Mr. H. E. ten Cate, Dr. C. J. K. van Aalst, Mr. Franz Koenigs, Mr. F. Gutmann, and Mrs. Hartogs. Among the private collectors in neighboring countries to whom we are especially grateful are Mr. R. W. Reford in Montreal, Mr. Frank P. Wood in

Toronto, the Hon. Oscar B. Cintas in Havana and Sir Harry Oakes, Bart., in Nassau.

An exhibition of such importance as the present one could be shown only in a building which, with all the precautionary planning and construction for the safety of the exhibits, combines aesthetic value. The architects, Messrs. Harrison & Fouilhoux, have designed an excellent structure of this type, the inner courtyard walls of which, by virtue of the gift of Mr. and Mrs. Ernest Kanzler of Detroit, could be decorated with murals by one of the leading American painters, Lyonel Feininger.

If, as we hope, real enjoyment and education will emanate from this building and its wonderful contents, it should be remembered by all those who share in this pleasure that it is due mainly to a very small group of public-minded citizens that the difficult task of presenting this loan exhibition has been accomplished. To create it was the original idea of Mr. Louis S. Levy, Chairman of the Board of Directors, who at a time when it seemed that there might be no Old Masters exhibition in the World's Fair, took the matter in hand, interested a sufficient number of private citizens in the undertaking, and with keen executive ability founded the organization of which Dr. Alexander Hamilton Rice became the President. The realization of this plan would not have been possible without the generosity and continuous interest of the Marquis and the Marquise de Cuevas, who made it financially possible to erect and equip the building, to defray the transportation and the insurance costs amounting to a value of thirty million dollars, as well as to obtain the necessary interior decoration. For their generous assistance in this essential, we are also deeply indebted to Mr. and Mrs. Murry Guggenheim, and to Senator and Mrs. Simon Guggenheim.

Those who are acquainted with the leading part taken by the art firms in this country in the formation of the collection will understand that an exhibition formed mostly of loans from American private collections could not have been assembled without their help. Special thanks are due to Mr. Charles R. Henschel, Chairman of the Executive Committee, to Mr. Armand Lowengard, to Messrs. Wildenstein, Germain Seligmann, Mr. Mitchell Samuels, Mr. Paul M. Byk, Mr. Parish Watson, Dr. K. Lilienfeld, Dr. H. Schaeffer, and many others.

The activities of the organizations necessitated by the present loan exhibition were manifold. A special committee, composed of two of the foremost restorers of old masters—Mr. Stephen S. Pichetto and Mr. William Suhr—is constantly engaged with studying the conditions of the paintings while they are on exhibition. Another, headed by Mr. H. R. Farjeon, undertook the complicated insurance problems. The publicity has been admirably managed by Dr. Alfred M. Frankfurter, the Editor of "The Art News", who was assisted by Mr. Robert Washburn. Also the special work of Dr. Frankfurter is the beautifully illustrated souvenir book which, as a supplement, we recommend to the buyers of the catalogue. As business manager, forming at the same time a contact between the architects and the World's Fair organization, Mr. Norman S. Mackie has done invaluable work, as has Mr. John S. Newberry of Detroit in a general capacity. In the compilation of the catalogue splendid work has been done by Mr. George H. McCall, whose knowledge, painstaking research and industry are apparent on every page of this production, in which he was ably assisted by Mr. Edgar T. Stanton. Finally special recognition is due for their untiring efforts both to Miss Joan Shepard, and Mr. Perry T. Rathbone, assistant to the Director and Secretary of the Executive Committee, without whose intelligent and faithful assistance the Director's tasks would have been insurmountable.

W. R. VALENTINER.

June 1939.

CATALOGUE OF PAINTINGS

CATALOGUE OF PAINTINGS

The Names of the Artists are arranged alphabetically.
Pictures illustrated are marked with Plate Number.

ALBERTI, ANTONIO *(Attributed)*

FERRARESE, C. 1390-1439

Born at Ferrara, and migrated to Urbino where he married in 1423 the sister of the painter Matteo Gennari, who might have been his master; he followed the manner of Gentile da Fabriano. He was also active at Città di Castello. His daughter became the mother of the painter Timoteo Viti.

1
6
The Madonna and Child, with Pietro Lardi and St. Maurilius.

Painted before 1431. The Latin inscription on the picture indicates that it was painted for the donor, Pietro Lardi, collector of taxes to Borso d'Este, Duke of Ferrara, during the Episcopacy of Pietro Boiardi, Archbishop of Ferrara (1400-1431), and that the Saint represented is St. Maurilius of Ferrara, his patron.

Panel: 43½ x 42 inches.

LENT BY MRS. ARTHUR LEHMAN, NEW YORK.

COLLECTIONS: The Certosa of Ferrara; Palazzo Costabili, Ferrara; Count A. Trotti.
BIBLIOGRAPHY: A. GUARINI: Compendio historico delle chiese di Ferrara, 1621, p. 392; G. LADERCHI: Descrizione della Quadreria Costabili, 1838, parte I, p. 24; S. REINACH: Répertoire de Peintures, Vol. I, 1905, p. 270, *Illust.*; ANON: Catalogo delle pitture in casa Costabili, 1914, p. 163, *Illust.*, D. ZACCARINI: In L'Arte, Vol. XVII, 1914, p. 170, *Illust.*, A. VENTURI: N. Ital. Painting of the Quattrocento Emilia, n.d. p. 11, *Illust.*, (*As Unknown Ferrarese painter*), R. LONGHI: Officina Ferrarese, 1934, p. 14, *Illust.* (*As Unknown Ferrarese painter contemporary with Alberti*).

ANDREA DEL SARTO

FLORENTINE, 1486-1531

Born in Florence, the son of a tailor, and a pupil of Piero di Cosimo, influenced by Fra Bartolommeo, Leonardo da Vinci, and Michelangelo. He married Lucrezia del Fedi in 1513. He went to Paris, on the invitation of Francis I, in 1518, and returned to Florence the following year, where he remained, having squandered money which the king had entrusted to him for the purchase of works of art. He painted extensively in fresco. Among his pupils were Vasari, Jacopo da Pontormo and Franciabigio.

2
16
Portrait of Lucrezia del Fedi, Wife of the Artist.

Painted about 1513. This is probably the earliest of Andrea's portraits of his wife;

he reproduced her features in his paintings many times, one of the most noted being the *Madonna dell'Arpie*, now in the Uffizi. Other portraits of her are in the Prado, Madrid, and the Berlin Gallery. A copy of the Gerini portrait is in the former convent of S. Servi, now a museum devoted to the memory of Andrea.

Canvas *(transferred)*: 33½ x 24¾ inches.

LENT BY MR. WILLIAM H. THOMPSON, INDIANAPOLIS.

COLLECTION: Marchese Andrea Gerini (1759), in whose Palazzo, in the Via Ricasoli, Florence, it remained until recently.

ENGRAVED in 1759.

BIBLIOGRAPHY: ANON: Raccolta di Stampe rappresentanti i quadri piu scelti de' Signori Marchesi Gerini, Firenze, 1759, No. XXVII, *Illust. with engraving,* E. GRIFI: Saunterings in Florence, 1906, p. 157; G. M. RICHTER: *In* Burl. Mag. Nov. 1938, pp. 191-192, *Illust.*

ANGELICO DA FIESOLE, FRA

FLORENTINE, 1387-1455

Born at Vicchio di Mugello. At the age of twenty he entered the Dominican Monastery at Fiesole, where he came under the influence of the mystic Fra Giovanni Domenici; in his art he was influenced by Lorenzo Monaco and possibly by Masaccio; his pupil was Benozzo Gozzoli. In 1436-1445 he decorated the cloisters, halls and cells of his Monastery of San Marco at Florence with frescoes from the life of Christ. Later he worked in Cortona, Orvieto and Rome, where he died. The greatest religious painter of the Florentine school. He combines a fine color-sense with an exceptional gift for decorative pattern.

3

Pl. 11

The Annunciation.

Two panels: The Archangel Gabriel, and Our Lady Annunciate. Painted between 1430 and 1440.

Panels: Each 14½ x 10 inches.

LENT BY MR. AND MRS. EDSEL B. FORD, DETROIT.

COLLECTIONS: Duke of Hamilton; John Edward Taylor; Charles Sedelmeyer; Lord Duveen of Millbank; Carl W. Hamilton.

EXHIBITIONS: Sedelmeyer Galleries, Paris, 1913; Duveen Galleries, New York, 1924; Detroit Institute of Arts, 1927 and 1933.

BIBLIOGRAPHY: ANON: Catalogue of the Hamilton Palace Collection, 1882, p. 51, No. 356, *Illust.,* C. SEDELMEYER: Paintings by Old Masters, 1913, No. 29, *Illust.,* R. OFFNER: *In* The Arts, 1924, p. 245; W. R. VALENTINER: Catalogue of Early Italian Paintings, Duveen Galleries, 1926, No. 3, *Illust.,* E. SINGLETON: Old World Masters, 1929, p. 32, *Illust.,* R. VAN MARLE: Italian Schools of Painting, Vol. X, 1928, p. 143; B. BERENSON: Italian Pictures, 1932, p. 20 (Ital. edn. 1936, p. 17, *Illust.*); W. HEIL: Old and Modern Masters, Detroit Inst. of Arts, 1927, No. 1, *Illust.,* L. VENTURI: Ital. Paintings in America, 1933, Nos. 176-177, *Illust.*

ANGELICO DA FIESOLE, FRA

FLORENTINE, 1387-1455

4 *Temptation of St. Anthony, Abbot.*

12 Painted about 1437. Related stylistically to the predella panels of the Madonna Altar of San Domenico, Perugia, now in the Vatican and Perugia Galleries. The scene represents St. Anthony fleeing from a heap of gold in his path as a snare of the devil.

Panel: 7½ x 11 inches.

LENT BY MR. PERCY S. STRAUS, NEW YORK.

COLLECTIONS: Wilhelm IV of Prussia; Count von Ingenheim; A. S. Drey; K. W. Bachstitz.
EXHIBITIONS: Bachstitz Gallery, The Hague, 1925; Rijksmuseum, Amsterdam, 1929; Art Institute, Chicago, 1933.
BIBLIOGRAPHY: Bull. of the Bachstitz Gall., 1925, pp. 97-98; *Ibid*, 1929, p. 16, *Illust.*, Art News, June 7, 1930, p. 1, *Illust.*, ANON: Catalogus, Vereenigung van Handelaeren, Rijksmuseum, 1929; F. W. HUDIG: *In* Parnassus, Nov. 1929, p. 19, *Illust.*, B. BERENSON: Ital. Pictures, 1932, p. 22 (It. ed. 1936, p. 19); D. C. RICH: Paintings and Sculpture, Art Inst. Chicago, 1933, p. 13, No. 81.

BARONZIO, GIOVANNI

RIMINESE, 1330?-1362?

Giovanni Baronzio da Rimini was a pupil of some local Byzantine; a follower of Cavallini; and the successful propagator of Giottesque art in Romagna; his only dated works are those of 1344 and 1345, but he must have been painting much before and after those years. He lived in the Marches, and mention of his tomb in the Tempio Malatestiano at Rimini as being of 1362 indicates that he must have died about that year. His frescoes still exist in various churches in Pomposa, Ravenna, and Rimini.

5 *Adoration of the Magi.*

Van Marle dates this picture considerably earlier than 1344.

Panel: 24 x 24 inches.

LENT BY THE SAMUEL H. KRESS FOUNDATION,
ART COLLECTION, NEW YORK.

COLLECTIONS: Captain Langton Douglas; Mrs. Otto H. Kahn; Lord Duveen of Millbank.
BIBLIOGRAPHY: W. R. VALENTINER: Unknown Masterpieces (Comment by R. van Marle), 1930, No. 1, *Illust.*, L. VENTURI: Italian Paintings in Amer., 1933, No. 115, *Illust.*, B. BERENSON: Ital. Pictures, 1932, p. 44 (Ital. Edn., 1936, p. 37).

BARTOLOMMEO VENETO

LOMBARDO-VENETIAN, ACTIVE 1502—AFTER 1530

Pupil of Giovanni Bellini along with Previtali and Francesco di Simone da S. Croce;

influenced by Solario and Boltraffio. In 1506-08 he worked at Ferrara for Lucrezia Borgia; after 1510 he worked in Milan for Maximilian Sforza. His last dated portrait, now in the Uffizi, was painted in 1555. While he appears to be a rather weak Bellini follower in his religious paintings, he is one of the finest portrait painters of North Italy, especially during his Milanese period.

6 Portrait of a Young Man.

Painted during the artist's Milanese period, between 1510-15.

Panel: 27¾ x 20¼ inches.

LENT BY MR. PERCY S. STRAUS, NEW YORK.

COLLECTIONS: Casa Mayno, Milan; Robert Stayner, Holford; Sir George Lindsay Holford; Thomas Agnew and Sons; Mrs. Edwin S. Bayer, Comtesse Sala; Arnold Seligmann, Rey and Co.
EXHIBITIONS: Royal Academy, London, 1893; New Gallery, London, 1893-94; Burlington Fine Arts Club, London, 1912 and 1921-22; Agnew Galleries, New York, 1927.
BIBLIOGRAPHY: G. F. WAAGEN: Treasures of Art, Vol. II, 1854, p. 107; ANON: Early Ital. Exhn. Folio, New Gallery, London, 1894, No. 253, Jllust., B. BERENSON: Venetian Painters, 1897, p. 81; A. VENTURI: In L'Arte, Vol. II, 1899, p. 454, Jllust., IDEM: Jn Galleria Crespi in Milano, 1900, pp. 89-91, Jllust., P. D'ACHIARDI: Jn Thieme-Becker's Lexikon, Vol. II, 1908, p. 579; ANON: Early Venetian Pictures, Burl. F. A. Club, 1912, p. 34, No. 32, Jllust., CROWE AND CAVALCASELLE: Painting in N. Italy, Ed. by T. Borenius, Vol. I, 1912, p. 300; A. VENTURI: Storia dell'Arte Ital. Vol. VII, 4, 1915, p. 698; S. REINACH: Répertoire, Vol. IV, 1918, p. 93, Jllust., ANON: Catalogue of Pictures, Holford Colln., Burl. F. A. Club, 1921-22, p. 15, No. 96, Jllust., R. H. BENSON: The Holford Collection, 1924, p. 50, No. 24, Jllust., S. DE RICCI: Jn Gaz. des B. Arts, Vol. LXVII, 1924, p. 39; ANON: Venetian School Exhibition, Agnew Gall. N. Y., 1927; E. MICHALSKI: Jn Zeitsch. für Bild. Kunst. Vol. LXI, 1927, p. 301, Jllust., A. L. MAYER: Jn Pantheon, June 1928, p. 571, Jllust., F. J. MATHER: Jn The Arts, Jan. 1929, p. 20, Jllust., B. BERENSON: Ital. Pictures, 1932, p. 52 (Ital. Edn., 1936, p. 44).

BARTOLOMMEO VENETO

VENETIAN, ACTIVE 1502-AFTER 1530

7 Maximilian Sforza, Duke of Milan (presumed).

Pl. 28

The two figures in the landscape are copied from a woodcut by Dürer. Massimiliano Sforza, born 1490, was the eldest son of Lodovico il Moro, and like his father, was exiled from Milan by the French. He was taken to France in 1515, and lived there until his death in 1535.

Panel: 30¼ x 23 inches.

LENT BY MR. SAMUEL H. KRESS, NEW YORK.

COLLECTIONS: Palazza Sforza, Milan; Casa Perego, Milan; Benigno Crespi; Henry Goldman; Lord Duveen of Millbank.
EXHIBITIONS: Metropolitan Museum of Art, New York, 1920; Royal Academy, London, 1930; California Palace of the Legion of Honor, San Francisco, 1938.
BIBLIOGRAPHY: G. FRIZZONI: Jn Arch. Storico dell'Arte, 1891, p. 284; A. VENTURI: Jn L'Arte, Vol. II, 1899, p. 342; IDEM: La Galleria Crespi in Milano, 1900, p. 81, Jllust., F. HERMANIN: Jn

L'Arte, Vol. III, 1900, pp. 155-157, *Illust.*, F. D'ACHIARDI: *In* Thieme-Becker's Lexikon, Vol. II, 1908, p. 579; J. BURCKHARDT: *In* Der Cicerone, Vol. III, 1910, p. 796; CROWE AND CAVALCASELLE: Hist. of Painting in N. Italy, Vol. II, 1912, pp. 384-385; A. VENTURI: Storia dell'Arte Ital., Vol. III, 5, 1915, p. 698, *Illust.*, B. BERENSON: Venetian Paintings in Amer., 1916, p. 260; W. R. VALENTINER: The Henry Goldman Collection, New York, 1922, No. 4, *Illust.*, A. L. MAYER: *In* Pantheon, Dec. 1928, p. 72, *Illust.*, E. SINGLETON: Old World Masters, 1929, p. 149, *Illust.*, LORD BALNIEL AND K. CLARK: Cat. Exh. Italian Art, Royal Acad., London, 1930, No. 342; L. VENTURI: Ital. Paintings in America, Vol. III, 1933, No. 476, *Illust.*, B. BERENSON: Ital. Pictures, 1932, p. 52, (Ital. Edn., 1936, p. 44, *Illust.*); H. TIETZE: Meisterw. Europ. Malerei, 1935, p. 329, *Illust.*, W. HEIL: Venetian Paintings, Cal. Pal. of the Legion of Honor, San Francisco, 1938, No. 3, *Illust. in color*, A. M. FRANKFURTER: *In* Art News, Mar. 1938, *Illust. in color*.

BELLINI, GIOVANNI

VENETIAN, 1430?-1516

The younger brother of Gentile Bellini, and a pupil of his father, Jacopo Bellini; influenced by his brother-in-law, Mantegna, and later by Antonello da Messina. Was the greatest Venetian painter of the fifteenth century, combining deep religious sentiment with rich imagination and an unusual color-sense. He was also a master of portraiture and became, especially in later life, interested in allegorical and mythological subjects. His powers remained undiminished until his eighties. As a septuagenarian he painted several "Allegories", now at Florence and Venice, and the "Portrait of Doge Loredano" in the National Gallery, London. Among his pupils were Titian and Giorgione.

8

The Madonna and Child.

23 Executed in the middle period of the artist, about 1475-1480. Workshop copies in the Academia Carrara and formerly Collection G. von Mallmann, Berlin. This picture was reproduced in miniature by David Teniers the Younger (1610-1690) in one of his noted paintings (now in the Brussels Museum) of the Archduke Leopold William's Picture Gallery in the Ducal Palace, Brussels, in the Inventory of which it was recorded under No. 274.

Panel: 28½ x 21½ inches.

LENT BY THE RALPH HARMAN BOOTH COLLECTION, DETROIT.

COLLECTIONS: Archduke Leopold William of Austria; Julius Böhler.

EXHIBITIONS: Detroit Institute of Art, 1923 and 1927; Metropolitan Museum of Art, New York, 1923.

BIBLIOGRAPHY: T. V. FRIMMEL: Kleine Galeriestudien, Vol. III, 1893; B. BERENSON: The Study and Criticism of Italian Art, Vol. III, 1916, p. 95; W. R. VALENTINER: *In* Bulletin, Detroit Inst. of Arts, March 1923, p. 54, *Illust.*, R. POLAND: *In* Art and Archeology, Vol. XVII, 1924, No. 3; A. VENTURI: Studi dal Vero, 1927, p. 238, *Illust.*, G. GRONAU: Giovanni Bellini, 1930, p. 113, *Illust.*, L. VENTURI: Italian Paintings in America, 1933, No. 392, *Illust.*, B. BERENSON: Italian Pictures of the Renaissance, 1932, p. 70; R. VAN MARLE: Italian Schools of Painting, Vol. XVII, 1935, p. 209; L. DUSSLER: Giovanni Bellini, 1935, p. 145; C. GAMBA: Giovanni Bellini, 1937, p. 207, *Illust.*

BELLINI, GIOVANNI

VENETIAN, 1430?-1516

9 *Madonna and Child.*

Pl. 23 Signed: *Joannes Bellinus.* Painted about 1488. One of the finest Madonna compositions of the master, in an unusually good state of preservation.

Panel: 30¼ x 23 inches.

LENT BY MRS. VAN WIE WILLYS, NEW YORK.

COLLECTIONS: Sir George Campbell of Garscube; Lord Duveen of Millbank; John N. Willys.

EXHIBITION: Reinhardt Galleries, New York, 1915; Metropolitan Museum of Art, New York, 1920; Knoedler Galleries, New York, 1929.

BIBLIOGRAPHY: B. BERENSON: *Jn* Art in Amer., June 1916, p. 204, *Jllust.,* IDEM: Venetian Painting in Amer., 1916, pp. 92 *et seq., Jllust.,* w. ROBERTS: Catalogue raisonné of the John N. Willys Colln., New York, 1917; W. M. IVINS: Ital. Paintings, Fiftieth Anniv. Exn. Metropolitan Mus., N. Y., July 1920, p. 160; G. FOGOLARI: *Jn* Rass. d'Arte, May 1920, p. 120, *Jllust.,* R. PLINT: *Jn* International Studio, Feb. 1925, pp. 363-366, *Jllust.,* ANON: Exhb. of Primitives, Knoedler Gall., 1929, No. 4; G. GRONAU: Giovanni Bellini (Klas. d. K.), 1930, p. 131, *Jllust.,* B. BERENSON: Ital. Pictures, 1932, p. 72 (Ital. Edn., 1936, p. 62); L. VENTURI: Ital. Paintings in Amer., 1933, No. 391, *Jllust.,* R. VAN MARLE: Ital. Schools, Vol. XV, 1934, p. 560, Vol. XVII, 1935, pp. 274, 294; L. DÜSSLER: Giovanni Bellini, 1935, p. 143; C. GAMBA: Giovanni Bellini, 1937, p. 105, *Jllust.*

BELLINI, GIOVANNI

VENETIAN, 1430?-1516

10 *Two Venetian Gentlemen.*

Painted during the master's late period. A somewhat similar double portrait, possibly representing the same models with the addition of a landscape background, is in the Louvre, Paris.

Canvas: 17¾ x 24½ inches.

LENT BY MR. PERCY S. STRAUS, NEW YORK.

COLLECTIONS: Edward Solly; Kaiser Friedrich Museum, Berlin; Achillito Chiesa.

BIBLIOGRAPHY: G. GRONAU: Gemäldegalerie der Kgl. Mus. Berlin, 1905, p. 41; G. LUDWIG: *Jn* Berlin Jahrbuch, Beiheft, Vol. XXVI, 1905, p. 73; H. POSSE: Gemäldegalerie d. Kaiser-Friedrich-Museums, 1909, p. 117; 1913, p. 127, *Jllust.,* CROWE AND CAVALCASELLE: Hist. of Painting in N. Italy, Vol. I, 1912, pp. 134, 135; SIR C. PHILLIPS: *Jn* Burl. Mag. Dec. 1913, pp. 157-158, *Jllust.* (attributed to *Cariani*); S. DE RICCI: Peintures du Louvre, 1913, p. 17; B. BERENSON: Venetian Painting in Amer., 1916, p. 261; G. DE NICOLA: Collection of Achillito Chiesa, Milan, 1925, No. 56, *Jllust.,* B. BERENSON: Ital. Pictures, 1932, p. 72; C. GAMBA: Giovanni Bellini, 1937, p. 174; M. VAUGHAN: *Jn* "Parnassus" May 1939, p. 7, *Jllust.*

BELLINI, JACOPO

VENETIAN, 1424-1470

Born in Venice. Father of Giovanni and Gentile Bellini, the latter being named after Gentile da Fabriano, under whom Jacopo studied. Influenced by Masolino, Castagno, Lamberti, and other Florentines. Founder of the great Bellini tradition which dominated Venetian painting throughout the XV Century. Worked in Verona, Ferrara, and Venice. His daughter Nicolosia married Andrea Mantegna in 1454. A great many of his drawings are preserved (mostly in the Louvre), but his paintings are very rare.

11 *The Madonna and Child.*

Painted during the artist's early period.

Panel: 34½ x 24¾ inches.

LENT BY MRS. JESSE ISIDOR STRAUS, NEW YORK.

EXHIBITION: California Palace of the Legion of Honor, San Francisco, 1938.

BIBLIOGRAPHY: L. VENTURI: *In* L'Arte, March, 1903, p. 180, *Illust.*, B. BERENSON: Italian Pictures, 1932, p. 75, (Ital. edn., 1936, p. 65, *Illust.*); L. VENTURI: Ital. Painting in Amer., Vol. II, 1933, No. 333, *Illust.*, R. VAN MARLE: Ital. Schools, Vol. XVII, 1935, pp. 105-106, *Illust.*, W. HEIL: Exhn. of Venetian Painting, Calif. Palace of the Legion of Honor, San Francisco, 1938, No. 9, *Illust.*, ANON: *In* Art News, Supplement, Mar. 26, 1938, *Illust.*

BELLOTTO, BERNARDO

VENETIAN, 1724-1780

Born in Venice; a nephew and pupil of Giovanni Antonio da Canale, also called Canaletto (1697-1768), which has often been the cause of their paintings being confused, particularly on account of the similarity of their works. While still young he accompanied his uncle to Rome, and in 1745 went to Dresden where he became a member of the Academy, and was known as Count Bellotto, there being over thirty of his paintings in the Dresden Gallery. He afterwards worked at Warsaw, Poland, where he died.

2 *The Lock at Dolo, near Venice.*

Canvas: 29 x 42¾ inches.

LENT BY THE GALLERY OF FINE ARTS, YALE UNIVERSITY,

NEW HAVEN, CONN.

COLLECTION: Duncan Phillips.

EXHIBITIONS: Yale University, since 1929; Springfield Museum, 1933; Cleveland Museum, 1936; California Palace of the Legion of Honor, San Francisco, 1938.

BIBLIOGRAPHY: D. PHILLIPS: A Collection in the making, 1926, p. 18, *Illust.*, T. SIZER: *In* Bulletin, Yale University, Vol. 3, 1929, p. 61, *Illust.*, E. V. MEEKS: School of Fine Arts Handbook, Yale University, 1931, p. 34, *Illust.*, T. H. PARKER: Catalogue, Springfield Museum Opening Exhibition, 1933, p. 27, No. 70, *Illust.*, H. S. FRANCIS: Catalogue, Great Lakes Exposition, Cleveland Museum, 1936, pp. 86 and 87, No. 213; T. C. HOWE: Catalogue of Venetian Paintings, Calif. Pal. Legion of Honor, San Francisco, 1938, No. 11, *Illust.*

BLANCHARD, JACQUES

FRENCH, 1600-1638

Born in Paris. A pupil of his uncle Nicolas Bollery, and worked from 1621 until 1624 with Horace Leblanc, a painter at Lyons in the service of the Duke of Angoulême. He then travelled to Venice, where he decorated the country mansion of a local nobleman. After two years he worked for the Duke of Savoy in Turin and from there went back to Lyons. Returning to Paris, he became a member of the Academy in 1628. Renowned as a colorist, he was known among his contemporaries as "the Titian of France". Very few portraits are known by him; a mythological painting, representing Angelique and Medor, is in the Metropolitan Museum.

13 *Portrait of a Young Cavalier.*

Signed and dated 1631.

Panel: 29½ x 23 inches.

LENT BY MRS. JOHN S. NEWBERRY, DETROIT.

COLLECTION: Colin Agnew.
EXHIBITIONS: Seventeenth Century French Painting, Detroit Institute of Arts, 1937.
BIBLIOGRAPHY: W. R. VALENTINER: *In* Bulletin of the Detroit Institute of Arts, March 1937, p. 100, *Illust.*

BOLTRAFFIO, GIOVANNI ANTONIO

MILANESE, 1467-1516

A pupil in Leonardo's studio from boyhood, he became one of his most ardent disciples; he sought with all reverence to follow the precepts and imbibe the spirit of his great master, but his original personality saved him from becoming a mere imitator. Although he is excellent in some of his altarpieces and smaller Madonna paintings, his portraits belong to the most fascinating paintings of the Milanese school.

14 *Portrait of a Youth.*

Pl. 25

Panel: 18½ x 13¾ inches.

According to De Hévesy the youth is Girolamo Casio, friend of Boltraffio, who painted him several times.

LENT BY THE RALPH HARMAN BOOTH COLLECTION, DETROIT.

COLLECTIONS: Baron Gustave de Rothschild; Sir Philip Sassoon; Lord Duveen of Millbank.
EXHIBITIONS: Detroit Institute of Arts, 1926 and 1927; Royal Academy, London, 1930; Chicago Art Institute, 1933; Detroit Institute of Arts, 1933.
BIBLIOGRAPHY: C. HOLMES: *In* Burl. Mag., Sept. 1921, p. 107, *Illust.*, W. R. VALENTINER: Loan Exhibition Catalogues, Detroit Inst. of Arts, 1926, No. 9, and 1927, No. 7, *Illust.*, W. SUIDA: Leonardo und sein Kreis, 1929, pp. 191, 287, *Illust.*, K. CLARK: Exhibition of Italian Art, Royal Academy, London, 1930, No. 310, *Illust.*, T. BORENIUS: *In* Pantheon, Feb. 1930, p. 89, *Illust.*, IDEM: *In* Apollo, March 1930, p. 160, *Illust.*, A. ALEXANDRE: *In* Renaissance, March 1930, p. 90, *Illust.*, L. VENTURI: Italian Paintings in America, 1933, No. 481, *Illust.*, B. BERENSON: Italian

Pictures of the Renaissance, 1932, p. 91; D. C. RICH: Catalogue of Paintings and Sculpture, Art Institute of Chicago, 1933, No. 106; W. R. VALENTINER: Italian Paintings, Detroit Inst. of Arts, 1933, No. 86; A. DE HÉVESY: *Jn* Pantheon, Oct. 1936, p. 323, *Jllust.*, M. VAUGHAN: *Jn* Parnassus, May 1939, p. 10, *Jllust.*

BOLTRAFFIO, GIOVANNI ANTONIO
MILANESE, 1467-1516

15 *Portrait of Clarice Pusterla*

A Milanese lady of the Court of Lodovico Maria Sforza (il Moro), Duke of Milan (1451-1508).

Panel: 26⅜ x 22 inches.

LENT ANONYMOUSLY.

COLLECTIONS: Contessa Teresa Soranzo-Mocenigo; Conte Luchino del Mayno, Milan.
EXHIBITION: Royal Academy, London, 1930.
BIBLIOGRAPHY: B. BERENSON: North Ital. Painters, 1907, p. 171; G. PAULI: *Jn* Thieme-Becker's Kunstler-Lexikon, Vol. IV, 1910, p. 257; F. M. VALERI: La Corte di Lodovico il Moro, Vol. I, 1913, pp. 496, 506, 507, *Jllust.*, Vol. III, 1917, pp. 81-82, *Jllust.*, W. SUIDA: Leonardo und sein Kreis, 1929, p. 189; F. WITTGENS: *Jn* Apollo, Feb. 1930, pp. 84-86, *Jllust.*, BALNIEL and CLARK: Exhibition of Italian Art, Royal Academy, London, 1930, p. 106, No. 308; B. BERENSON: Italian Pictures, 1932, p. 92, (Ital. edn., 1936, p. 79).

BOSCH, HIERONYMUS
FLEMISH, 1462?-1516

Known also as Hieronymus van Aeken; born at 's Hertogenbosch (Bois-le-Duc), Brabant, and worked there most of his life. In 1484 he became a member of a religious society. In 1502 he painted for Philip II of Spain the "Last Judgment", and it is presumed that he was invited to the Court of Spain by that monarch. He made a whimsical choice of subjects for his pictures, which are generally grotesque representations of spectres, demons and incantations which he treated with singular ingenuity. His fantastic art was a connecting link between the Dutch and the Flemish, especially the Antwerp School, and he had many followers in the Netherlands through the XVI century, the greatest of them being Pieter Brueghel the Elder.

16 *The Mocking of Christ.*

54 Painted after 1500.

Panel: 20 x 21 inches.

LENT BY THE JOHN G. JOHNSON COLLECTION, PHILADELPHIA.

COLLECTIONS: W. B. Paterson; John G. Johnson.
EXHIBITION: Worcester-Philadelphia Exhn. of Flemish Painting, 1939.
BIBLIOGRAPHY: R. FRY: *Jn* Burl. Mag., Sept. 1903, p. 92, *Jllust.*, C. PHILLIPS: *Jn* Burl Mag., Sept. 1910, p. 322; W. COHEN: *Jn* Thieme-Becker's Lexikon, Vol. IV, 1910, p. 389; W. R. VALEN-

TINER: Catalogue of the John G. Johnson Collection, 1913, No. 352, *Illust.*, W. SCHÜRMEYER: Hieronymus Bosch, 1923, p. 40; M. J. FRIEDLÄNDER: Hieronymus Bosch, 1927, No. 78, *Illust.*, H. TIETZE: Meisterwerke Europäischer Malerei in Amerika, 1935, p. 138, *Illust.*, H. MARCEAU and others: Catalogue of the Worcester-Philadelphia Exhn., 1939, p. 34, No. 41, *Illust.*

BOSCH, HIERONYMUS

FLEMISH, 1462?-1516

17 *Temptation of St. Anthony.*

Panel: 10½ x 8¼ inches.

LENT BY MR. F. B. GUTMANN, HAARLEM, HOLLAND.

COLLECTION: From Spain.
BIBLIOGRAPHY: M. J. FRIEDLÄNDER: Geertgen van Haarlem und Hieronymus Bosch, 1927, p. 150, No. 92, *Illust.*

BOSCH, HIERONYMUS

FLEMISH, 1462?-1516

18 *The Betrayal of Christ.*

Pl. 54 Signed in full on the sword at upper right. Painted about 1500. A painting of similar composition, but entirely different in color scheme is in the Rijks-Museum, Amsterdam.

Panel: 20 x 32 inches.

LENT BY THE FINE ARTS GALLERY OF SAN DIEGO, CALIFORNIA.

COLLECTIONS: Baron H., Westphalia; Lilienfeld Galleries.
BIBLIOGRAPHY: "The Art News", N. Y., Dec. 31, 1938, p. 6, *Illust.*, "The Art Digest", N. Y., Mar. 1, 1939, p. 21, *Illust.*

BOTTICELLI, SANDRO

FLORENTINE, 1444-1510

Allesandro di Mariano Filipepi, called Botticelli, first studied with Fra Filippo Lippi (1458); influenced by Antonio Pollaiuolo, Verrocchio and Castagno. He worked mostly at Florence; from 1474-1475 he was in Pisa; in 1482-1483 in Rome. His range of subjects extended from great scriptural compositions through the most touching scenes in the life of the Madonna, to events in classic history, including allegorical and mythological subjects. He painted the "Allegory of Spring", and the "Birth of Venus", for Lorenzo de' Medici. He was a profound student of Dante whose Divine Comedy he illustrated, and he espoused the cause of Savonarola. Characteristic for his great art is a linear style of unusual sensitiveness, a rare poetical conception and a profound religious sentiment.

19 The Legend of St. Mary Magdalen.

. 17

Christ Preaching; The Feast in the House of Levi; "Noli me tangere"; The last
Moments of the Magdalen, forming the predella of an altarpiece, painted for the
monastery of the Convertite, of which the patron Saint was Mary Magdalen. This
altarpiece has been identified either as the one in the Academy in Florence
(C. Gamba), or as the one in the possession of Lord Lee (H. P. Horne and
Y. Yashiro). The first was painted about 1471, the second about 1480.

Panels: Each 7⅛ x 16½ inches.

LENT BY THE JOHN G. JOHNSON COLLECTION, PHILADELPHIA.
COLLECTION: Monastery of S. Elizabetta delle Convertite, Florence.
EXHIBITION: Royal Academy, London, 1930.
BIBLIOGRAPHY: H. P. HORNE: Jn Rassegna d'Arte, Sept. 1913, pp. 147-154, Jllust., B. BEREN-
SON: Catalogue of the John G. Johnson Collection, 1913, Nos. 44-47, Jllust., W. VON BODE: Sandro
Botticelli, 1925, pp. 126-7, Jllust., IDEM: Botticelli (Kl. der Kunst), 1926, No. 84-85, Jllust., A.
VENTURI: Botticelli, 1925, p. 38; Y. YASHIRO: Jn Burl. Mag., April 1925, pp. 157-167, Jllust.,
IDEM: Sandro Botticelli, 1929, p. 208, Jllust., K. CLARK: Exhibition of Italian Art, Royal Academy,
London, 1930, pp. 78-79, Nos. 225-228, Jllust., R. VAN MARLE: Italian Schools, Vol. XII, p. 58;
C. GAMBA: Jn Dedalo, Feb. 1931, pp. 595-6, Jllust., IDEM: Botticelli, 1936, p. 226, Jllus., L. VEN-
TURI: Italian Paintings in America, 1933, Nos. 247-248, Jllust., B. BERENSON: Italian Pictures,
1932, p. 105.

BOTTICELLI, SANDRO

FLORENTINE, 1444-1510

20 The Annunciation.

12

Painted about 1474.

Panel: 9½ x 14⅜ inches.

LENT BY MR. ROBERT LEHMAN, NEW YORK.
COLLECTIONS: Barberini Palace, Rome; Oscar Huldschinsky.
EXHIBITION: Berlin Academy, 1914.
BIBLIOGRAPHY: COUNT PLUNKETT: Botticelli, 1900, p. 117; W. VON BODE: Jn Berlin Jahrbuch,
Vol. XXVII, 1906, pp. 245 ff, Jllust., IDEM: Die Sammlung Huldschinsky, 1908, p. 9, Jllust.,
A. SCHMARSOW: Botticelli, 1923, p. 45, Jllust., B. BERENSON: Jn Art in Amer., Vol. XII, 1924, p. 188,
Jllust., W. VON BODE: Botticelli, 1925, pp. 113, 126, Jllus., IDEM: Botticelli (Kl. d. K), 1926, No.
80, Jllust., A. VENTURI: Botticelli, 1927, p. 121; M. J. FRIEDLANDER: Jn Cicerone, Vol. XX, 1928,
p. 2, Jllust., Y. YASHIRO: Sandro Botticelli, 1929, p. 239, Jllust., R. VAN MARLE: Ital. Schools, Vol.
XII, 1931, p. 148; B. BERENSON: Ital. Pictures, 1932, p. 105; L. VENTURI: Ital. Paintings in Amer.,
1933, No. 245, Jllust., C. GAMBA: Botticelli, 1937, p. 168, Jllust., J. MESNIL: Botticelli, 1938,
p. 225.

BOTTICELLI, SANDRO

FLORENTINE, 1444-1510

21 *The Madonna Adoring the Child.*

Pl. 18 Painted about 1490.

Panel: Diameter 22½ inches.

LENT ANONYMOUSLY.

COLLECTIONS: M. Paravey; Mme. Raynaud; Wildenstein Galleries.

EXHIBITIONS: Detroit Institute of Arts, 1933; Century Club, New York, 1935; Art Institute of Chicago, 1933.

BIBLIOGRAPHY: ANON: Tableaux Anciens, Collection de M. Paravey, Conseiller d'Etat, Paris, 1878; A. VENTURI: Botticelli, 1925, No. 108, *Illust.*, A. L. MAYER: *In* Pantheon, Vol. VI, 1930, pp. 392-394, *Illust. in color*, IDEM: *In* Art News, Sept. 13, 1930, and May 13, 1933, *Illust.*, W. R. VALENTINER: Ital. Paintings, Detroit Inst., 1933, No. 24, *Illust.*, IDEM: *In* Pantheon, Aug. 1933, p. 238; L. VENTURI: Ital. Paintings in Amer., Vol. II, 1933, No. 246, *Illust.*, D. C. RICH: Paintings and Sculpture, Art Inst. of Chicago, 1933, p. 17, No. 109; ANON: Exhib. of Ital. Paintings of the Renaissance, Century Club, New York, 1935, No. 2; J. MESNIL: Botticelli, 1938, p. 225.

BOUCHER, FRANÇOIS

FRENCH, 1703-1770

First employed by Jean François Cars, and afterwards studied under François Le Moine; went to Rome in 1727, and returned to Paris in 1731. In 1733 he married Marie Jeanne Buseau, and in 1734 became a member of the French Academy, his reception picture being "Rinaldo and Armida", now in the Louvre. In 1755 he was appointed Director of the Gobelins, and ten years later *premier peintre du roy*. He was the *protégé* of Madame de Pompadour, whose patronage had a very considerable influence on his career. His fertile imagination and voluptuous grace gave to him the title of the "Anacreon of Painting."

22 *The Messenger of Love.*

Signed and dated 1765.

Canvas, oval: 12¾ x 10½ inches.

LENT BY MRS. I. D. LEVY, NEW YORK.

COLLECTIONS: Sir Anthony Rothschild; The Hon. Mrs. Yorke; Lady Battersea; Wildenstein Galleries.

BIBLIOGRAPHY: International Studio, April 1928, p. 37, *Illust. in color.*

BOUTS, AELBERT

FLEMISH, 1460-1549

Second son of Dirk Bouts, born probably at Löwen, where he died; doubtless trained under his father. He married twice, in 1481 and 1491. He followed in his compositions closely the style of his father, but the execution of his paintings is less precise and the colors are lighter in key.

23 *The Annunciation.*

Painted about 1480. There are two other versions by this artist of the same subject, one in the Kaiser Friedrich Museum, and a second at Leningrad.

Panel: 19¾ x 16⅜ inches.

LENT BY THE ESTATE OF JOHN L. SEVERANCE, CLEVELAND.

COLLECTIONS: Von Kramm-Siersdorf, Driburg; Eugen Schweitzer, Berlin; Knoedler Galleries, New York.

EXHIBITIONS: Cleveland Museum of Art, 1931; and 1936.

BIBLIOGRAPHY: M. J. FRIEDLÄNDER: Dierick Bouts und Joos van Gent, 1925, No. 44a, *Illust.*, H. S. FRANCIS: Exhibition of Painting, Cleveland Museum, 1936, p. 78, No. 185, *Illust.*

BOUTS, DIRK

FLEMISH, 1400?-1475

Born at Haarlem, and possibly studied under Van der Weyden, about 1435-1440. He settled at Louvain about 1448, when he was appointed official portrait-painter of that city, and in the same year he was commissioned to paint the important "Last Supper", now in the Church of St. Pierre, Louvain, the shutters of which are now at Berlin and Munich respectively. He is the earliest and most important master of the Haarlem school of the fifteenth century.

24 *The Madonna and Child.*

49   Panel: 11½ x 8¼ inches.

LENT BY THE JULES S. BACHE COLLECTION, NEW YORK.

COLLECTIONS: Gabriel J. P. Weyer; Prince Karl von Hohenzollern; Royal Museum, Sigmaringen; Lord Duveen of Millbank.

EXHIBITIONS: Sigmaringen Gallery, Pinakothek, Munich, 1918; Kleinberger Galleries, New York, 1929; Brussels, 1935.

BIBLIOGRAPHY: G. J. P. WEYER: Collection de Tableaux Anciens, Cologne, 1862; F. WINKLER: *In* Belgische Kunstdenkmäler, Vol. I, 1923; F. RIEFFEL: *In* Städel Jahrbuch, Frankfort, a/M., 1924, pp. 57-58, Plate XV; M. J. FRIEDLÄNDER: Dierick Bouts und Joos van Gent, 1925, p. 127, No. 95a; W. HEIL: *In* Art News, April 27, 1929, p. 32, *Illust.*, W. R. VALENTINER: Unknown Masterpieces, 1930, No. 36, *Illust.*, BARONNE HOUTART: Catalogue, Cinq Siecles d'Art, Brussels, 1935, p. 38, No. 78; ANON: Catalogue of the Bache Collection, New York, 1938; No. 19, *Illust.*, W. SCHÖNE: Dieric Bouts und seine Schule, 1938, p. 215, No. 146.

BOUTS, DIRK

FLEMISH, 1400?-1475

25 *Moses Before the Burning Bush.*

50   Panel: 17⅛ x 13⅝ inches.

LENT BY THE JOHN G. JOHNSON COLLECTION, PHILADELPHIA.

COLLECTIONS: T. Lloyd Roberts; Henry Willett; Rodolphe Kann; Lord Duveen of Millbank; John G. Johnson.

EXHIBITIONS: Manchester Art Treasures, 1857; Royal Academy, London, 1892; Burlington Fine Arts Club, London, 1892; Worcester-Philadelphia Exhn. of Flemish Paintings, 1939.

BIBLIOGRAPHY: w. bürger: Trésors d'Art exposés à Manchester en 1857, p. 154; e. michel: *In* Gaz. des Beaux-Arts, June, 1901, p. 498; p. heiland: Dirk Bouts, 1903, p. 126; k. voll: Altniederländische Malerei von Jan van Eyck bis Memling, 1906; e. heidrich: Altniederländische Malerei, 1910; w. von bode: Catalogue of the Rodolphe Kann Collection, Paris, Vol. II, 1907, No. 97, *Illust.*; w. r. valentiner: Catalogue of the John G. Johnson Collection, 1913, No. 339, *Illust.*; m. j. friedländer: Dierick Bouts, 1925, p. 108, *Illust.*; l. baldass: *In* Jahrb. der Kunsth. Sammlungen in Wien, 1932; w. schöne: Dieric Bouts und seine Schule, 1938, p. 179, No. 65, *Illust.*; h. tietze: Meisterwerke Europäischer Malerei in Amerika, 1935, p. 129, *Illust.*; h. marceau and others: Catalogue of the Worcester-Philadelphia Exhn., 1939, p. 21, No. 10, *Illust.*

BRONZINO, ANGELO ALLORI

FLORENTINE, 1502?-1572

Born at Monticelli. First studied under Raffaelino del Garbo; pupil of Pontormo; influenced by Michelangelo. He executed several works in fresco and oil for the public buildings of Florence and its vicinity, and was much employed by the Grand Duke Cosimo I. as a portrait painter. He was both poet and painter, and a member of the Florentine Academy.

26 *Portrait of Fernando de' Medici* (Presumed)

Painted about 1548; very similar in style to the portrait of Giannettino Doria in the Doria Palace, Rome, and in harmony to the portrait of Don Garcia de' Medici in the Ashmolean Museum, Oxford.

Canvas: 22¼ x 16 inches.

LENT BY MR. AND MRS. ROBERT W. REFORD, MONTREAL, CANADA.

COLLECTIONS: Sir William Drummond; Col. George Wyndham, first Earl of Egremont; Lord Leconfield; Colin Agnew.

BIBLIOGRAPHY: g. f. waagen: Art Treasures, Vol. III, 1854, p. 41; c. h. collins baker: Catalogue of the Leconfield Colln., Petworth, 1920, p. 11, No. 172, *Illust.*; a. mc comb: Agnolo Bronzino, 1928, p. 108; a. venturi: Storia dell'Arte Ital., Vol. IX, 6, 1932, p. 28; l. venturi: Ital. Paintings in America, Vol. III, 1933, No. 464, *Illust.*

BROSAMER, HANS

GERMAN, 1500?-1554

Born at Fulda; painter, designer of woodcuts, and engraver, known chiefly as a portraitist. Earliest dated work 1520. Active mostly in Fulda and Erfurt, where he made a large woodcut representing Duke Philip of Hesse. Only a small number of painted portraits are known by him.

27 *Portrait of a Gentleman.*

Painted about 1530. The attribution is due to M. J. Friedländer.

Panel: 18⅝ x 12 inches.

COLLECTIONS: S. Neumans, Brussels; Wildenstein Galleries.
BIBLIOGRAPHY: c. h. kuhn: German Paintings in American Collections, 1936, p. 35, No. 74, *Illust.*, *In* Burl. Mag., Dec. 1938, Suppl., *Illust.*

BRUEGHEL THE ELDER, PIETER

FLEMISH, 1525?-1569

The founder of a family of noted painters; born in the village of Brueghel, near Breda; died at Brussels. He painted chiefly the pleasures of rustic life with human understanding and a great sense of humour, and is regarded as the founder of genre painting. He was a pupil and son-in-law of Pieter Coeck van Aalst of Antwerp, and became a member of the Antwerp Guild in 1551. He settled in Brussels in 1563. His son Pieter (1564-1637) is called 'Hellish Brueghel' because he loved to paint scenes with devils, hags, or robbers; a younger son Jan (1568-1625), called 'Velvet Brueghel', was known chiefly as a flower and landscape painter. The art of Rubens and other seventeenth century painters could not be imagined without the precedence of Pieter Brueghel, with whose colorism and decorative style modern art in the North begins.

28 *The Wedding Dance.*

59 Dated 1566. Many contemporary copies of the painting are known, one in the Antwerp Museum, and another in the Kaiser Friedrich Museum, Berlin.

Panel: 47 x 62 inches.

LENT BY THE DETROIT INSTITUTE OF ARTS.
COLLECTION: Arthur James Sulley.
EXHIBITIONS: Century of Progress, Chicago Art Institute, 1933; Brussels, 1935.
BIBLIOGRAPHY: w. r. valentiner: *In* Bulletin of the Detroit Inst. of Arts, Nov. 1930, pp. 16-18, *Illust.*, idem: *In* Apollo, Dec. 1930, pp. 395-399, *Illust.*, idem: Catalogue of Paintings, Detroit Inst. of Arts, 1930, No. 22, *Illust.*, idem: *In* Art in America, April, 1931, p. 101, *Illust.*, e. michel: Brueghel, 1931, No. 10; g. gluck: Brueghels Gemälde, 1932, pp. 69-71, No. 24, *Illust.*, d. c. rich: Catalogue of Paintings and Sculpture, Art Institute of Chicago, 1933, No. 34, *Illust.*, h. tietze: Europäische Malerei in Amerika, 1935, p. 147, *Illust.*, baronne houtart: Cinq Siècles d'Art, Brussels, 1935, No. 137; m. j. friedländer: Pieter Brueghel, 1937, pp. 30-31, *Illust.*

BRUGES MASTER OF 1473

FLEMISH,

29 *Madonna and Child, with Donors.*

51 A Triptych, painted in 1473, by an artist whose work shows the influence of Van der Weyden and Memling. The coats-of-arms have made possible the identification of the donors: Jan de Witte, Burgomaster of Bruges, and his second wife Maria

Hoose. The inscription on the frame informs us that the picture was finished on July 27, 1473, and that Jan was 30 years of age and his wife 18 years. On the reverse of the right wing is a representation of Christ with His Mother and St. John, painted in *grisaille*.

Panel: 33 x 54 inches.

LENT BY MR. SOLOMON R. GUGGENHEIM, NEW YORK.

COLLECTIONS: Gabriel Johann P. Weyer; Prince Karl von Hohenzollern-Sigmaringen; Royal Museum, Sigmaringen; A. S. Drey.
EXHIBITIONS: Bruges, 1902; Sigmaringen Gallery, Alte Pinakothek, Munich, 1928; A. S. Drey Galleries, New York, 1929.
BIBLIOGRAPHY: G. J. P. WEYER: Collection de Tableaux anciens, Cologne, 1862; F. A. VON LEHNER: Furstlich Hohenzollern'sches Museum zu Sigmaringen, 1883, No. 140, *Illust.*, W. H. J. WEALE: Primitifs flamands, Bruges, 1902, pp. 21-22, No. 49; G. H. DE LOO: Catalogue critique, Bruges, 1902, p. 14, No. 49; M. J. FRIEDLÄNDER: *In* Rep. für Kunstw., Vol. XXVI, 1903, p. 86; IDEM: Memling u. Gerard David, 1928, pp. 59, 60, 136, *Illust.*, IDEM: Flemish Primitives in the Hohenzollern-Sigmaringen Collection, 1928, No. 3, *Illust.*, F. RIEFFEL: *In* Städel-Jahrbuch, Vols. III-IV, 1924, p. 58; A. L. MAYER: *In* Pantheon, Vol. I, 1928, p. 59, *Illust.*, H. WILM: *In* Cicerone, Vol. XX, 1928, p. 636.

BURCH, HENDRIK VAN DER

DUTCH, 1614-1678?

Son of Hendrik the elder, an engraver; born in Frankenthal near Mannheim, where his father lived from 1586 until 1627 when the family moved to Frankfurt. In 1636 Hendrik the younger became the protégé of the Earl of Arundel, who sent him to Italy with Dr. Hervey, to make drawings of art objects and with the view of training him to become the custodian of the Arundel collection; he arrived in London in 1637 and remained there until 1642, when he accompanied Arundel to Antwerp; he became a member of the Delft Guild in 1649, and worked in close connection with Pieter de Hooch and Jan Vermeer; he was in Amsterdam in 1652 and in Leyden in 1658. He probably spent the remainder of his life in Amsterdam. *See also under* HOOCH, PIETER DE (No. 203).

30 *The Game of Cards.*

Painted about 1660-65. Formerly attributed to Pieter de Hooch whose signature has been falsely inscribed.

Canvas: 26 x 30½ inches.

LENT BY MR. AND MRS. J. WARNER PRINS, NEW YORK.

COLLECTIONS: Jean Louis Laneuville; William Tilden Blodgett; Miss Eleanor E. Blodgett; Miss Gertrude Buttenwieser.
EXHIBITION: Metropolitan Museum of Art, New York, 1909.
BIBLIOGRAPHY: J. L. LANEUVILLE: Collection de Tableaux, 1813, No. 35; C. HOFSTEDE DE GROOT: Catalogue raisonné, Vol. I, 1907, p. 536, No. 217; W. R. VALENTINER: Pieter de Hoogh and H. v. d. Burch, n.d., p. 296, No. 250, *Illust.*, W. R. VALENTINER: Dutch Old Masters, Metropolitan Mus. of Art (Hudson-Fulton Celebration), 1909, p. 205, No. 56, *Illust.*

BURGKMAIR, HANS

GERMAN, 1473-1531

Born at Augsburg. Studied with his father, and perhaps with Schongauer and Albrecht Dürer. He made several trips to Italy. Celebrated also as an engraver on wood, many of his works in this medium representing the triumphs of Maximilian I. He was the leading figure of the Renaissance in Augsburg.

31 *Portrait of an Architect.*

Painted in 1507. Signed, upper right: *Johanes Burgkmaier pingebat in Augusta Regia,* and on left: *Etatis annor 25-1501.*

Panel: 13 x 9¾ inches.

LENT BY MRS. ERNST ROSENFELD, NEW YORK.

COLLECTIONS: Palazzo Florio, Udine; Ernst Rosenfeld.

EXHIBITIONS: Nuremberg, 1873; Knoedler Galleries, New York, 1935.

BIBLIOGRAPHY: o. BENESCH: Das Schwäbische Museum, 1930, p. 79; F. DÖRNHOFFER: Burgkmair Austellung, 1931, No. 9; ANON: Jn Art News, May 16, 1931, Jllust., A. BURKHARD: Hans Burgkmair d. Ae., 1932, pp. 78-79; o. BENESCH: Jn Berlin Jahrbuch, Vol. LIV, 1933, p. 243; ANON: Fifteenth Century Portraits, Knoedler Galleries, N. Y., 1935, No. 17, Jllust., ANON: Jn Art News, Apr. 20, 1935; C. L. KUHN: German Paintings in Amer. Collns., 1936, p. 66, No. 279, Jllust.

BUYTEWECH, WILLEM PIETERSZ

DUTCH, 1591-1624

Son of Pieter J. Buytewech; born in Rotterdam. He was married at Haarlem in 1613. In 1616 he returned to Rotterdam. He worked in the style of Dirk Hals and Esaias van der Velde, and must have been in close relationship with Frans Hals in Haarlem. His paintings are very rare, and have been rediscovered only in recent years. He was also a noted engraver and etcher. He made his will in 1624, and his widow sold their house in 1627. He was one of the finest genre painters of the Frans Hals period in Holland.

32 *The Ordeal of the Rose.*

Painted about 1616. According to the coat-of-arms on the *grille,* and the dog holding a rose in its mouth, alluding to his crest, the youth at the left is a member of the Van Duyvelandt van Rhoon family of Rotterdam. The scene depicts him as a victim of irresolution—the old story that 'faint heart ne'er won fair lady'. While hesitating to offer his hand to the younger sister, she has taken advantage of his indecision and accepted another. The elder sister, anxious to fill her place, resorts to an old Dutch custom with a chance of winning him. Having held two roses behind his back, from which he is to make his choice, she tricks him by crossing her hands, and offers him the rose favorable to herself—much to his further disappointment. When the picture came to the Rijksmuseum, the rosebuds had been painted over, indicating, perhaps, that a later generation of the Van Rhoon's disapproved of the artifice by which their grandmother had won her husband.

Canvas: 22¼ x 27¾ inches.

LENT BY THE RIJKSMUSEUM, AMSTERDAM.

COLLECTIONS: Johan v. d. Linden van Slingeland, 1785; Rijksmuseum, Amsterdam, since 1926.

EXHIBITION: Royal Academy, London, 1930.

BIBLIOGRAPHY: M. D. HENKEL: *Jn* Kunstwanderer, 1926, pp. 240-241, *Jllust.*, H. F. W. JELTES: *Jn* Elsevier, Vol. LXXI, 1926, pp. 300-301; J. Q. VAN REGTEREN ALTENA: *Jn* Maandblad v. beeldende Kunsten; Vol. III, 1926, pp. 165-168, *Jllust.*, J. SIX: *Jn* Oud-Holland, Vol. XLIII, 1926, pp. 97-100, *Jllust.*, W. J. J. C. BIJLEVELD: *Jn* Maandblad de Nederlandsche leeuw, Vol. XLIV, 1926, pp. 144-146; G. POENSGEN: *Jn* Berlin Jahrb, Vol. XLVII, 1926, p. 97, *Jllust.*, H. SCHNEIDER and W. G. CONSTABLE: Exhn. of Dutch Art, Royal Acad., London, 1929 (1930), p. 24, No. 78 (*Jllust. in Souvenir*, p. 16, *No. 9*).

CAPPELLE, JAN VAN DE

DUTCH, 1624-1679

A native of Amsterdam, and son of a dyer; he followed his father's business throughout his life, yet he was the greatest marine painter in Holland during the seventeenth century. As a painter he was self-taught but based his style on Simon de Vlieger and other marine painters. The dates on his pictures range from 1649. He was a friend of Rembrandt, who painted his portrait; he was also a noted art collector.

33 *A Seascape.*

Signed in full.

Canvas: 23½ x 26¾.

LENT BY MR. H. E. TEN CATE, ALMELO, HOLLAND.

COLLECTIONS: Jan de Kommer (?) 1767; Miss Jane M. Seymour, Knoyle; D. Katz.

EXHIBITIONS: Amsterdam, 1938; Museum Boymans, Rotterdam, 1938; Schaeffer Galleries, New York, 1939.

BIBLIOGRAPHY: EXHIBITION Catalogue, D. Katz Collection, Amsterdam, 1938, No. 11, *Jllust.*, D. HANNEMA: Meesterwerken uit vier eeuwen, 1400-1800, Museum Boymans, Rotterdam, 1938, p. 17, No. 60, *Jllust.*, A. M. FRANKFURTER: *Jn* Art News, Feb. 4, 1939, p. 8, *Jllust.*

CARAVAGGIO, MICHELANGELO

ROMAN, 1569-1609

Michelangelo Amerighi, or Merigi, was born at Caravaggio in the Milanese. He first painted at Milan, then went to Venice, and afterwards to Rome where he was employed by Cav. Cesare d'Arpino to paint fruits and flowers into his own works. He afterwards became an independent painter, and produced his first altarpiece in the Contarelli Chapel. He had a violent temper, and killed his companion at a tennis-match, which compelled him to flee to Naples and later to Malta. At the latter place he quarrelled with one of the Knights and was cast into prison, but escaped and fled to Syracuse. On his way to Rome, having been pardoned for homicide, he was robbed of his property and died at Porto Ercole from a fever at the age of forty. His realistic style, built upon the strongest contrast of light and shadows, had an extraordinary influence in Italy as well as in other countries of Europe.

4 *A Table of Fruits.*

Canvas: 20 x 28¼ inches.

LENT BY MR. SAMUEL H. KRESS, NEW YORK.

EXHIBITION: Painters of Still-life, Wadsworth Atheneum, Hartford, Conn., 1938.
BIBLIOGRAPHY: R. LONGHI: *In* Pinacotheca, 1928, p. 274, *Illust.,* A. F. AUSTIN and H. R. HITCHCOCK: Painters of Still-life, Wadsworth Atheneum, 1938, No. 3, *Illust.;* IDEM: Aesthetic of the Still-life. *In* Art News, Feb. 5, 1938, p. 13, *Illust.,* M. VAUGHAN: *In* Parnassus, May 1939, p. 9, *Illust.*

CARAVAGGIO, MICHELANGELO DA

ROMAN, 1569-1609

5 *The Card-Players.*

Painted about 1590-1595. This painting is closely related to the 'Card Sharpers', formerly in the Sciarra Collection, now in private possession in Germany.

Canvas: 38 x 46 inches.

LENT BY THE FOGG ART MUSEUM, HARVARD UNIVERSITY.

COLLECTIONS: Durlacher Bros.
EXHIBITIONS: Wadsworth Atheneum, Hartford, Conn., 1930; Durlacher Galleries, New York, 1932.
BIBLIOGRAPHY: A. K. MC COMB: Ital. Paintings of the Sei- and Settecento, Wadsworth Atheneum, 1930, p. 9, No. 3, *Illust.,* IDEM: *In* Wadsworth Atheneum Bulletin, Vol. VIII, 1930, No. 1, p. 4, *Illust.,* IDEM: *In* Fogg Art Museum Notes, 1930, pp. 199-202, *Illust.,* L. VENTURI: Italian Paintings in America, 1933, No. 580, *Illust.*

CARPACCIO, VITTORE

VENETIAN, C. 1455-1526

Vittore Scarpaza, called Carpaccio, was born in Istria, and lived and worked in Venice; he was a pupil and follower of Gentile Bellini, and influenced by Giovanni Bellini and Giorgione. The knowledge of Oriental costumes shown in some of his works has led to the opinion that he accompanied Gentile to Constantinople. He is the most entertaining narrator of the Venetian school and his cycles representing the life of S. George in S. Giorgio degli Schiavoni, and the life of S. Ursula in the Venice Academy, belong to the most popular compositions in his native town.

36 *A Lady Reading.*

A female figure of almost identical position appears in Carpaccio's 'Birth of the Virgin' in the Academy in Bergamo.

Panel: 30¾ x 20 inches.

LENT BY THE SAMUEL H. KRESS FOUNDATION,
ART COLLECTION, NEW YORK.

COLLECTIONS: The Earl of Exeter, acquired in Italy between 1690-1700; Burleigh House; Robert and Evelyn Benson; Lord Duveen of Millbank.

EXHIBITIONS: New Gallery, London, 1894-1895; Royal Academy, London, 1910; Burlington Fine Arts Club, London, 1912.

BIBLIOGRAPHY: B. BERENSON: Venetian Painters, 1894, p. 101; G. GRONAU: *In* Gaz. des B.A., Mar. 1895, p. 259; SIR S. COLVIN: *In* Berlin Jahrb, Vol. XVIII, 1897, p. 196; LUDWIG AND MOL-MENTI: V. Carpaccio, 1906, p. 224, *Illust.*, SIR L. CUST: *In* Les Arts, Oct. 1907, p. 7, *Illust.*, A. VON BECKERATH: *In* Rep. für Kunstw., Vol. XXXIII, 1910, p. 282; B. BERENSON: Study and Crit. of Ital. Art, Vol. I, 1912, pp. 119 *et seq;* CROWE AND CAVALCASELLE: Hist. of P. in N. Italy, Ed. by T. Borenius, Vol. I, 1912, p. 211; T. BORENIUS: Catalogue of the Benson Colln., 1912, pp. 151-152, *Illust.*, IDEM: *In* Rassegna d'Arte, Vol. XII, 1912, p. 90, *Illust.*, R. FRY: *In* Burl. Mag., May 1912, p. 96; A. VENTURI: Storia dell'Arte, Vol. VII, 4, 1915, p. 730; G. FIOCCO: Carpaccio, 1931, p. 77, *Illust.*, L. VENTURI: Ital. Ptgs. in America, Vol. II, 1933, No. 410, *Illust.*, A. M. FRANK-FURTER: *In* Art News, Mar. 1935, p. 162, *Illust.*

CHARDIN, JEAN BAPTISTE SIMÉON

FRENCH, 1699-1779

Born in Paris; studied under Pierre-Jacques Cazes and later with Noel-Nicolas Coypel. His ability as a still-life painter was recognized before he was thirty years of age, when he entered the Académie Royale in 1728. About 1737 he turned his attention to figure painting and most of his noted genre subjects follow this date. From 1755 to 1774 he was Treasurer of the Académie, and had rooms at the Louvre. One of the greatest masters of still-life and genre painting of all times.

37 *Le Bénédicité ('Grace before meals').*

Pl. 82 One of the masterpieces of the artist, painted about 1740.

Canvas: 19¼ x 15¼ inches.

LENT BY THE MUSÉE DU LOUVRE, PARIS.

COLLECTIONS: Royal Collections from 1744; Versailles, 1760.

EXHIBITIONS: Salon, Paris, 1740; California Palace of the Legion of Honor, San Francisco, 1934.

ENGRAVED by Lepicié, Petit, and Decisy; LITHOGRAPHED by Bouchot; ETCHED by Jardin, Gauchard, and Courboin.

BIBLIOGRAPHY: Mercure de Fränce, Oct.-Nov. 1740, and Dec. 1744; ABBÉ DESFONTAINES: Observation sur les écrits modernes, 1740; P. J. MARIETTE: Abecedario, Vol. I, 1853, p. 358; F. ENGERAND: Inventaire des Tableaux commandés par la Direction des Batiments du Roi, 1710 a

1792, p. 80; F. VILLOT: Notice des Tableaux, Musée du Louvre, 1855, No. 99; E. AND J. DE GON-
COURT: In Gaz. des Beaux-Arts, Dec. 1863, pp. 520-527; Feb. 1864, pp. 146, 149 and 153; H. DE
CHENNEVRIERES: In Gaz. des Beaux-Arts, July 1888, p. 58, and Feb. 1889, p. 121, Illust., LADY
DILKE: French Painters of the XVIII century, 1899, p. 120; L. DE FOURCAUD: Chardin, 1900, p. 25,
Illust., A. DAYOT AND L. VIALLET: L'Oeuvre de Chardin, N.D., p. V.; P. G. KONODY AND M. BROCK-
WELL: The Louvre, 1910, p. 268, Illust. in color, H. E. A. FURST: Chardin, 1911, pp. 88 and 121,
No. 92; P. VITRY: Catalogue du Musée du Louvre, 1913, p. 170, No. 93; T. KLINGSOR: Chardin,
1924, p. 65, Illust., G. BRIERE: Catalogue des Peintures, Musée National du Louvre, Paris, 1924,
p. 26, No. 92; F. HEYWOOD: Important Pictures of the Louvre, 1927, p. 283, Illust., G. WILDEN-
STEIN: Chardin, 1933, No. 74; Catalogue of Exhibition of French Painting, California Palace
of the Legion of Honor, San Francisco, 1934, No. 23, Illust.

CHARDIN, JEAN BAPTISTE SIMÉON
FRENCH, 1699-1779

Bouteilles de Savon ('Soap Bubbles')

Signed J. S. Chardin. A smaller version of the same subject is in the Nelson Gallery, Kansas City; another example is in the Louvre. Exhibited at the Salon of
1739 as L'Amusement frivole. Its pendant, Les Osselets ('Knuckle-bones'), is in the
Baltimore Museum.

Canvas: 35¼ x 28 inches.

LENT BY MRS. JOHN W. SIMPSON, NEW YORK.

COLLECTIONS: M. Boscry, 1781; M. Gruel, 1811; Wildenstein Galleries, Paris.
ENGRAVED by Filloeul in 1739.
EXHIBITIONS: Salon du Louvre, Paris, 1739; Art Institute of Chicago, 1933; Cleveland Mu-
seum of Art, 1936.
BIBLIOGRAPHY: ANON: Livret de Salon, Paris, 1739, p. 13; ANON: Notice des Tableaux,
Colln. de M. Boscry, 1781, No. 17; ANON: Catalogue de Tableaux, Colln. M. Gruel, 1811, No. 5;
A. DAYOT et J. GUIFFREY: J. B. S. Chardin, n.d., p. 7; IDEM, et O. VAILLAT: L'Oeuvre de Chardin,
1907, No. 18, Illust., G. WILDENSTEIN: Chardin, 1933, pp. 68, 166, No. 134, Illust., D. C. RICH:
Exhibition of Paintings, Art Inst., Chicago, 1934, p. 24, No. 134, Illust., H. S. FRANCIS: Exhibi-
tion of the Cleveland Mus., 1936, p. 31, No. 56, Illust.

CHARDIN, JEAN BAPTISTE SIMÉON
FRENCH, 1699-1779

Still Life with Hare.

Painted in 1757; Signed: Chardin.

Canvas: 25½ x 32 inches.

LENT BY MR. HENRY P. MC ILHENNY, GERMANTOWN, PA.

COLLECTIONS: Chevalier de Damery; Michel Francois d'André-Bardon; M. Laperlier; Baron
de Beurnonville; Léon Michel-Lévy; M. M. Wildenstein.
ENGRAVED by L. Monzies.
EXHIBITIONS: Salon du Louvre, Paris, 1757; Galerie Martinet, Paris, 1860; Musée des Arts

Decoratifs, Paris, 1880; Galerie Georges Petit, Paris, 1892; and 1907; Wildenstein Galleries, New York, 1926.

BIBLIOGRAPHY: ANON: Explication des Peintures, Salon du Louvre, Paris, 1757, p. 16, No. 36; CATALOGUE de Tableaux, provenans de M. D'André Bardon, peintre du Roi, 1783, No. 27; ANON: Tableaux de l'Ecole française, Galerie Martinet, Paris, 1860, No. 106; E. et J. DE GONCOURT: L'Art du XVIIIe siecle Chardin, 1864, p. 189; ANON: Tableaux de l'Ecole française, Collection Leperlier, 1867, No. 22; 1879, No. 3; ANON: Catalogue des Tableaux, Colln. Baron de Beurnonville, 1881, p. 14, No. 20, *Illust. with Monzies' engraving,* A. WOLFF: Cent Chefs-d'oeuvre, Galerie Georges Petit, Paris, 1892, No. 6; J. GUIFFREY: *In* Revue de l'Art, 1907, p. 109; IDEM: L'Oeuvre de Chardin et Fragonard, 1907, p. IX, No. 47, *Illust.,* M. TOURNEUX: *In* Gaz. des B.-Arts, Vol. XXXVIII, 1907, p. 95, *Illust.,* J. GUIFFREY: Chardin, Catalogue raisonné, 1908, p. 83, No. 166; H. E. A. FURST: Chardin, 1911, p. 127; G. WILDENSTEIN: Exhibition of Paintings by Chardin, New York, 1926, No. 9, *Illust.,* G. WILDENSTEIN: Chardin, 1933, p. 209, No. 706, *Illust.*

CHRISTUS, PETRUS

FLEMISH, 1410?-1473

Born at Baerle, and in 1444 was made a free citizen of Bruges. He was strongly influenced by Jan Van Eyck, from whom he seems to have taken over his studio when the latter died in 1441. His signed works are dated from 1446 to 1457. He simplified the forms of Jan van Eyck and developed perspective and modelling by contrasting stronger light and shadows. He has little temperament and is best in representations of quiet content and in portraits. See also under EYCK, JAN VAN (No. 114).

40 *Dionysius the Carthusian (?).*

Signed: Petrus. Xri. me Fecit, Ao. 1446. Dionysius the Carthusian (Denys van Leeuwen) was born in 1402, at Ryckel, a small village near St. Trond, in Belgium. In 1415 he was sent to Zwolle where he entered upon the study of Philosophy and the practice of religious life. At the age of 18 he determined to acquire the "science of saints" in the order of St. Bruno. In 1423 he was admitted to the Carthusian Monastery of Roermond. He died in 1471. The cause of his beatification has never been explained, but writers of note have styled him "Blessed".

Panel: 11½ x 8 inches.

LENT BY THE JULES S. BACHE COLLECTION, NEW YORK.

COLLECTIONS: Viceroy Don Ramon de la Cruz; Marquéz de Dos Aguas; Knoedler Galleries.

EXHIBITIONS: Royal Academy, London, 1927; Knoedler Galleries, New York, 1935; Princeton University, 1937.

BIBLIOGRAPHY: R. AGROSOT: *In* Museum, revista mensuel, Barcelona, Vol. I, 1911, pp. 9-18, *Illust.,* M. J. FRIEDLANDER: Die Van Eyck und Petrus Christus, 1924, pp. 145 *et seq, Illust.,* SIR M. CONWAY, Edr.: Catalogue of Flemish and Belgian Art, Royal Academy, London, 1927, No. 16, Plate XII; T. BORENIUS: *In* Apollo, May 1928, p. 212, *Illust.,* R. FRY: *In* The Burl. Mag., Feb. 1927, p. 62, *Illust.,* SIR P. LAMBOTTE, and others: Flemish-Belgian Art, 1500-1900, 1927, p. 142, No. 16; E. SINGLETON: Old World Masters, 1929, pp. 169-172, *Illust.,* H. TIETZE: Meisterwerke Europäischer Malerei in Amerika, 1935, No. 124, *Illust.,* ANON: Catalogue of the Bache Collection, New York, 1938, No. 20, *Illust.,* W. SCHÖNE: Dieric Bouts und seine Schule, 1938, p. 56, No. 4.

CHRISTUS, PETRUS

FLEMISH, 1410?-1473

1 *Madonna and Child.*

Painted about 1450-70. A replica is in the Prado, Madrid.

Panel: 19½ x 12½ inches.

LENT BY DR. PRESTON P. SATTERWHITE, NEW YORK.

COLLECTIONS: Marchesa Cierrega, Madrid; Knoedler Galleries.

EXHIBITION: Toledo Museum of Art, 1935.

BIBLIOGRAPHY: PARNASSUS: Dec. 1930, p. 27, *Illust.*, BLAKE-MORE GODWIN: French and Flemish Primitives, Toledo Mus., 1935, No. 4, *Illust.*, *In* Art News, Nov. 23, 1935, p. 4, *Illust.*

CIMA DA CONEGLIANO

VENETIAN, C. 1459-1517

Probably a pupil of Alvise Vivarini; he was also influenced by Antonello and Giovanni Bellini. His earliest dated work was painted in 1489 at Vicenza, and in the following year he finally settled at Venice. In 1494 he painted the 'Baptism' for the Church of San Giovanni in Venice. From Giovanni Bellini he differs notably in the clearness of outlines and the silvery shades of color. One great beauty of his paintings is the landscape backgrounds, many of which represent the neighborhood of Conegliano.

2 *The Madonna with SS. Catherine and Nicolas.*

Painted after 1509.

Canvas: 21¼ x 28¼ inches.

LENT BY MR. AND MRS. CHARLES V. HICKOX, NEW YORK.

COLLECTIONS: Nicolas Baronowsky; Städelinstitut, Frankfurt-am-Main.

BIBLIOGRAPHY: H. WEIZSÄCKER: Katalog der Gemälde Gallerie des Städelschen Kunstinstituts in Frankfurt, 1900, No. 40; B. BERENSON: Venetian Painters, 1894, p. 104; R. BURCKHARDT: Cima da Conegliano, 1905, p. 116; B. BERENSON: Italian Pictures, 1932, p. 146 (Ital. Edn. 1936, p. 126); R. VAN MARLE: Italian Schools, Vol. XVII, 1935, p. 451.

CLAUDE LORRAIN

FRENCH SCHOOL, 1600-1682

Claude Gellée, called Claude Lorrain, was born at Chamagne in the Duchy of Lorraine, and is said to have been brought up as a pastry cook, and went to Rome in 1613 in that capacity, entering the service of Agostino Tassi, a painter, which gave him a stimulus to follow his master's calling. He spent most of his life in Rome where the Poussins and Salvator Rosa were his fellow-workers. He is the outstanding exponent of the classical trend of French landscape art in the seventeenth century.

43 *St. George Slaying the Dragon.*

Painted in 1646 for Cardinal Poli, the *proefectus domi* at the Vatican. A drawing of this picture, No. 73, is in the *Liber Veritatis* (a sketch-book containing 200 pen drawings, washed with bistre, made by Claude as a record of his original pictures, and which is now in the possession of the Duke of Devonshire).

Canvas: 44 x 58½ inches.

LENT BY THE WADSWORTH ATHENEUM, HARTFORD, CONN.

COLLECTIONS: Cardinal Faustus Poli; Cardinal Antonio Barberini; Charles Alexandre de Colonne, Prime Minister of France; Charles d'Arveley; Edmund Antrobus; William Beckford; Durlacher Galleries.

ETCHED in 1668 by Dominique Barriere, and Engraved by Lerpiniere.

EXHIBITIONS: Berkshire Museum, Pittsfield, Mass., 1937; Durlacher Galleries, New York, 1938.

BIBLIOGRAPHY: SKINNER AND DYKE: Catalogue of the Calonne Collection, 1795, No. 65; JOHN SMITH: Catalogue raisonné, Vol. VIII, 1837, p. 230, No. 73; LADY DILKE: Claude Lorrain, sa vie et ses Oeuvres, 1884; O. J. DULLEA: Claude Gellée, 1887, pp. 38 and 107; E. DILLON: Claude, 1905, p. 75; M. DAVIDSON: In Art News, Jan. 16, 1937, p. 18, Illust.

CLAUDE LORRAIN

FRENCH, 1600-1682

44 *A Seaport at Sunset.*

A characteristic classical composition of the artist of the type which influenced Turner's style.

Canvas: 30 x 40 inches.

LENT BY PRESIDENT FRANKLIN DELANO ROOSEVELT, WASHINGTON, D. C.

COLLECTIONS: William Tilden Blodgett, acquired about 1870; Miss Eleanor E. Blodgett.

CLAUDE LORRAIN

FRENCH, 1600-1682

45 *Classical Landcape.*

Pl. 6   Canvas: 20 x 25 inches.

LENT BY MR. AND MRS. ERNEST KANZLER, DETROIT.

COLLECTION: Lilienfeld Galleries, New York.

EXHIBITION: California Palace of the Legion of Honor, San Francisco, 1934.

BIBLIOGRAPHY: W. HEIL: French Painting, California Pal. Legion of Honor, 1934, p. 33, No. 15; In Art News, June 9, 1934, p. 9, Illust.

CLEVE, JOOS VAN

FLEMISH, c. 1485-1540

Born in the neighborhood of Cleve, he probably learned his art from Jan Joest of Calcar; when the latter, in 1508, settled at Haarlem, Joos van Cleve may have gone with him. In 1511 he settled in Antwerp and about 1530 he seems to have been in France in the service of Francis I. In 1536 he went to England and painted a portrait of Henry VIII, and afterwards, it is presumed, he went to Genoa and painted certain altarpieces. Together with Quentin Massys, the leading painter of the Antwerp school in the first half of the sixteenth century, he excelled especially in portraits.

6 *The Holy Family.*

Panel: 9½ x 8 inches.

LENT BY MR. AND MRS. JOHN E. ALDRED, NEW YORK.

COLLECTIONS: Johann Peter Weyer; Prince Karl von Hohenzollern; The Royal Sigmaringen Museum; A. S. Drey.

EXHIBITIONS: Sigmaringen Collection, Pinakothek, Munich, 1928; Drey Galleries, New York, 1928.

BIBLIOGRAPHY: F. A. VON LEHNER: Fürstlich Hohenzollern'sches Museum zu Sigmaringen, 1883; M. J. FRIEDLÄNDER: Joos van Cleve, 1931, p. 135, No. 56g.

CLEVE, JOOS VAN

FLEMISH, c. 1485-1540

7 *Portrait of a Man.*

57 Painted about 1538.

Panel: 20¾ x 17 inches.

LENT FROM THE WILLIAM GOLDMAN COLLECTION, NEW YORK.

COLLECTION: Dr. Hans Wendland.

EXHIBITION: Kleinberger Galleries, New York, 1929.

BIBLIOGRAPHY: KLEINBERGER: Exhibition of Flemish Primitives, 1929, p. 178, No. 59, *Illust.*, M. J. FRIEDLÄNDER: Joos van Cleve, 1931, p. 142, No. 99.

CLEVE, JOOS VAN

FLEMISH, 1490?-1640

8 *Portrait of a Young Man.*

Painted about 1521-24.

Panel: 10 x 8⅝ inches.

LENT BY THE JOHN G. JOHNSON COLLECTION, PHILADELPHIA.

EXHIBITIONS: Worcester Art Museum, 1939; Philadelphia Museum of Art, 1939.

BIBLIOGRAPHY: W. R. VALENTINER: Flemish and Dutch Paintings in the John G. Johnson Collection, Phila., 1913, p. 36, No. 375, *Illust.*, L. BALDASS: Joos van Cleve, der Meister des Todes Maria, 1925, p. 27, No. 64, *Illust.*, H. MARCEAU and others: The Worcester-Philadelphia Exhn. of Flemish Painting, 1939, p. 43, No. 64, *Illust. on cover.*

CLEVE, JOOS VAN

FLEMISH, C. 1485-1540

49 *Portrait of a Woman.*

Attributed to Joos van Cleve by M. J. Friedländer. Painted about 1540.

Panel: 9½ x 8 inches.

LENT BY MR. JOHN BASS, NEW YORK.

CLOUET, FRANÇOIS (Workshop)

FRENCH, 1510?-1572

Son of Jehan Clouet; of Flemish birth or extraction, probably born at Tours; held for some time the office of *Valet de chambre* to Francis I, afterwards official painter under Henry II, Francis II, and Charles IX.

50 *Jean Babou, Seigneur de La Bourdaisière.*

Painted in 1553. Secretary of Francis I, and brother of Cardinal Philibert Babou; ambassador to Rome, 1560, Governor of Blois, and Grand master of Artillery, 1567; his wife and his six daughters were known as the "Seven Capital Sins" on account of their beauty. He died in 1569.

Panel: 12½ x 9 inches.

LENT BY THE MUSÉE DU LOUVRE, PARIS.

COLLECTIONS: Jean-Baptiste Colbert de Torcy; François Roger de Gaignieres, 1717. Comes from a collection of portraits assembled by Louis XV, at the Cabinet des Ordres du Roi, situated at the Grands Augustins, Paris; taken in 1792 to the Musée des Monuments Français in 1817.
BIBLIOGRAPHY: ANON: Inventory of the Grands-Augustins, No. 76 or 39, Gagnières Collection (1642-1715); F. VILLOT: Notice des Tableaux, Musée du Louvre, Ecole Française, 1855, No. 121; P. VITRY: Le Musée du Louvre, 1913, p. 121, No. 133B; H. S. EDE: Jn Burl. Mag., Mar. 1923, p. 117; G. BRIÈRE: Catalogue des Peintures, Musée National du Louvre, 1924, p. 37, 133B; E. MOREAU-NELATON: Les Clouet, Vol. I, p. 76, Vol. III, p. 254, 1924; L. DIMIER: Le Portrait en France au XVI siecle, Vol. I, p. 109, Vol. II, p. 145, No. 1, and p. 135, No. 549, 1925.

CORNEILLE DE LYON

FRENCH, 1520?-1574

Of Netherlandish origin, he is possibly identical with Cornelis de Capelle of the Hague. After working in Paris he went to Lyons, where he met the poet, Jean Second, in 1533. He settled in that city in 1544, and obtained French nationalization in 1547. In 1561 he was visited by Catherine de Médicis, and afterwards painted her portrait with her three children. Several of his portraits of various members of the royal house were engraved, as medallions, in *Promtuarium iconum* (Roville, Lyon, 1553).

51 *Seigneur de Boisy, Grand Ecuyer de France.*

Panel: 6½ x 5¼ inches.

LENT BY MRS. HERBERT N. STRAUS, NEW YORK.

COLLECTION: Frédéric Spitzer.

CORNEILLE DE LYON

FRENCH, 1520?-1574

52 *Portrait of a Man.*

Panel: 6½ x 5¼ inches.

LENT BY MRS. HERBERT N. STRAUS, NEW YORK.

COLLECTION: La Rochefoucauld-Bisaccia.

CORNEILLE DE LYON

FRENCH, 1520?-1574

53 *Portrait of a Lady.*

Panel: 6 inches diameter.

LENT BY MRS. HERBERT N. STRAUS, NEW YORK.

COLLECTION: La Rochefoucauld-Bisaccia.

CORNELISZ, JACOB

DUTCH, 1470?-1533?

Jacob Cornelisz van Oostsanen (or Jacob van Amsterdam) was born at Oostzaan in North Holland. He was a painter and engraver, and worked at Amsterdam from 1500 until 1533, where he died before October 18, 1533. Prints by him dealing with the 'Life of Christ' and other subjects, and dated 1517 and 1518, are still preserved. He was the second master of Jan Scorel, and the father of Dirck Jacobsz. Next to Lucas van Leyden and Jan Scorel, the leading Dutch master in the earlier part of the sixteenth century.

54 *The Holy Family with St. Anne, St. Joachim, and the Angel Annunciate.*

Painted about 1500. An early work of the master under the influence of Geertgen.

Panel: 36¾ x 33½ niches.

LENT BY MR. AND MRS. CHARLES V. HICKOX, NEW YORK.

COLLECTIONS: Prince Schaumburg-Lippe, Schloss Bückeburg, Westphalia.

EXHIBITION: Century of Progress, Chicago Art Institute, 1933.

BIBLIOGRAPHY: D. C. RICH: Catalogue of Paintings and Sculpture, Art Institute of Chicago, 1933, No. 38, *Illust.*; L. SCHEIBLER: *In* Jahrbuch der Konigl., Preuss, Kunstsammlung, 1882, p. 19; K. STEINBART: *In* Pantheon, Nov. 1933, p. 337, *Illust.*

CRANACH THE ELDER, LUCAS

GERMAN, 1472-1553

Lucas Cranach, whose family name is uncertain, is commonly called Cranach from his native town of Kronach, in Upper Franconia. He was a pupil of his father and mastered the arts of painting and engraving on copper and wood. He accompanied the Elector Frederick the Wise on his pilgrimage to the Holy Land, and afterwards took up his residence at Wittemberg where he was afterwards twice burgomaster. In 1502-4 he was in Vienna, and in 1508 in the Netherlands. His principal works were painted between 1506 and 1540, during which period it was his custom to use the device of a crowned winged serpent instead of a signature. He was an intimate friend of Luther and painted his portrait several times. From 1547 until 1552 he accompanied Elector John Frederick in exile in Innsbruck, after which he retired to Weimar, where he died.

55 *A Woman with a Gold Chain.*

Painted about 1538-1540.

> LENT FROM THE WILLIAM GOLDMAN COLLECTION, NEW YORK.
> Panel: 21½ x 13½ inches.

COLLECTIONS: F. B. Gutman; Julius Goldschmidt.

EXHIBITIONS: Van Diemen Galleries, New York, 1929; Reinhardt Galleries, New York, 1929; Schaeffer Galleries, New York, 1937; Wadsworth Atheneum, Hartford, Connecticut, 1937.

BIBLIOGRAPHY: L. GOODRICH: *In* The Arts, Dec. 1929, p. 255, *Illust.*, F. E. W. FREUND: *In* Der Cicerone, Jan. 1932, p. 35, *Illust.*, M. J. FRIEDLÄNDER and J. ROSENBERG: Die Gemälde von Lucas Cranach, 1932, p. 81, No. 283 d; ANON: Catalogue of Early German Paintings, Schaeffer Galleries, New York, 1937; A. M. FRANKFURTER: *In* The Art News, Feb. 1937, p. 7, *Illust.*, A. E. AUSTIN: Forty-three Portraits, Wadsworth Atheneum, 1937, No. 9, *Illust.*

CRANACH THE ELDER, LUCAS

GERMAN, 1472-1553

56 *The Feast of Herod.*

Pl. 41 Signed and dated 1531. The Herod in this picture is presumed to be the portrait of Prince Frederick the Wise, Elector and Duke of Saxony (1463-1525).

> Panel: 46 x 31½ inches.

> LENT BY THE WADSWORTH ATHENEUM, HARTFORD, CONN.

COLLECTIONS: A. Langen; Julius Böhler; M. van Gelder; Durlacher Bros.

EXHIBITIONS: Cranach Exhibition, Munich, 1901; Schaeffer Galleries, New York, 1937.

BIBLIOGRAPHY: ANON: Cranach Ausstellung, Munich, 1901, No. 150, *Illust.*, M. J. FRIEDLÄNDER U. J. ROSENBERG: Die Gemälde von Lucas Cranach, 1932, p. 63, No. 182, *Illust.*, A. M. FRANKFURTER: *In* Art News, Feb. 20, 1937, p. 17.

CRANACH, LUCAS

GERMAN, 1472-1553

57 *Portrait of a Bearded Man.*

Signed, with winged serpent device, and dated 1532.

Panel: 20 x 14¼ inches.

LENT BY DR. F. H. HIRSCHLAND, HARRISON, NEW YORK.

COLLECTION: Georg Hirth; Van Diemen Galleries.

EXHIBITION: Koninklijke Kunstzaal Kleykamp, The Hague, 1924; Kaiser-Friedrich Museums Verein, Berlin, 1925.

BIBLIOGRAPHY: E. LÜTHGEN: Catalogue des tableaux et sculptures, Kunstzaal Kleykamp, 1924, No. 7, *Illust.*, H. ZIMMERMANN: Zeitwende, 1925, Part 1, p. 1, *Illust.*, E. HEYCK: Lucas Cranach, 1727, p. 96; M. J. FRIEDLÄNDER U. J. ROSENBERG: Die Gemälde von Lucas Cranach, 1932, p. 79, No. 273; C. L. KUHN: German Paintings in American Collections, 1936, p. 43, No. 132.

CRANACH THE ELDER, LUCAS

GERMAN, 1472-1553

58 *The Nymph of the Spring.*

Signed, with winged serpent device, beneath the quiver on the tree.   Inscribed,—
FONTIS NYMPHA SACRI SOMNVM NERVMPE QVIESCO. (Compare, No. 59.)

Panel: 6 x 8 inches.

LENT BY MR. ROBERT LEHMAN, NEW YORK.

COLLECTIONS: James Simon; Rudolf Chillingworth.

EXHIBITIONS: Kleinberger Galleries, New York, 1928; Knoedler Galleries, New York, 1939.

BIBLIOGRAPHY: Exhn. Catalogue of German Primitives, Kleinberger Gall., 1928, No. 27; M. J. FRIEDLÄNDER and J. ROSENBERG: Die Gemälde von L. Cranach, 1932, p. 89, No. 324b; ANON: Classics of the Nude Exhibition, Knoedler Galleries, 1939, p. 13, No. 5, *Illust.*, J. J. SWEENEY: *In Parnassus, Apr. 1939, p. 19, Illust.*

CRANACH THE ELDER, LUCAS

GERMAN, 1472-1553

59 *The Nymph of the Spring.*

Signed, with winged serpent device, on the rock. Inscribed: FONTIS NYMPHA SACRI SOMNVM RVMPE QVIESCO. (Compare No. 58).

Panel: 18¾ x 28¾ inches.

LENT BY MR. AND MRS. CLARENCE Y. PALITZ, NEW YORK.

COLLECTIONS: Burg Flechtingen, Magdeburg; Baron von Schenck.

EXHIBITION: Knoedler Galleries, New York, 1939.

BIBLIOGRAPHY: M. J. FRIEDLÄNDER AND J. ROSENBERG: Die Gemälde von Lucas Cranach, 1932, p. 89, No. 324, *Illust.*, ANON: Exhibition of Classics of the Nude, Knoedler Galleries, N. Y., 1939, p. 11, No. 5A.

CRANACH THE ELDER, LUCAS

GERMAN, 1472-1553

60 *Portrait of a Prince of Saxony* (Companion to No. 61).

Dr. Friedländer suggests that it may represent Prince Friedrich, son of George the Bearded, Duke of Saxony (1471-1539); the prince was born in 1504, and died young.

Panel: 16¾ x 13 inches.

LENT BY THE RALPH HARMAN BOOTH COLLECTION, DETROIT.

COLLECTIONS: Julius Böhler; A. Salomon; Ralph H. Booth.

EXHIBITIONS: Detroit Institute of Arts, 1926; Chicago Art Institute, 1936.

BIBLIOGRAPHY: w. r. valentiner: Catalogue of Paintings by Old Masters, Detroit Institute of Arts, 1926, No. 18, *Illust.*, International Studio, Oct. 1929, *Reproduced in Color*, m. j. friedländer and j. rosenberg: Die Gemälde von Lucas Cranach, 1932, p. 50, No. 104, *Illust.*, d. c. rich: Catalogue of Paintings and Sculpture, Art Institute of Chicago, 1933, p. 3, No. 116; c. l. kuhn: German Paintings in American Collections, 1936, p. 37, No. 90; m. vaughan: *In* Parnassus, May 1939, p. 10, *Illust.*

CRANACH THE ELDER, LUCAS

GERMAN, 1472-1553

61 *Portrait of a Princess of Saxony* (Companion to No. 60).

Dr. Friedländer suggests that it may represent Princess Christine, daughter of George the Bearded, Duke of Saxony (1471-1539); the Princess was born in 1505, and died young.

Panel: 16¾ x 13 inches.

LENT BY THE RALPH HARMAN BOOTH COLLECTION, DETROIT.

COLLECTIONS: Julius Böhler; A. Salomon; Ralph H. Booth.

EXHIBITIONS: Detroit Institute of Arts, 1926; Chicago Art Institute, 1933.

BIBLIOGRAPHY: w. r. valentiner: Catalogue of Paintings by Old Masters, Detroit Inst. of Arts, 1926, No. 17, *Illust.*, m. j. friedländer and j. rosenberg: Die Gemälde von Lucas Cranach, 1932, p. 50, No. 105, *Illust.*, d. c. rich: Catalogue of Paintings and Sculpture, Art Institute of Chicago, 1933, p. 3, No. 16; c. l. kuhn: German Paintings in American Collections, 1936, p. 37, No. 91, *Illust.*, m. vaughan: *In* Parnassus, May 1939, p. 10, *Illust.*

CRANACH THE ELDER, LUCAS

GERMAN, 1472-1553

62 *Saint Christopher.*

Panel: 16 x 10½ inches.

LENT BY MR. AND MRS. EDWARD F. FISHER, DETROIT.

COLLECTIONS: Böhler and Steinmeyer; Howard Young.

CRESPI, GIUSEPPE MARIA
BOLOGNESE, 1665-1747

Called Lo Spagnuolo. He studied under several Baroque masters, and was influenced by Guercino. He was employed for some time by the Grand-Duke Ferdinand, for whom he executed several works in the Pitti Palace at Florence. He was also a capable engraver. His style is distinguished by his use of silvery highlights. Crespi's *chefs d'oeuvre* are his series of the 'Seven Sacraments' in the Dresden Gallery.

3 *Self Portrait before his Easel.*

Painted about 1710.

Canvas: 22½ x 16½ inches.

LENT BY THE WADSWORTH ATHENEUM, HARTFORD, CONN.

EXHIBITIONS: Mostra del Settecento, Bologna, 1935; Durlacher Galleries, 1936; Wadsworth Athenaeum, since 1937; Metropolitan Museum, New York, 1938.

BIBLIOGRAPHY: c. foresti: Catalogo, Mostra del Settecento in Bologna, 1935; anon: *In* Art News, Jan. 2, 1937, pp. 8 and 20, *Illust.*, a. m. frankfurter: *In* The Art News, Jan. 16, 1937, pp. 11-12; h. b. wehle: Tiepolo and his contemporaries, Met. Mus., N. Y., 1938, No. 5.

CRIVELLI, CARLO
VENETIAN, 1430?-1495?

A fellow pupil with Bartolomeo Vivarini under Antonio da Murano and Squarcione. About 1468 he settled at Ascoli, and in that neighborhood spent the rest of his life. His first dated picture, 1468, is the ancona painted for the church of S. Silvestro at Massa Fermana; the large ancona in the National Gallery, London, is dated 1476. In 1490 he was knighted by Prince Ferdinand of Capua. The "Coronation of the Virgin", in the Brera, is dated 1493; later than this no date concerning him is known. The brilliancy of Crivelli's pictures, seldom impaired by time, is due to his exclusive employment of tempera.

4 *The Madonna and Child.*

0 Panel: 14 x 9 inches.

LENT BY THE JULES S. BACHE COLLECTION, NEW YORK.

COLLECTIONS: Walter Jones, of Clytha; The Earls of Northbrook; Lord Duveen of Millbank.

EXHIBITIONS: Royal Academy, Winter Exhibition, 1872; New Gallery, London, 1894-1895; Burlington Fine Arts Club, London, 1912; Royal Academy, Italian Exhibition, 1930; Exposition de l'Art Italien, Paris, 1935; Cleveland Museum, 1936.

BIBLIOGRAPHY: g. f. waagen: Galleries and Cabinets of Art in Great Britain, Vol. IV, 1857, p. 95; j. p. richter: Catalogue of Pictures belonging to the Earl of Northbrook, 1880, p. 126, No. 174; lord r. gower, *Edr.*: The Northbrook Gallery, 1885, p. 4, Plate I; g. m. rushforth: Carlo Crivelli, 1894, pp. 44 *et seq, Illust.*, crowe and cavalcaselle: Painting in North Italy, Ed. by T. Borenius, Vol. I, 1912, p. 92; b. berenson: The Study and Criticism of Italian Art, Vol. I, 1912, p. 102; anon: Burl. Fine Arts Club: Catalogue of Early Venetian Pictures, 1912, p. 24, Plate

VII; A. VENTURI: Storia dell'Arte Italiana, Vol. VII, Part 3, 1914, p. 376, *Illust.*, F. DREY: Carlo Crivelli und seine Schule, 1927, pp. 128-129, Plate XXV; B. BERENSON: Italian Pictures, 1932, p. 162 (Ital. edn., 1936, p. 140, *Illust.*); L. VENTURI: Italian Paintings in America, Vol. II, 1933, No. 363, *Illust.*, ANON: Catalogue of the Bache Collection, 1938, No. 5, *Illust.*

CRIVELLI, CARLO

VENETIAN, 1430?-1495?

65 Saints Anthony, Christopher, Sebastian, and Thomas Aquinas.

Painted during the master's middle period, c. 1470.

Panels: Each, 17 x 4 inches.

LENT BY SENATOR AND MRS. SIMON GUGGENHEIM, NEW YORK.

COLLECTIONS: Count Grégoire Stroganoff; Count Alessandro Contini.

BIBLIOGRAPHY: G. BERNARDINI: *Jn* Rassegna d'Arte, Vol. I, 1901, p. 120; L. POLLAK et A. MUNOS: Collection du Comte Grégoire Stroganoff a Rome, 1912, *Illust. pl. 7;* F. DREY: *Jn* New York Sun, Apr. 15, 1929, *Illust.*, B. BERENSON: Italian Pictures, 1932, p. 162 (Ital. Edn. 1936, p. 140); R. VAN MARLE: Italian Schools, Vol. XVIII, 1936, p. 29, *Illust.*

CUYP, AELBERT

DUTCH, 1620-1691

Born at Dordrecht, and studied under his father, Jacob Gerritz Cuyp. His pictures date from 1639, and comprise portraits, mainly of children, animals, landscapes, filled with the glow of high summer, winter pieces, night pieces, scenes on the Rhine and the Maas, etc. Characteristic is the warm golden atmosphere of his landscapes of his developed period. The paintings of his earlier period are under Van Goyen's influence and pale in tone. Together with Ruysdael and Hobbema, the leading landscape painter in Holland in the Rembrandt period.

66 The Flight into Egypt.

Pl. 77   Signed: A. Cuyp.

Panel: 35⅝ x 27 inches.

LENT BY MR. AND MRS. CHARLES T. FISHER, DETROIT.

COLLECTIONS: Servad, Amsterdam; Stanislaus II, last King of Poland; Prince de Talleyrand; Alexander Baring, first Lord Ashburton; Alfred Charles de Rothschild.

EXHIBITIONS: British Institution, London, 1819; Knoedler Galleries, New York, 1925; Detroit Institute of Arts, 1926, 1927 and 1929.

BIBLIOGRAPHY: G. F. WAAGEN: Treasures of Art in Great Britain, 1854, Vol. II, p. 110; W. BUCHANAN: Memoirs of Painting, Vol. II, 1824, pp. 321-323; ANON: Catalogue of Dutch Masters of the XVII century, Knoedler Galleries, New York, 1925, No. 2, *Illust.*, W. R. VALENTINER: Catalogue of Dutch Paintings of the XVII century, Detroit Institute of Arts, 1929, No. 16, *Illust.*, IDEM: *Jn* Art News, Oct. 19, 1929, p. 8, *Illust.*

CUYP, AELBERT

DUTCH, 1620 - 1691

7 Fishingboats on the Maas.

77 Signed: A. Cuyp. Painted at the beginning of the master's middle period.

Panel: 18 x 28 inches.

LENT BY THE JOHN G. JOHNSON COLLECTION, PHILADELPHIA.

COLLECTIONS: Macalester Loup; Van Saceghem of Ghent; J. A. Tardieu; Jean Dollfus; John G. Johnson.

EXHIBITIONS: Orphelins d'Alsace-Lorraine, Musée de Louvre, Paris, 1885; Kleinberger Galleries, Paris, 1912.

BIBLIOGRAPHY: ANON: Catalogue de l'Exposition de Tableaux au profit des Orphelins d'Alsace-Lorraine, Paris, 1885, p. 35, No. 96; C. HOFSTEDE DE GROOT: Catalogue Raisonné, Vol. II, 1909, p. 198, 661a; W. R. VALENTINER: Catalogue of Flemish and Dutch Painters in the John G. Johnson Collection, Philadelphia, 1913, p. 147, No. 627, Illust.

CUYP, AELBERT

DUTCH, 1620 - 1691

8 A View on the River Scheldt.

Panel: 11 x 13½ inches.

LENT BY MR. AND MRS. EDGAR B. WHITCOMB, DETROIT.

COLLECTIONS: J. S. Phillips; J. E. Fordham.

EXHIBITIONS: Old Masters, Royal Academy, London, 1878; Dutch Paintings of the XVII Century, Detroit Institute of Arts, 1929.

BIBLIOGRAPHY: ANON: Catalogue of Old Masters, Royal Academy, London, 1878, No. 85; C. HOFSTEDE DE GROOT: Catalogue Raisonné, Vol. II, 1909, p. 200, No. 668; W. R. VALENTINER: Catalogue of Seventeenth Century Dutch Paintings, Detroit Institute of Arts, 1929, No. 14, Illust.

CUYP, AELBERT

DUTCH, 1620 - 1691

9 An Old Inn at a Ferry.

Belong to Cuyp's earlier middle period. A drawing which the artist used for this composition is in the Munich Printroom.

Canvas: 17 x 37¾ inches.

LENT BY MR. ADOLF MAYER, NEW YORK.

COLLECTIONS: Carl Schoen; Lilienfeld Galleries, New York.

EXHIBITION: Detroit Institute of Arts, 1939.

BIBLIOGRAPHY: W. R. VALENTINER: Exhibition of Paintings, Detroit Inst. of Arts, 1939, No.

34

CUYP, AELBERT

DUTCH, 1620-1691

70 *Landscape with Riders.*

Signed: A. Cuyp. Painted about 1660-70.

Canvas: 41 x 57 inches.

LENT BY MR. AND MRS. CHARLES V. HICKOX, NEW YORK.

COLLECTION: The Duke of Leinster.

EXHIBITIONS: Art Institute of Chicago, 1927 and 1933.

BIBLIOGRAPHY: C. HOFSTEDE DE GROOT: Catalogue Raisonné, Vol. II, 1909, p. 148, No. 484;
D. C. RICH: Catalogue of Paintings, Institute of Chicago, 1933, p. 10, No. 58, *Illust.*

CUYP, AELBERT

DUTCH, 1620-1691

71 *Cows and Herdsmen in a Landscape.*

Signed, A. Cuyp, below on the right. Characteristic work of the best middle period
of the master.

Panel: 23 x 28½ inches.

LENT BY DR. C. J. K. VAN AALST, HOEVELAKEN, HOLLAND.

COLLECTIONS: Duke of Leinster; Frank Partridge.

BIBLIOGRAPHY: C. HOFSTEDE DE GROOT: Catalogue raisonné, Vol. II, 1909, p. 65, No. 189;
W. R. VALENTINER: Catalogue of Paintings in the Van Alst Collection, 1939, p. 14, *Illust.*

DADDI, BERNARDO

FLORENTINE, c. 1290-after 1355

Bernardo Daddi has been identified with the master who signed himself Bernardus
de Florentin, by whom there are three pictures signed and dated. He was a pupil
of Giotto, influenced by the Master of S. Cecilia, by Ambrogio Lorenzetti and
more especially by French art. He matriculated in the Arte de'Medici e Speziali,
about 1317. About 1330 he painted the frescoes in Santa Croce, Florence, and in
1335 acquired the third share of a house on the Via Larga. One of the leading
painters in Florence in the first half of the fourteenth century.

72 *The Crucifixion.*

Pl. 1   Panel: 12⅝ x 8 inches.

LENT BY THE DAN FELLOWS PLATT ESTATE, ENGLEWOOD, NEW JERSEY.

COLLECTION: N. van Slochem.

EXHIBITIONS: Fogg Art Museum, Cambridge, Mass., 1915; Kleinberger Galleries, New York,
1917; The Century Club, New York, 1935.

BIBLIOGRAPHY: F. M. PERKINS: *In* Rass. d'Arte, Vol. XI, 1911, p. 1; O. SIREN: *In* Art in
Amer., Vol. II, 1914, p. 264; G. H. EDGELL: *In* Art and Archaeology, July 1915, p. 13; O. SIREN:
Giotto and some of his followers, 1917, p. 168; IDEM and M. BROCKWELL: Loan Exh. of Primitives,

Kleinberger Gall., N. Y., 1917, p. 17, No. 3, *Illust.*, R. VAN MARLE: Ital. Schools, Vol. III, 1924, p. 378; L. VENTURI: Italian Paintings in America, 1933, No. 44, *Illust.*, B. BERENSON: Ital. Pictures, 1932, p. 165 (Ital. Edn. 1936, p. 142); R. OFFNER: Corpus of Flor. Painting, Vol. III, 1933, p. 5; ANON: Ital. Paintings of the Renaissance, Century Club, N. Y., 1935, No. 4.

DADDI, BERNARDO
FLORENTINE, C. 1290-AFTER 1355

3 *The Holy Eucharist.*

Attributed convincingly by B. Berenson to Giovanni del Biondo.

Panel: 19⅛ x 16⅛ inches.

LENT BY MR. FRANK C. SMITH, JR., WORCESTER, MASS.
COLLECTION: Capt. R. Langton Douglas.
BIBLIOGRAPHY: L. VENTURI: Ital. Paintings in Amer., 1933, No. 41, *Illust.*

DADDI, BERNARDO
FLORENTINE, C. 1290-AFTER 1355

a *The Extreme Unction.*

Attributed convincingly by B. Berenson to Giovanni del Biondo.

Panel: 19⅛ x 16⅛ inches.

LENT BY MR. FRANK C. SMITH, JR., WORCESTER, MASS.
COLLECTION: Capt. R. Langton Douglas.
BIBLIOGRAPHY: L. VENTURI: Ital. Paintings in America, 1933, No. 42, *Illust.*

DADDI, BERNARDO
FLORENTINE, C. 1290-AFTER 1355

4 *The Madonna and Child Enthroned.*

Painted during the late period of the master; near in style to the Polyptych in the Uffizi, Florence.

Panel: 42½ x 24 inches.

LENT BY THE DUMBARTON OAKS COLLECTION, WASHINGTON, D. C.
COLLECTION: Durlacher Galleries, New York.
BIBLIOGRAPHY: L. VENTURI: Italian Paintings in America, Vol. I, 1933, No. 48, *Illust.*

DAVID, GERARD
FLEMISH, 1464?-1523

Born at Oudewater, Holland. He probably studied in Haarlem under Geertzen tot Sint Jans, or Dirk Bouts. Since 1484 he worked in Bruges, where he became the last great master of this school towards the end of the century. His first important commission was in 1488, the 'Judgment of Cambyses,' now in the Bruges

Museum. In 1509 he presented an altarpiece to the Carmelite nuns of Sion, at Bruges; it is now at Rouen. In 1515 he went to Antwerp, and was elected a member of the Guild of St. Luke. His wife, Cornelia Cnoop, whom he married in 1488, was famous for her skill as a miniaturist.

75 *The Madonna and Child.*

Painted about 1485-90. Repeats with slight variations the Madonna of the Altarpiece in the Louvre.

Panel: 13¾ x 9¼ inches.

LENT BY MR. AND MRS. PAUL KLOTZ, NEW YORK.

COLLECTION: Leopold Koppel.

BIBLIOGRAPHY: M. J. FRIEDLÄNDER: Memling u. Gerard David, 1928, p. 145, No. 165c.

DAVID, GERARD

FLEMISH, 1464?-1523

76 *The Annunciation.*

Painted about 1490. Of the earlier period of the master, soon after he moved from Holland to Bruges. On the wall of the interior hangs a painting representing Moses and the Burning Bush.

Panel: 13½ x 9 inches.

LENT BY THE DETROIT INSTITUTE OF ARTS.

COLLECTION: Private Collection in Russia.

EXHIBITION: Detroit Institute of Arts, since 1927.

BIBLIOGRAPHY: W. R. VALENTINER: In Detroit Inst. Bulletin, May 1927, pp. 92-93, *Illust.*, M. J. FRIEDLÄNDER: Memling u. Gerard David, 1928, p. 147, No. 175; Catalogue of Paintings in the Detroit Inst., 1930, No. 50, *Illust.*

DAVID, GERARD

FLEMISH, 1464?-1523

77 *The Madonna and Child, "The Rest on the Flight to Egypt".*

Pl. 53   Painted about 1500-1510. The scene is obviously intended as an episode during the Flight into Egypt, and represents the Madonna resting on the journey. The subject of the *Riposo* has recommended itself to various masters of landscape painting on account of its romantic and pastoral character.

Panel: 20 x 17 inches.

LENT BY THE JULES S. BACHE COLLECTION, NEW YORK.

COLLECTIONS: Frank Stoop, J.P.; Lord Duveen of Millbank.

EXHIBITIONS: Guildhall, London, 1906; Royal Academy, London, 1927; Kleinberger Galleries, New York, 1929.

BIBLIOGRAPHY: A. G. TEMPLE: Works by Early Flemish Painters, Guildhall, London, 1906,

No. 52; s. REINACH: Répertoire de Peintures, Vol. III, 1910, p. 286, *Illust.*, M. J. FRIEDLÄNDER: Von Eyck bis Breughel, 1921, p. 190; SIR M. CONWAY: The Van Eycks and their Followers, 1921, p. 285; IDEM, Edr.: Catalogue of Flemish and Belgian Art, Royal Academy, London, 1927, p. 47, No. 104; SIR R. WITT: Exhibition of Flemish and Belgian Art, 1300-1900, 1927, p. 42, *Illust.*, SIR P. LAMBOTTE, and others: Flemish and Belgian Art, 1300-1900, 1927, p. 145, No. 104, *Illustrated in color*, p. 43; M. J. FRIEDLÄNDER: Memling und Gerard David, 1928, p. 154, No. 212a, Plate XCV; R. CORTISSOZ: *In* The Amer. Mag. of Art, Vol. XXI, p. 248, *Illust.*, ANON: Catalogue of the Bache Collection, New York, 1938, No. 22, *Illust.*

DAVID, GERARD

FLEMISH, 1464?-1523

8   *The Annunciation.*

Painted about 1515-1520. One of the masterpieces of the artist's later (Antwerp) period. The two panels formed very likely the wings of an altarpiece of which the center part is missing.

Canvas: 24 x 30 inches.

LENT BY MR. EDWARD S. HARKNESS, NEW YORK.

COLLECTIONS: Gabriel J. P. Weyer; Prince Karl von Hohenzollern; Royal Museum, Sigmaringen, Prussia.

EXHIBITIONS: International Picture Exhibition, Munich, 1869; Primitive Flemish Paintings, Bruges, 1902; The Old Pinakothek, Munich, 1928; Sixteen Masterpieces, Knoedler Galleries, New York, 1930, Nos. 9-10.

BIBLIOGRAPHY: CROWE AND CAVALCASELLE: Early Flemish Painters, 1872, p. 129; A. SPRINGER: Altniederländischen Malerei, 1875, pp. 131 and 348; M. J. FRIEDLÄNDER: Meisterwerke der Niederländische Malerei, Bruges, 1902, p. 17, *Illust.*, IDEM: Die Brugger Leihausstellung von 1902, No. 128 bis; H. HYAMS: *In* Gaz. des Beaux-Arts, Oct. 1902, pp. 294-295; H. FIERENS-GEVAERT: Les Primitives Flamands, 1902, p. 152; E. VON BODENHAUSEN: Gerard David und seine Schule, 1905, pp. 173-175, *Illust.*, E. HEINRICH: Alt-Niederländische Malerei, 1910, *Illust.*, SIR M. CONWAY: The Van Eycks and their Followers, 1921, p. 283; M. J. FRIEDLÄNDER: Von Eyck bis Bruegel, 1921, p. 191; F. WINKLER: Die Altniederländische Malerei, 1923, p. 138; M. J. FRIEDLÄNDER: Memling-Gerard David, 1928, No. 173.

DAVID, JACQUES LOUIS

FRENCH, 1748-1825

Born in Paris. Studied under Vien, a leader of the Neo-classicists. Received the Prix de Rome in 1774, where he stayed until 1780, and returned to Paris. Became an academician in 1782, and acquired a conspicuous name in 1789 during the Revolution, when he painted his finest pieces. He destroyed the Academy in 1793 and removed his rival painters. He paid court to Napoleon, and after Waterloo returned to Brussels. He created the Empire style and had a considerable influence on the following generations by introducing again the classical tendencies into French art.

79
Pl. 84

Portrait of the Marquise d'Orvilliers,
née Jeanne Robertine Rilliet (1772-1862).

Signed and dated—1790.

Canvas: 49 x 37¾ inches.

LENT BY THE MUSÉE DU LOUVRE, PARIS.

COLLECTIONS: Comte de Turenne; Comtesse Robert de Fitz-James.

EXHIBITIONS: Salon, Paris, 1790; Exposition des Alsace-Lorraine, 1874; Exposition des Portraits Nationaux, 1878; Exposition des Portraits du Siecle, 1885; Exposition David, 1913.

BIBLIOGRAPHY: P. DORBEC: *Jn* Gaz. des Beaux-Arts, April 1907, pp. 328-330, *Jllust.*, L. DUMONT-WILDEN: Le Portrait en France, 1909, p. 171; L. ROSENTHAL: Louis David, n.d., pp. 129 and 161; L. HOURTICQ: A Guide to the Louvre, 1923, p. 124, No. 202; G. BRIERE: Catalogue des Peintures, École Française, Musée National du Louvre, Paris, 1924, p. 69, No. 3062, *Jllust.*, R. H. WILENSKI: French Painting, 1931, p. 182.

DAVID, JACQUES LOUIS
FRENCH, 1748-1825

80
Pl. 84

Madame de Richemond, and her son Eugène.

Painted about 1800. One of the finest works of the master of the "Madame Recamier" period; the costume and lines conceived entirely in the spirit of the Empire, in a style which, in its prime, was largely inspired by the influence of David's art.

Canvas: 45¾ x 35½ inches.

LENT BY MISS JULIA BERWIND, NEW YORK.

COLLECTIONS: The Richemond family; Sigismund Bardac; Vicomte G. Chabert; Wildenstein Galleries, Paris; Edward J. Berwind.

EXHIBITIONS: L'Ecole des Beaux-Arts, Paris, 1897; Royal Academy, London, 1932; Art Institute of Chicago, 1933.

BIBLIOGRAPHY: ANON: Catalogue de l'Expos. des Portraits de Femmes a l'Ecole des B.-Arts, Paris, 1897, p. 23, No. 45; H. CARO-DELVAILLE: *Jn* Art in America, Vol. VII, 1919, p. 145, *Jllust.*, W. R. VALENTINER: Jacques Louis David and the French Revolution, 1928, p. 26; IDEM: Unknown Masterpieces, 1930, No. 83, *Jllust.*, A. M. FRANKFURTER: *Jn* Art News, May 16, 1931, p. 4, *Jllust.*, R. H. WILENSKI: French Painting, 1931, p. 181; J. E. BLANCHE: *Jn* Gazette des Beaux-Arts, Jan. 1932, p. 81, *Jllust.*, T. BORENIUS: *Jn* Pantheon, Jan. 1932, p. 19, *Jllust.*, D. C. RICH: Catalogue of Paintings, etc., Chicago Art Inst., 1933, No. 213, *Jllust.*

DEVIS, ARTHUR WILLIAM
ENGLISH, 1763-1822

Born in Preston, Lancashire, and studied under his father, a noted painter of 'conversation pieces'. He afterwards went to Calcutta and painted several portraits of noted officials in the India service; he returned to England in 1795 and became prominent as a painter of historical subjects, among his most successful paintings being the "Death of Nelson" which he painted on board 'The Victory', and, the "Detection of Babington's Conspiracy".

1 *Master Simpson.*

Painted about 1810. James Alexander Simpson, born about 1806, became in later life (from 1852-1860) Solicitor to the Foundling Hospital in London.

Canvas: 49 x 39½ inches.

LENT ANONYMOUSLY.

COLLECTION: Mrs. William Harnes Simpson.

ENGRAVED in Mezzotint by M. Raeburn, and E. Milner.

EXHIBITIONS: British Institution, London, 1863; Arden Art Galleries, New York, 1937; Museum of Modern Art, Washington, D. C., 1938.

BIBLIOGRAPHY: ANON: Catalogue of the British Institution, London, 1863, No. 151; In The Illustrated London News, Christmas No. 1936, *Reproduced in color.*

DOSSI, DOSSO

FERRARESE, 1479-1542

Born near Ferrara. He was a disciple of Lorenzo Costa; later influenced by Giorgione, Titian and Raphael. In 1511-12 he was in Mantua and later became painter to Alfonso I of Ferrara and his wife Lucrezia Borgia. By his contemporaries he was classed with Mantegna, Leonardo, Bellini, and Michelangelo. Leading Ferrarese master in the first half of the sixteenth century. With his fantastic conceptions he combined a remarkable chiaroscuro and an unusually free impressionistic technique.

2 *Circe and her Lovers.*

32 One of the earliest works of the master, and the one nearest to the spirit of Giorgione; painted possibly for Alfonso d'Este of Ferrara. Circe, a mythical sorceress, was a daughter of Helios (the Sun) by the Oceanid Perse. By means of drugs and incantations she was able to change her lovers into animal forms. She was found on her solitary island of Aenea by Odysseus and his companions; the latter she changed into swine, but Odysseus fortified himself against her powers of metamorphosis by eating a magic root.

Canvas: 38 x 52 inches.

LENT ANONYMOUSLY.

COLLECTIONS: William Graham; Robert and Evelyn Benson; Lord Duveen of Millbank.

EXHIBITIONS: Burlington Fine Arts Club, 1894; Royal Academy, London, 1896; Grafton Galleries, London, 1909-1910; Manchester Art Gallery, 1927; Wadsworth Atheneum, Hartford, Conn.; Albright Gallery, Buffalo, N. Y.; Detroit Institute of Arts, 1933; Palazzo dei Diamanti, Ferrara, 1933; Knoedler Galleries, New York, 1939.

BIBLIOGRAPHY: R. H. BENSON: Catalogue of the Ferrarese Exhn., Burl. F. A. Club, 1894, No. 54, *Illust.,* S. REINACH: Répertoire de Peintures, Vol. I, 1905, p. 635, *Illust.,* B. BERENSON: North Ital. Painters, 1907, p. 209; SIR L. CUST: In Les Arts, Oct. 1907, p. 22, *Illust.,* H. COOK and M. BROCKWELL: Catalogue of the National Loan Exhn., Grafton Gall., Lond., 1909-10, No. 87, *Illust.,* T. BORENIUS: Catalogue of the Benson Colln., 1912, pp. 115-116, No. 60, *Illust.,* L. VENTURI: Giorgione e il Giorgionismo, 1913, p. 195; H. MENDELSOHN: Das Werk der Dossi, 1914, pp. 64 *et seq*, *Jllust.*, A. VENTURI: Storia dell'Arte Ital., Vol. IX, 3, 1928, pp. 937-938, *Jllust.*, BALNIEL and CLARK: Exhbn. of Ital. Art, Royal Acad., London, 1930, No. 337; ANON: Catalogo d. Esposizione d. Pittura Ferrarese, Ferrara, 1933, p. 153, No. 184, *Jllust.*, L. VENTURI: Ital. Paintings in Amer., 1933, No. 499, *Jllust.*, A. VENTURI: *Jn* L'Arte, Sept. 1933, p. 386; C. H. WEIGELT: *Jn* Pantheon, July 1933, p. 218, *Jllust.*, W. R. VALENTINER: Ital. Paintings of the XIV to XVI, C. Detroit Inst. of Arts, 1933, No. 83, *Jllust.*, ANON: Exhn. of Classics of the Nude, Knoedler Galleries, N. Y., 1939, p. 14, No. 7.

DOSSI, DOSSO

FERRARESE, 1479-1542

83 Departure of the Argonauts.

Pl. 32   In Greek legend, the heroes who sailed to Aea (afterwards called Colchis) in the Argo to carry off the Golden Fleece, soon after the Trojan War. The expedition was led by Jason, with demigods and heroes in his retinue.

Panel: 23⅝ x 34⅝ inches.

LENT BY MR. SAMUEL H. KRESS, NEW YORK.

COLLECTION: Conte Alessandro Contini-Bonacossi, Florence.
EXHIBITION: Palazzo dei Diamanti, Ferrara, 1933.
BIBLIOGRAPHY: R. LONGHI: Una favola del Dosso. *Jn* Vita Artistica, 1927, pp. 92-95; ANON: Catalogo d. Esposizione d. Pittura Ferrarese, Ferrara, 1933, p. 12, No. 198, *Jllust.*, R. LONGHI: Officina Ferrarese, 1934, pp. 142, 146, 176, 217, Nos. 198-201, *Jllust.*, C. H. WEIGELT: *Jn* Pantheon, July 1933, p. 218; A. VENTURI: *Jn* L'Arte, Sept. 1933, p. 386.

DROUAIS, FRANÇOIS HUBERT

FRENCH, 1727-1775

Born in Paris. Studied successively under his father, Hubert Drouais, Nonotte, Carle Van Loo, Natoire, and Boucher. He was received as an Academician in 1758, which led to his introduction to the Court, where he painted portraits of the whole Royal Family, and celebrities and beauties of the period. He exhibited at the Salon from 1755 to 1775.

84 Un Jeune Elève ('The Young Pupil') (Companion to No. 85).

Signed and dated, *Drouais fils, 1760*. This picture was reproduced by Cozette, to the order of the Marquis de Marigny, as a tapestry, in 1762, at the Royal Gobelins Manufactory, Paris, an example of which is now in the Museum of Tours, and another is in the Wallace Collection, London.

Canvas: 24 x 19½ inches.

LENT BY MR. CHARLES E. DUNLAP, NEW YORK.

COLLECTIONS: Marquise de Pompadour; Marquis de Marigny; Duc de Penthièvre-Chante-

loup; Madame Roussel; Maurice de Rothschild; Wildenstein Galleries; Edward Julius Berwind.
EXHIBITION: Salon du Louvre, Paris, 1761.
BIBLIOGRAPHY: ANON: Explication des Peintures, L'Académie Royale, Paris, 1761, p. 24, No.
83, (A copy of this catalogue, with marginal drawings by Gabriel de St. Aubin, is preserved in
the Bibliothéque Nationale, Paris; reissued in fac-similé in 1911, showing a sketch of this picture);
L. ABBÉ DE LA PORTE: Jn L'Observateur littéraire, Paris, 1761; Jn Société d'Amateurs, 1763; F. BASAN
ET F. C. JOUILLAIN: Le Cabinet de M. le Marquis de Ménars-Marigny, 1781, No. 36; ANON: Inven-
taire d'Amboise et de Chanteloup, 1794, Jn Nouvelles Archives de l'Arts français, Vol. I, 1879;
C. STRYIENSKI: Jn Gazette des B.-Arts, 1903, part 2, p. 75, Jllust., M. GABILLOT: Jn Gazette des
B.-Arts, 1905, part 2, p. 398; M. FENAILLE: Tapisseries des Gobelins, Vol. IV, 1907, pp. 341-342,
Jllust., ANON: Catalogue des Tableaux anciens, Colln. Mme. Roussel, Paris, 1912, pp. 14-15,
Jllust., L. REAU: Hist. de la Peinture Française au XVIII siècle, Vol. I, 1925, p. 72; A. M. FRANK-
FURTER: Jn Art News, Supplement, May 16, 1931, p. 3, Jllust.

DROUAIS, FRANÇOIS HUBERT

FRENCH, 1727-1775

85 *La Fillette au chat* ('Young Girl with a Cat')
(Companion to No. 84).

Signed and dated, *Drouais le fils, 1763*. This picture was reproduced by Cozette,
to the order of the Marquis de Marigny, as a tapestry, in 1764, at the Royal Gobelins Manufactory, Paris, an example of which is now in the Museum of Tours, and
another in the Wallace Collection, London.

Canvas: 25½ x 21¼ inches.

LENT BY MR. CHARLES E. DUNLAP, NEW YORK.

COLLECTIONS: Marquise de Pompadour; Marquis de Marigny; Duc de Penthièvre-Chante-
loup; Madame Roussel; Baron Maurice de Rothschild; Wildenstein Galleries; Edward Julius Berwind.
EXHIBITION: Salon du Louvre, Paris, 1763.
BIBLIOGRAPHY: ANON: Explication des Peintures, L'Academie Royale, Paris, 1763, p. 25, No.
117; M. MATHAN: Un Lettre a Mme. . . . sur les peintures exposées au salon, 1763; D. DIDEROT:
Jn Salon de 1763; F. BASAN ET F. C. JOUILLAIN: Le Cabinet de M. le Marquis de Ménars-Marigny,
1781, No. 37; ANON: Inventaire d'Amboise et de Chanteloup, 1794. Jn Nouvelles Archives de l'Art
français, Vol. I, 1879; M. GABILLOT: Jn Gazette des B.-Arts, 1905, part 2, p. 398; M. FENAILLE:
Tapisseries des Gobelins, Vol. IV, 1907, pp. 341-342, Jllust., ANON: Catalogue des Tableaux
anciens, Colln. Mme. Roussel, Paris, 1912, pp. 16-18, Jllust., L. REAU: Hist. de la Peinture Française au XVIII siècle, Vol. I, 1925, p. 72.

DUCCIO DI BUONINSEGNA

SIENESE, ACTIVE 1279-1319

Born in Siena. Obviously trained by one of the Byzantine masters, many of whom
worked at this time in Italy, followed by Roman and Gothic influences, the latter
being particularly evident in his great Maestà, once in the Cathedral at Siena, part

of which is now in the Opera del Duomo in that city. His influence on the art of Siena and indirectly upon that of all Italy was tremendous. According to B. Berenson he was "the last of the great artists of antiquity, in contrast with Giotto, who was the first of the moderns."

86 The Madonna and Child, with Saints and Angels.

Pl. 3 This work, together with the "Crucifixion", No. 86A, constitutes a diptych.

Panel: 15 x 11 inches.

LENT BY MR. ROBERT LEHMAN, NEW YORK.

COLLECTIONS: Cathedral of Lemberg; Philip Lehman.
BIBLIOGRAPHY: R. LEHMAN: The Philip Lehman Collection, 1928, No. 14, *Illust.*; L. VENTURI: Ital. Paintings in America, 1933, No. 23, *Illust.*

DUCCIO DI BUONINSEGNA

SIENESE, ACTIVE 1279-1319

86a The Crucifixion.

Pl. 3 This work, together with the "Madonna, Saints and Angels", No. 86, constitutes a diptych.

Panel: 15 x 11 inches.

LENT BY MR. ROBERT LEHMAN, NEW YORK.

COLLECTIONS: Cathedral of Lemberg; Philip Lehman.
BIBLIOGRAPHY: R. LEHMAN: The Philip Lehman Collection, 1928, No. 15, *Illust.*, L. VENTURI: Ital. Paintings in America, 1933, No. 24, *Illust.*

DÜRER, ALBRECHT *

GERMAN, 1471-1528

Born and died at Nuremberg. Worked in his father's goldsmith shop, and then apprenticed to Michel Wolgemut. In 1490 he left Nuremberg, and wandered for four years. He returned to Nuremberg, married Agnes Frey, and went to Italy. In 1495 he was in Nuremberg again, where he remained for ten years, during which period his best work was designed for engravings. In 1505-6 he went to Venice. His chief paintings were produced from 1507, after his return to Nuremberg, until 1520, and are unequalled in their fullness of invention. In 1520 he went to Antwerp and met Erasmus, and stayed in the Low Countries for a year. He is regarded as the great typical exponent in art of German thought.

* As it was not possible to represent Dürer by paintings in this exhibition, an exception has been made in this case—a number of his drawings, woodcuts, and engravings, etchings and drypoints, are being shown instead, and will give an idea of the work of this great artist. Such a representation of his art in black and white is not inadequate, as he is perhaps even greater as a graphic artist and draughtsman than as a painter.

7 A Girl in Dance Costume.

A Drawing in ink, washed in green, dated 1501. Inscribed: *Also gand dy Juncfrou-wen zum dancz in Noermarck 151.* (*Trans.* This is how the young maiden of Noermarck went to dances in 15(0)1.). Belongs to the series, 'Nuernberger Trach-tenstudien', in the Albertina, Vienna. Dürer used the same figure in his celebrated engraving, 'The Coat-of-Arms with a Skull', 1503. *See* No. 97E.

Paper: 12¾ x 8¼ inches.

LENT BY MRS. LE ROY M. BACKUS, SAN FRANCISCO.

COLLECTIONS: Baron Dominique Vivant-Denon, Director of the French Imperial Museums (1825); General Comte Antoine Francois Andréossy; Dr. Henri Angst; Frédéric Engel-Gros; Mme. Gertrude Paravicini.

BIBLIOGRAPHY: A. N. PERIGNON: Tableaux, dessins, etc., collection Baron Vivant-Dinon, 1826, No. 617; F. LANEUVILLE: Tableaux et dessins, collection Général Comte Andréossy, 1864, No. 72; F. LIPPMANN AND F. WINKLER: Zeichnungen von A. Dürer, Vol. VI, 1883-29, p. 22, No. 703, *Illust.,* P. GANZ: La Collection Engelgros, 1925, Vol. I, p. 45, Vol. II, No. 80, *Illust.,* H. TIETZE: Kritisches Verz. der Werke A. Dürers, Vol. I, 1928, p. 56, No. 188, *Illust.;* E. FLECHSIG: Albrecht Dürer, Vol. II, 1931, p. 435, No. 248; F. WINKLER: Die Zeichnungen des A. Dürer, 1936, Vol. I, No. 227, *Illust.,* A. M. FRANKFURTER: *In* Art News, Feb. 25, 1939, p. 96, *Illust. in color.*

DÜRER, ALBRECHT

GERMAN, 1471 - 1528

8 The Artist's Brother Hans.

A drawing in silver point, signed and dated 1503.

Paper: 8⅛ x 5¾ inches.

LENT BY MR. LESSING J. ROSENWALD, PHILADELPHIA.

COLLECTIONS: Pierre-Jean Mariette; H. Danby Seymour.

EXHIBITION: Albright Gallery, Buffalo, 1935.

BIBLIOGRAPHY: F. LIPPMANN: Zeichnungen von Albrecht Dürer, 1883, No. 711; H. TIETZE: *In* Art Bulletin, Vol. XV, 1933, p. 259, *Illust.,* A. MONGAN: Master Drawings, Albright Art Gallery, Buffalo, 1935, No. 21, *Illust.,* F. WINKLER: Die Zeichnungen A. Dürers, Vol. II, 1937, No. 280, *Illust.*

DÜRER, ALBRECHT

GERMAN, 1471 - 1528

9 Portrait of a Woman.

Drawing in black chalk, with greenish washes. Dated 1505, monogram. A Slo-vanian peasant, drawn by Dürer during his second journey to Italy.

Paper: 13⅝ x 10⅜ inches.

LENT BY MR. FRANZ KOENIGS, HAARLEM, HOLLAND.

COLLECTIONS: Heinrich Wilhelm Campe (1770-1862); Eduard Viewig; Heinrich Viewig; Dr. Max Eisler.
EXHIBITIONS: Museum Boymans, 1934-35, and 1938; Berlin Museum, 1936.
BIBLIOGRAPHY: F. LIPPMANN: Zeichnungen von A. Dürer, 1896, No. 180; F. WINKLER: Sammlung Viewig, Braunschweig, 1930, *Vorwort*, p. 2; IDEM: Die Zeichnungen A. Dürers, Vol. II, 1937, No. 371, *Illust.*, D. HANNEMA: Meesterwerken uit vier eeuwen, 1400-1800, Museum Boymans, Rotterdam, 1938, p. 61, No. 261, *Illust.*

DÜRER, ALBRECHT

GERMAN, 1471-1528

90 *Lamentation over Christ.*

A drawing in ink, dated 1521.

Paper: 11¾ x 8½ inches.

LENT BY THE PAUL J. SACHS COLLECTION,
FOGG ART MUSEUM, CAMBRIDGE.

BIBLIOGRAPHY: F. LIPPMANN: Zeichnungen von Albrecht Dürer, 1883, No. 379; E. SCHILLING: *In* Städel-Jahrbuch, Vol. I, 1921, p. 127; H. TIETZE: *In* Art Bulletin, Vol. XV, 1933, p. 254, *Illust.*

DÜRER, ALBRECHT

GERMAN, 1471-1528

91 *A Young Woman.*

Pl. 42 Signed and dated 1521. Possibly one of the drawings mentioned in Dürer's diary: "I also sketched in black and white on gray paper two Netherlandish costumes" (*Conway*).

Gray paper: 11⅛ x 7¾ inches.

LENT BY MR. JOSEPH E. WIDENER, PHILADELPHIA.

COLLECTIONS: Baron Arthur de Schickler; Count Hubert de Pourtalès.
BIBLIOGRAPHY: C. EPHRUSSI: Albert Dürer et ses Dessins, 1882, pp. 299-300, 424, *Illust.*, SIR M. CONWAY: Literary Remains of Albrecht Dürer, 1889, p. 120; F. LIPPMANN: Zeichnungen von Albrecht Dürer, 1896, No. 30, *Illust.*, F. WINKLER: Die Zeichnungen Albrecht Dürers, Vol. IV; H. TIETZE: *In* Art Bulletin, Vol. XV, 1933, p. 259, *Illust.*

DÜRER, ALBRECHT

GERMAN, 1471-1528

92 *Musical Angels.*

Pen drawing, signed and dated 1521. "Intended to find a place in a great composition with many saints adoring the Holy Virgin with which Dürer was occupied in 1521-22. Some of the angels are repeated in other drawings for the same composition" (*Tietze*).

Paper: 6½ x 9 inches.

COLLECTION: John Postle Heseltine.
BIBLIOGRAPHY: F. LIPPMANN: Zeichnungen von Albrecht Dürer, 1883, No. 170; H. TIETZE: In Art Bulletin, Vol. XV, 1933, p. 259, Illust.

DÜRER, ALBRECHT

GERMAN, 1471-1528

33 *Study of a Woman's Head.*

Black chalk drawing heightened with white, circa 1521.

Green paper: 7⅞ x 6 inches.

EXHIBITION: Lyman Allen Museum, New London, Conn., 1936.
BIBLIOGRAPHY: C. DODGSON: Old Master Drawings, Vol. 10, 1935, p. 49, No. 39, Illust.; ANON: Catalogue of the Exhibition of Drawings, Lyman Allen Mus., New London, 1936, No. 41, Illust.

DÜRER, ALBRECHT

GERMAN, 1471-1528

34 *Susanna of Bavaria.*

Wife of Prince Casimir of Brandenburg-Ansbach. A drawing in ink, dated upper right, 1525.

Black and green paper: 15⅞ x 11⅝ inches.

COLLECTIONS: Ambroise Firmin-Didot; John Postle Heseltine.
BIBLIOGRAPHY: C. EPHRUSSI: Albert Dürer et ses Dessins, 1882, p. 331; F. LIPPMANN: Zeichnungen von Albrecht Dürer, 1883, No. 172; C. DODGSON: In Burlington Mag., Vol. II, 1903, pp. 289-290; IDEM: In Dürer Society, Vol. VI, Plate VIII; J. P. HESELTINE: Original Drawings, chiefly of the German School, 1912, No. 15; H. TIETZE: In Art Bulletin, Vol. XV, 1933, p. 254.

DÜRER, ALBRECHT

GERMAN, 1471-1528

35 *Apollo.*

Pen drawing, signed. Belongs to a group of studies executed by the master in order to fix the canonic male figure; derived from Apollo and Diana (Lippman, L. 233) in the British Museum.

Paper: 9 x 6 inches.

COLLECTION: Sir Edward J. Poynter, P.R.A.
BIBLIOGRAPHY: F. LIPPMANN: Zeichnungen von Albrecht Dürer, 1896, No. 179; F. LUGT: Les Marques de Collections, 1921, p. 155; E. PANOFSKY: In Berlin Jahrbuch, Vol. XLI, p. 376; H. TIETZE: In Art Bulletin, Vol. XV, 1933, p. 253.

DÜRER, ALBRECHT

GERMAN, 1471 - 1528

96 Ten Woodcuts.
Engraved between 1495-1511.

LENT ANONYMOUSLY.

A.—The Men's Bath.
Attributed date 1495-1498.
Watermark: Reichsapfel.
Bartsch 128; Dodgson 4.

B.—The Martrydom of St. Catherine.
Attributed date 1495-1498.
Watermark: Reichsapfel.
Bartsch 120; Dodgson 7.

C.—The Holy Family with Three Hares.
Attributed date 1495-1498.
Watermark: Reichsapfel.
Bartsch 102; Dodgson 9.

D.—The Woman of Babylon.
Attributed date 1498, or earlier. From the "Apocalypse" Series.
Watermark: Reichsapfel.
Bartsch 73; Dodgson 12.

E.—The Crucifixion.
Attributed date 1497-1500. From the "Great Passion" Series.
Watermark: Bull's Head with Cross and Serpent.
Bartsch 11; Dodgson 19.

F.—The Last Supper.
Dated 1510. From the "Great Passion" Series.
Bartsch 5; Dodgson 102.

16 *G.—The Death of the Virgin.*
Dated 1510. From the "Life of the Virgin" Series.
Watermark: Bull's Head with Cross and Flower.
Bartsch 93; Dodgson 106.

H.—The Adoration of the Magi.
Dated 1511.
Watermark: Bull's Head.
Bartsch 3; Dodgson 115.

I.—The Holy Family with SS. Joachim and Anne.
Dated 1511.
Bartsch 96; Dodgson 119.

J.—The Trinity.
Dated 1511.
Bartsch 122; Dodgson 116.

DÜRER, ALBRECHT

GERMAN, 1471-1528

17 *Eleven Engravings, Etchings, and Drypoints.*
Engraved between 1495-1516.

A.—The Holy Family with a Butterfly.
Attributed date 1495-1496, Monogram.
Watermark: Shield with Foliage and St. Anthony's Cross.
COLLECTIONS: Wilhelm H. F. K. Graf von Lepell (1755-1826); Emperor Friedrich Wilhelm III; Berlin Museum (duplicate).
Bartsch 44; Koehler 2; Dodgson 4.

LENT ANONYMOUSLY.

B.—St. Jerome in Penetence.
Attributed date 1497.
Watermark: Crowned Shield with Imperial Eagle.
Bartsch 61; Dodgson 11.

LENT ANONYMOUSLY.

C.—The Virgin with a Monkey.
Attributed date 1498-1499, Monogram.
Bartsch 42; Koehler 13; Dodgson 22.

LENT BY MR. LOUIS S. LEVY, NEW YORK.

97 D.—*The Effects of Jealousy.*

Known also as "Hercules". Attributed date 1500, Monogram.

Watermark: High Crown.

COLLECTION: August Artaria (1807-1893).

Bartsch 73; Dodgson 29; British Museum B. 73.

Mentioned by Giorgio Vasari, 1568.

LENT BY MR. LOUIS S. LEVY, NEW YORK.

E.—*The Coat of Arms with a Skull.*

Dated 1503, Monogram (*See* No. 87 in this catalogue).

COLLECTION: Dr. William August Ackermann (1793-1865).

Bartsch 101; Koehler 30; Dodgson 36.

LENT ANONYMOUSLY.

F.—*Adam and Eve.*

Dated 1504.

Watermark: Bull's Head.

COLLECTION: Henry Harper Benedict.

Bartsch 1; Dodgson 39.

LENT BY MR. LOUIS S. LEVY, NEW YORK.

G.—*The Knight, Death, and the Devil.*

Dated 1513, Monogram.

Bartsch 98; Koehler 69; Dodgson 70.

Mentioned by Giorgio Vasari, 1568.

LENT BY MR. LOUIS S. LEVY, NEW YORK.

H.—*The Virgin Seated by a Wall.*

Dated 1514, Monogram.

COLLECTION: Vinzent Mayer (1831-1918).

Bartsch 40; Koehler 75; Dodgson 72.

LENT BY MR. LOUIS S. LEVY, NEW YORK.

J.—*Melancholia.*

Dated 1514, Monogram.

Bartsch 74; Koehler 70; Dodgson 73.

Mentioned by Giorgio Vasari, 1568.

LENT ANONYMOUSLY.

J.—*Christ on the Mount of Olives.*

Etching, dated 155, Monogram.

Bartsch 19; Koehler 82; Dodgson 82.

LENT ANONYMOUSLY.

97 *K.—The Rape of Proserpine?*
Etching on iron, dated 1516, Monogram.
Watermark: Anchor in Circle.
Bartsch 72; Koehler 84; Dodgson 83.

LENT ANONYMOUSLY.

DYCK, SIR ANTHONY VAN

FLEMISH, 1599-1641

Born at Antwerp. At the age of ten he became the pupil of Hendrik van Balen, but his great instructor was Rubens. Before his twentieth birthday he was admitted a Master of the Antwerp Corporation of Painters. By the advice of Rubens, he visited Italy, and remained there five years. In 1630 he visited England, but not meeting with the reception he had anticipated, he returned to his own country. In 1632, Charles I sent an express invitation to him to return to London, and on this occasion he was most courteously received, being lodged by the King at Blackfriars, and in the following year knighted. His success as a portrait-painter enabled him to live in luxurious style. Next to Rubens the greatest master of the Flemish school of the seventeenth century.

98 *Self Portrait.*
Painted during his first Antwerp period, about 1620.

Canvas: 47 x 33½ inches.

LENT BY THE JULES S. BACHE COLLECTION, NEW YORK.

COLLECTIONS: Earl of Arlington (1618-1685); Dukes of Grafton; Lord Duveen of Millbank.
ENGRAVED by P. Pontius; etched by Geddes, and reproduced in "The True Effigies of the Most Eminent Painters," London, 1694, Plate 33.
EXHIBITIONS: Grosvenor Gallery, London, 1887; Royal Academy, Winter Exhibition, London, 1900; Detroit Institute of Arts, 1929.
BIBLIOGRAPHY: J. SMITH: Catalogue Raisonné, Part III, 1831, pp. 210-211, No. 742; E. SCHAEFFER: Van Dyck (Kl. der Kunst), 1909, p. 171, *Illust.*, L. CUST: Anthony Van Dyck, 1900, p. 19, *Illust.*, G. GLÜCK: Van Dyck (Kl. der Kunst), 1931, p. 532, No. 122a, *Illust.*, W. HEIL: In The Art News, April 27, 1929, p. 15, *Illust.*, ANON: Catalogue of the Bache Collection, New York, 1938, No. 26, *Illust.*

DYCK, SIR ANTHONY VAN

FLEMISH, 1599-1641

9 *Thomas Howard, Earl of Arundel.*
Painted about 1620-21, during the artist's first visit to England. Thomas Howard, 2nd Earl of Arundel, and Earl of Surrey and of Norfolk, was born in 1585, and died at Padua in 1646. He was employed in various diplomatic missions by Charles

I, and formed the first large collection of works of art in England, which was dispersed after his death. He was one of Van Dyck's most distinguished patrons.

Canvas: 44½ x 31½ inches.

LENT BY MRS. DANIEL GUGGENHEIM, NEW YORK.

COLLECTIONS: The Earl of Arundel; Citizen Róbit 1801; Duc d'Orleans; Duke of Sutherland; Fritz von Gans; Kurt W. Bachstitz.

ENGRAVED by G. Tardieu; G. W. Sharp; P. W. Tomkins.

EXHIBITIONS: Royal Institution, London, 1820; Royal Academy, London, 1876, 1890, 1900; Detroit Institute of Arts, 1929.

BIBLIOGRAPHY: w. y. ottley: Marquis of Stafford's Collection, Vol. III, 1818, p. 74, *Illust.*, J. smith: Catalogue Raisonné, Vol. III, 1831, p. 93, No. 322; g. f. waagen: Treasures of Art, Vol. II, 1854, p. 69; J. guiffrey: Antoine van Dyck, 1882, p. 256, No. 350; sir l. cust: Anthony Van Dyck, 1900, p. 268; m. rooses: Anthony van Dyck, 1900, p. 90; lord r. s. gower: Stafford House, Vol. I, 1910, *Illust.*, g. gronau: The Bachstitz Gallery, 1923, p. 4, No. 26, *Illust.*, w. r. valentiner: Van Dyck Exhibition, Detroit Inst., 1929, No. 14, *Illust.*, idem: *In* Zeitschrift für Bild. Kunst, Aug. 1929, pp. 105-111, *Illust.*, w. heil: *In* Pantheon, July 1929, p. 302, *Illust.*, g. glück: Van Dyck (Kl. der Kunst), 1931, p. 124, *Illust.*, a. m. frankfurter: *In* Art News, May 16, 1931, *Illust.*, idem: *In* Antiquarian, Oct. 1931, pp. 20-23, *Illust.*

DYCK, SIR ANTHONY VAN

FLEMISH, 1599-1641

100 *The Madonna and Child.*

Pl. 63

Painted during the Italian period of the artist (1621-27), or shortly afterward. A studio replica is in the 'Residence' at Munich. The model for the Madonna and Child is said to be Isabella Brandt, Rubens' first wife, and her boy, Nicholas; the types, however, are those familiar from a number of the other religious paintings by Van Dyck.

Panel: 25⅜ x 19½ inches.

LENT BY MRS. HENRY GOLDMAN, NEW YORK.

ENGRAVED by Lorenzi.

COLLECTIONS: The Earls of Harrington (whose family tradition declared it to be a direct purchase from Van Dyck).

BIBLIOGRAPHY: J. smith: Catalogue raisonné, Vol. III, 1831, p. 119, No. 429; g. f. waagen: Galleries of Art in Great Britain, Vol. IV, 1857, p. 238; f. j. mather: *In* Art in America, April 1919, pp. 103-104, *Illust.*, w. r. valentiner: Catalogue of the Henry Goldman Collection, 1922, No. 12, *Illust.*, idem: *In* Art News, May 1927, p. 15, *Illust.*

DYCK, SIR ANTHONY VAN

FLEMISH, 1599-1641

101 *John the Baptist in the Wilderness.*

Painted in Italy about 1625. Probably identical with the 'St. John in the Desert' described by Bellori (*Vite de Pittori, 1728, p.* 157) as the property of Sir Kenelm Digby, English Ambassador at the court of Pope Urban VIII.

Canvas: 56 x 46 inches.

LENT BY MR. STEPHEN S. PICHETTO, NEW YORK.

COLLECTIONS: Buen Retiro Palace, Madrid; Persigny family; Jean-Victor Fialin, Duc de Persigny; Maurice Cottier; Walter P. Fearon.

EXHIBITIONS: Detroit Institute of Arts, 1925 and 1929.

BIBLIOGRAPHY: G. GLÜCK: The Early Work of Van Dyck, 1925, pp. 26-31, *Illust.*, IDEM: *In* Zeitschrift für bildende Kunst, Vol. LIX, 1925-26; IDEM: Van Dyck (*Kl. der Kunst*), 1931, p. 534, No. 138, *Illust.*, W. R. VALENTINER: Van Dyck Exhn. Catalogue, Detroit Inst., 1929, No. 18, *Illust.*

DYCK, SIR ANTHONY VAN
FLEMISH, 1599-1641

2 *A Young Genoese Noblewoman.*

Painted about 1625 during the Genoese period of the artist.

Canvas: 25½ x 20½ inches.

LENT BY SENATOR AND MRS. SIMON GUGGENHEIM, NEW YORK.

COLLECTIONS: Private Collection in London; Count Alessandro Contini-Bonacossi; Julius Böhler.

BIBLIOGRAPHY: G. GLÜCK: Van Dyck (*Kl. der Kunst*), 1931, p. 159, *Illust.*, *In* International Studio, March, 31, p. 20, *Illust. in color.*

DYCK, SIR ANTHONY VAN
FLEMISH, 1599-1641

3 *Madonna and Child with St. Catherine.*

3 Painted about 1627. It is claimed by some authorities that this painting had been placed on the altar of Marie de' Medici's chapel in Brussels by the Infanta Isabella, and sent to London in 1631 by Sir Balthazar Gerbier, agent of Charles I of England. A slightly smaller replica, said to have come from the Palazzo Durazzo, Genoa, is in the Chicago Art Institute (presented by A. H. Sprague).

Canvas: 43½ x 36 inches.

LENT BY MR. AND MRS. WILLIAM R. TIMKEN, NEW YORK.

COLLECTIONS: Church of the Récollets, Antwerp; Welbore Ellis Agar; Robert, Earl Grosvenor; Duke of Westminster.

ENGRAVED by Bolswert, Blooteling, Snyers, Guzzi, Ragot, and others.

EXHIBITIONS: Grosvenor Gallery, London, 1887; Antwerp, 1899; Royal Academy, London, 1900; Detroit Institute of Arts, 1929.

BIBLIOGRAPHY: J. YOUNG: Pictures at Grosvenor House, London, 1820, p. 34, No. 96, *Illust.*, J. SMITH: Catalogue raisonné, Vol. III, 1831, p. 3, No. 3; W. H. CARPENTER: Memoir of Sir A. Van Dyck, 1844, pp. 57-64; G. F. WAAGEN: Treasures of Art, Vol. II, 1854, p. 165; J. GUIFFREY: Antoine Van Dyck, 1882, pp. 163, 245, No. 57; SIR L. CUST: Van Dyck, 1900, pp. 86-87, 200, 208,

219, 249, *Illust.*, M. ROOSES: Fifty Masterpieces of Van Dyck, 1900, p. 111, *Illust.*, J. LA FARGE AND A. F. JACCACI: Noteworthy Paintings in Amer. Comments by Guiffrey, Menotti, and Glück, 1907, pp. 475-491; E. SCHAEFFER: Van Dyck (Kl. der Kunst), 1909, p. 498, No. 81, *Illust.*; W. R. VALENTINER: Van Dyke Exhn. Catalogue, Detroit, 1929, No. 19, *Illust.*, W. R. VALENTINER: Van Dyck Exhn. Catalogue, Detroit, 1929, No. 19, *Illust.*, G. GLÜCK: Van Dyck (Kl. der Kunst), 1931, p. 543, No. 229, *Illust.*

DYCK, SIR ANTHONY VAN

FLEMISH, 1599-1641

104 Donna Polixena Spinola.

Painted during the second Antwerp period, 1628-32. Donna Polixena was the wife of Don Diego Filippo Guzman, Marchese di Leganez, Ambassador of Philip IV. of Spain to the Genoese Republic; he later served in the Netherlands.

Canvas: 44 x 38 inches.

LENT BY MR. SAMUEL H. KRESS, NEW YORK.

BIBLIOGRAPHY: Ambrogio Doria Palace, Genoa; Count Contini.
COLLECTIONS: INVENTORY of the Casa Doria, Genoa, 1680; M. MENOTTI: *In* Archivo Storico dell'Arte, II, 1897, pp. 281, 360, 432; SIR L. CUST: Van Dyck, 1900, p. 242; G. GLÜCK: Van Dyck *(Klas. der Kunst)*, 1931, *Illust.*, A. BURROUGHS: *In* Burl. Mag., Apr. 1933, pp. 175-176, *Illust.*, D. C. RICH: Catal. of Paintings and Sculpture, Art. Inst. of Chicago, 1933, p. 10, No. 59.

DYCK, SIR ANTHONY VAN

FLEMISH, 1599-1641

105 Jean Baptiste Van Bisthoven.

Rector of the Jesuit College, Antwerp. Painted during the artist's second Antwerp period, about 1630-32.

Canvas: 77 x 48 inches.

LENT BY MR. AND MRS. WALTER O. BRIGGS, DETROIT

COLLECTIONS: Wynn Ellis; Lord Battersea; Van Diemen Galleries, New York.
ENGRAVED by Adrian Lommelin (1636-1673).
EXHIBITIONS: Royal Academy, London, 1900; Guildhall, London, 1906; Detroit Institute of Arts, 1929.
BIBLIOGRAPHY: G. F. WAAGEN: Treasures of Art in Great Britain, Vol. II, 1854, p. 295; ANON: Pictures by Dutch and Flemish Masters, Wynn Ellis Colln., 1876, p. 17, No. 128 (As a Portrait of 'Mutio Viteleschi, General of the Jesuits'); ANON: Exhibition of Works by Van Dyck, Royal Academy, London, p. 32, No. 77; SIR A. G. TEMPLE: Catalogue of Old Masters, Guildhall, London, 1906, No. 91; W. R. VALENTINER: Paintings by Anthony Van Dyck, Detroit Inst. of Arts, 1929, No. 33, *Illust.*

DYCK, SIR ANTHONY VAN

16 *Robert Rich, Earl of Warwick.*

Painted about 1632-35. Robert Rich, second Earl of Warwick, was born in 1587. He was one of the original members of the company for the plantation of the Bermudas (1614), and was granted a seat on the council of the New England Company (1620). In 1624 he was made a member of the council of the Virginia government, and his name is connected indissolubly with the early history of the New England colonies. In 1632 he granted "the old patent of Connecticut", under which the town of Saybrook was established. In 1643 he was appointed Lord High Admiral of the Fleet, and bore the title of Governor-in-chief of all the colonies and other plantations subject to the English crown, on which authority he became associated with the foundation of the State of Rhode Island. Warwick died on April 19, 1658, and was buried at Felstead, Essex.

Canvas: 83 x 49 inches.

LENT BY THE JULES S. BACHE COLLECTION, NEW YORK.

COLLECTIONS: Marquess of Breadalbane; Hon. Mrs. Robert Baillie-Hamilton; Lord Duveen of Millbank.

EXHIBITION: Royal Academy, London, 1893.

BIBLIOGRAPHY: SIR L. CUST: Anthony van Dyck, 1900, p. 285; E. SINGLETON: Old World Masters, 1929, pp. 187-191, Illust., W. HEIL: In The Art News, April 27, 1929, p. 32, Illust., G. GLÜCK: Van Dyck (Kl. der Kunst), 1931, p. 562, No. 395, Illust., ANON: Catalogue of the Bache Collection, New York, 1938, No. 27, Illust.

DYCK, SIR ANTHONY VAN

17 *William Villiers, Viscount Grandison.*

54 Painted about 1632-33. Son of Sir Edward Villiers and nephew of the famous Duke of Buckingham, was born in 1613, and succeeded to the title of Viscount on the death of his great uncle, in 1630; he took part in the Civil War on the side of the Crown, and during the siege of Bristol, in 1643, was fatally wounded by a musket shot. A XVIIc. drawing in water-color by Boudan, after this portrait, is in the Bibliothéque Nationale (Gaignières colln.), Paris, called 'Henry de Lorraine, Duc de Guise'. Another portrait of Viscount Grandison by Van Dyck, painted some years later, is in the collection of the Earl of Clarendon.

Canvas: 82 x 49 inches.

LENT BY MRS. HARRY PAYNE WHITNEY, NEW YORK.

COLLECTIONS: Francois Roger de Gaignieres(?); Earl de Grey; Mrs. R. Bright of Stocks

House, Tring, Herts; Arthur Kay; Jacob Herzog; H. O. Miethke; William Collins Whitney; Harry Payne Whitney.

EXHIBITIONS: Antwerp, 1899; Royal Academy, London, 1893; Detroit Institute of Arts, 1929. BIBLIOGRAPHY: T. VON FRIMMEL: In Kunst-chronik, 1895, p. 386, Illust., SIR L. CUST: Van Dyck, 1900, pp. 127-128, 213, 275, Illust.; 1906 ed. p. 107, Illust.; M. ROOSES: Fifty Masterpieces of Van Dyck, 1900, p. 39, Illust., H. FIERENS-GEVAERT: Van Dyck, n.d. p. 95, Illust., W. R. VALENTINER: Art of the Low Countries, 1914, p. 213, Illust., W. R. VALENTINER: Van Dyck Exhn. Detroit, 1929, No. 40, Illust., W. HEIL: In Pantheon, 1929, p. 301, Illust., G. GLÜCK: Van Dyck (Kl. der Kunst), 1931, p. 565, No. 413, Illust., F. M. KELLY: In Apollo, Aug. 1935, pp. 91-94 (Identifies it as the Gaignieres picture), Illust.

DYCK, SIR ANTHONY VAN

FLEMISH, 1599-1641

108 Lucy, Countess of Carlisle.

Painted in 1637. Daughter of Henry Percy, 9th Earl of Northumberland, and his wife Dorothy, sister of the Earl of Essex; born 1600, married in 1617, James Hay, 1st Earl of Carlisle. She was one of the best known ladies of Charles I's court. Browning extolled her in his tragedy of "Stafford." She died in 1660. A study in chalk for this portrait, on greenish-gray paper, is in the British Museum.

Canvas: 85¾ x 50¾ inches.

LENT ANONYMOUSLY.

COLLECTIONS: Philip, Lord Wharton (1613-1695); Sir Robert Walpole; James West; Lord Frederick Campbell (1729-1816); Lord Gwydyr; Lord Duveen of Millbank.
ENGRAVED by Pieter van Gunst (1667-1724).
EXHIBITIONS: Detroit Institute of Arts, 1929; Nassau, B. W. I., 1938.
BIBLIOGRAPHY: J. GUIFFREY: Antoine Van Dyck, 1882, pp. 206 and 260, No. 435B; SIR LIONEL CUST: Anthony Van Dyck, 1900, p. 271, No. 36; L. BINYON: In Burl. Mag., Nov. 1906, p. 74, Drawing illust., W. R. VALENTINER: Van Dyck Exhibition, Detroit Inst., 1929, No. 47, Illust.; ANON: American Mag. of Art, June 1929, p. 363; W. HEIL: In Pantheon, July 1929, p. 305; A. M. FRANKFURTER: In Antiquarian, Oct. 1931, pp. 20-23, Illust., G. GLÜCK: Van Dyck (Kl. der Kunst), 1931, p. 447, Illust.

DYCK, SIR ANTHONY VAN

FLEMISH, 1599-1641

109 Prince Karl Ludwig, Elector Palatine.

Painted about 1637. Son of Friedrich V, King of Bohemia, and Princess Elizabeth, daughter of James I of England, was born 1617, and died 1680. In 1648, at the peace of Westphalia, he regained the Palatinate lost by his father in 1623. His sister Sophia was the mother of George I of England; his brother, Prince Rupert, was the hero of the English civil war. Another portrait of Prince Karl, with Rupert, by Van Dyck, is in the Louvre, Paris.

Canvas: 39¾ x 31¾ inches.

COLLECTIONS: Thomas Howard, Earl of Arundel (1592-1646); George Cranstoun, Lord Corehouse of Lanark; Col. Charles E. H. Edmondstoune-Cranstoun of Corehouse; Lieut-Col. Charles J. Edmonstoune-Cranstoun; Capt. Robert Langton Douglas.
ENGRAVED with inscription, by Wenzel Hollar, 1646; Thomas Jenner; and by John Payne, as a bust.
EXHIBITIONS: National Gallery, Edinburgh, 1883; Grosvenor Gallery, London, 1886-87.
BIBLIOGRAPHY: J. SMITH: Catalogue raisonné, Vol. III, 1831, p. 163, No. 569; VAN DYCK Exhibition Catalogue, National Gallery, Edinburgh, 1883, No. 417; F. G. STEPHENS: Sir A. Van Dyck Exhibition, Grosvenor Gall. London, 1887, p. 47, No. 52 (As Frederick V); G. GLÜCK: Van Dyck (Kl. der Kunst), 1931, p. 578, No. 514, Illust.

DYCK, SIR ANTHONY VAN

FLEMISH, 1599-1641

0 *John, Count of Nassau-Siegen* (Presumed).

62 Inscribed, *Aet 48. Ao.* Born 1585, died 1638; he was a cousin of William II of Orange, and Commander of the Forces of the Netherlands in 1630. He married Ernestine, daughter of the Comte de Ligne. The authenticated portraits of the Court of Nassau (Liechtenstein Gallery and Panshanger) seem to represent another personality. The painting is undoubtedly executed during Van Dyck's Genoese period, and is one of the finest portraits of this time. It has been recorded in the Balbi Palace Inventory as the Marquis Spinola, Italian General, with whose portrait, however, it has little likeness. It represents probably another Italian General whom Van Dyck painted in Genoa.

Canvas: 54 x 48 inches.

COLLECTIONS: Francesco M. Balbi, Balbi Palace, Genoa; A. Wilson; Lord Radstock; Alexander, first Lord Ashburton; Lord Duveen of Millbank; Mary M. Emery.
ENGRAVED by Paul Pontius.
EXHIBITIONS: British Gallery, London, 1821; Royal Academy, London, 1871, 1890, 1900, 1927; Detroit Institute of Arts, 1929.
BIBLIOGRAPHY: C. G. RATTI: In Instruzione, 1790, p. 193; J. SMITH: Catalogue Raisonné, Vol. III, 1831, pp. 106-107; G. F. WAAGEN: Treasures of Art, Vol. II, 1854, p. 108; H. SCHNEIDER: In Zeitsch. für Bild. Kunst, May 1927, p. 44; T. BORENIUS: Flemish and Belgian Art, Royal Acad., London, 1927, p. 63, No. 143, Illust.; W. R. VALENTINER: Paintings by Anthony Van Dyck, Detroit Inst., 1929, No. 27, Illust.; W. H. SIPLE: In Bulletin, Cincinnati Art. Mus., Jan. 1930, p. 7, Illust.; G. GLÜCK: Van Dyck (Kl. der Kunst), 1931, p. 539, No. 179, Illust.; PORTFOLIO of pictures, Mary M. Emery Colln., In Art Quarterly, Detroit, Winter, 1939, p. 96, Illust.

DYCK, SIR ANTHONY VAN

FLEMISH, 1599-1641

Portrait of Charles II. when a Boy.

Painted about 1639. Son of Charles I and Henrietta Maria; born 1630; after his father's execution in 1649 he lived in exile till his restoration in 1660. Died in 1685.

Canvas: 62 x 42 inches.

LENT BY THE HON. OSCAR B. CINTAS, HAVANA, CUBA.

COLLECTIONS: Earl of Harrington; Frank Sabin.

BIBLIOGRAPHY: A. C. R. CARTER: *Jn* The Year's Art, 1918, p. 313.

EWORTH, HANS

FLEMISH, ACTIVE 1540-1574

Born in Antwerp, where he was a member of the Guild. He went to England and settled at Southwark, about 1543, afterwards being employed as a painter by the Office of Revels. Between 1547 and 1573 he painted a considerable number of portraits of Tudor celebrities, most of which are still in the great mansions of England, many of them bearing the monogram HE. He was strongly influenced by Antonio Moro, and Hans Holbein.

112 *Queen Mary I. of England.*

Signed, and dated: HE 1554. Mary Tudor, called 'Bloody Mary', was the daughter of Henry VIII by his first wife Catherine of Aragon; she succeeded her half-brother, Edward VI. In 1553 she married Philip of Spain (later Philip II) the following year, and died in 1558. During her reign the total number of heretics against the papal power who were burned at the stake amounted to three-hundred.

Panel: 8½ x 7 inches.

LENT BY MR. FREDERICK R. BAY, NEW YORK.

COLLECTIONS: Lord Chesham; Wildenstein Galleries; Mrs. Cooper Hewitt.

EXHIBITIONS: Royal Academy, London, 1879; Wildenstein Galleries, 1928.

BIBLIOGRAPHY: CATALOGUE of the Royal Academy, London, 1879, No. 212 *(as Hans Holbein)*, M. BRYAN: Dictionary of Painters, Vol. II, 1904; *(as De Heere)*, SIR L. CUST: The Painter HE, *Jn* Walpole Society Annual, 1913, p. 15, *Jllust.*, G. BIERMANN: *Jn* Der Cicerone, Vol. XXI, 1929, p. 36, *Jllust.*

EYCK, JAN VAN

FLEMISH, 1385?-1441

Born at Maaseyck, Holland. In 1422 Jan was engaged as *valet de chambre* in the household of John of Bavaria at The Hague; in 1426 he left Holland for Flanders and entered the service of Philip III, Duke of Burgundy; soon afterwards he moved to Lille, and in 1428 went to Portugal. While at Lisbon he painted the portrait of the Infanta Isabella, the betrothed of Philip, and the following year returned to Bruges. He afterwards worked at Ghent on the famous Altarpiece left unfinished by his brother Hubert. He died at Bruges, and was buried in the Church of St. Donatian. Greatest of the fifteenth century Flemish masters, and founder of the School of Bruges.

3 The Madonna and Child.

46 Known as the 'Ince Hall Madonna'.

Painted in 1433, a year later than the celebrated Altarpiece at Ghent. *Signed:*
COMPLETV ANO D. MCCCCXXXIII P. IOHEM DE EYC BRVGIS; *also in-
scribed:* ALS JXH XAN ("As well as I can do"). First recognized as the work of
Jan Van Eyck by Dr. Waagen in 1854; previously it had been labelled "Dürer"!
Panel: 10⅜ x 7⅝ inches.

LENT BY THE NATIONAL GALLERY OF VICTORIA,

MELBOURNE, AUSTRALIA.

COLLECTIONS: Henry Blundell (1724-1810), Ince Hall, Lancashire; Charles Robert Blundell
(d. 1837); Thomas Weld-Blundell; Charles J. Weld-Blundell of Ince.
EXHIBITIONS: Royal Academy, London, 1884; Burlington Fine Arts Club, London, 1892;
Guildhall, London, 1906; National Gallery, London, 1922; National Gallery of Victoria, Mel-
bourne, since 1922.
BIBLIOGRAPHY: G. F. WAAGEN: Treasures of Art, Vol. III, 1854, p. 249; CROWE AND CAVAL-
CASELLE: Early Flem. Painters, 1857, pp. 338-341; W. H. J. WEALE: Jn Revue de l'Art Chrétien,
1883, pp. 193-195; F. G. STEPHENS: Jn Athenaeum, Oct. 6, 1883, p. 440; H. VON TSCHUDI: Jn
Rep. für Kunstw., Vol. XVI, 1893, p. 440; L. KAEMMERER: H. u. J. van Eyck, 1898, pp. 58-60;
K. VOLL: Die Werke des J. van Eyck, 1900, pp. 87-90; W. VON BODE: Jn Berlin, Jahrb., 1901, p. 122;
M. DVORAK: Jn Austrian Jahrb., Vol. XXIV, 1904, pp. 195-196; H. FIERENS: Etudes sur l'Art Flam.,
1905, p. 142; K. VOLL: Altn. Malerei, 1906, p. 35; SIR A. G. TEMPLE: Early Flem. Painters, Guild-
hall, London, 1906, No. 3; M. J. FRIEDLÄNDER: Jn Rep. Kunstw., Vol. XXIX, 1906, p. 574; W. H. J.
WEALE: Jn Burl. Mag., Vol. IX, 1906, p. 184; M. SIEBERT: Die Madonnendarstelling, 1906, p. 11;
E. DURAND-GREVILLE: Jn Arts anc. Flandre, Vol. II, 1907, pp. 62-63; H. HYMANS: Les Van Eyck,
1907, p. 72, Jllust.; W. H. J. WEALE: H. et J. Van Eyck, 1908, p. 65, Jllust.; E. C. GREVILLE: H. et
J. Van Eyck, 1910, p. 133, Jllust.; W. H. J. WEALE AND M. BROCKWELL: The Van Eycks, 1912,
p. 109, Jllust., SIR M. CONWAY: The Van Eycks, 1921, p. 68; M. J. FRIEDLÄNDER: Van Eyck bis
Bruegel, 1921, p. 183; SIR C. J. HOLMES: Jn Burl. Mag., Nov. 1922, pp. 232-235, Jllust.; M. W.
BROCKWELL: Jn Art in Amer., Apr. 1923, pp. 143-149, Jllust.; M. J. FRIEDLÄNDER: Die Van Eyck,
1924, p. 53, Jllust.; M. VAUGHAN: Jn Parnassus, May 1939, p. 6, Jllust.

EYCK, JAN VAN, and PETRUS CHRISTUS

FLEMISH SCHOOL, XV C.

4 St. Jerome in his Study.

7 Dated on the wall to the right of the chair in very small cyphers: 1442. Jan Van
Eyck died in 1441; Petrus Christus, his closest pupil, seems to have taken over his
studio, but did not become a member of the Guild until 1444. The present painting
comes in style nearer to Jan van Eyck, and is superior in quality in most parts than
any other known painting by Petrus Christus. It seems, therefore, possible that Jan
van Eyck began the painting and left it unfinished, and that after his death it was
completed and dated by Petrus Christus, and sold under the name of Van Eyck.
If we accepted this supposition the painting would be identical with the St. Jerome

by Jan van Eyck mentioned in the possession of Lorenzo de' Medici in 1492, and with the one described in the house of Antonio Pasqualino at Venice, in the third decade of the sixteenth century (according to Marc Antonio Michiel, the 'Anonimo Morelli ano'). This painting was acquired by the former owner from a private collection in Venice. That its composition was known in Florence at the time of Lorenzo de' Medici is proved by the fact that Domenico Ghirlandajo was clearly influenced by it when he painted the fresco in the Ognissanti in Florence in 1480.

Panel: 8¼ x 5¼ inches.

LENT BY THE DETROIT INSTITUTE OF ARTS, DETROIT.

EXHIBITIONS: Royal Academy, London, 1927; Chicago Art Institute, 1933; Worcester Art Museum, 1939; Philadelphia Museum of Art, 1939.

BIBLIOGRAPHY: w. r. valentiner: Jn Bull. of the Detroit Inst. of Arts, March, 1925, pp. 58-59, Jllust., anon: May, 1925, p. 290, Jllust., m. j. friedländer: Jn Der Kunstwanderer, May, 1925, p. 297; t. borenius: Catalogue of Flemish and Belgian Art, Royal Academy, London, 1927, No. 14, Jllust., r. fry: Jn Burlington Magazine, Feb. 1927, p. 59, Jllust., p. lambotte: Jn Apollo, Jan. 1927, p. 51, Jllust., l. baldass: Jn Belvedere, Vol. XI, 1927, p. 82; f. winkler: Jn Festschrift für Max J. Friedländer, 1927, pp. 94-98, Jllust., w. r. valentiner: Catalogue of Paintings in the Detroit Institute, 1930, No. 33, Jllust., m. j. friedländer: Jn Die Altniederländische Malerie, Vol. XIV, 1937, p. 79, Jllust., h. marceau, and others: The Worcester-Philadelphia Exhn. of Flemish Painting, 1939, p. 17, No. 2, Jllust.

FABRITIUS, CAREL

DUTCH, 1622-1654

Born at De Beemster, near Amsterdam, and was killed in the explosion at Delft, Oct. 12, 1654. Shortly after his marriage in 1641 he settled at Amsterdam, and studied under Rembrandt, of whom he was the most notable pupil. In 1650, eight years after the death of his first wife, he went to Delft, and married there for the second time. Vermeer was probably his pupil at Delft. Characteristic of his style is that he places his figures generally dark against a light background, reversing thus a method of his master who usually lights his figures strongly against a dark background.

115 *Portrait of Rembrandt.*

Pl. 70   Painted about 1648. One of the rare portraits of Rembrandt done by one of his pupils, which should be compared with the many self-portraits known by Rembrandt.

Canvas: 14¾ x 12 inches.

LENT BY DR. C. J. K. VAN AALST, HOEVELAKEN, HOLLAND.

COLLECTION: Otto von Wesendonck.

EXHIBITION: Provinzial-Museum, Bonn, for several years.

BIBLIOGRAPHY: w. cohen: Provinzial Museum in Bonn, Katalog der Gemäldegalerie, 1927; m. lempertz: Wesendonck-von Bissing Sammlung, 1935, No. 85; w. r. valentiner: Catalogue of Paintings in the Van Aalst Collection, 1939, p. 19, Jllust.

FOUQUET, JEAN

FRENCH, 1415?-1480?

Court painter to Louis XI. In 1447 he travelled in Italy and painted, in Rome, the portrait of Pope Eugenius IV, for the sacristy of Minerva. He returned to France and grafted the elements of the Tuscan style of painting upon the style of the Van Eycks, and thus became the founder of an important new school; one of his sponsors was Etienne Chevalier, Treasurer of France, for whom he painted the celebrated Book of Hours. One of his most important paintings was a diptych for the Cathedral of Melun, now separated between the Antwerp and Berlin Galleries.

6 *Portrait of Jean, Batard d'Orléans.*

Count of Dunois and Langueville, Grand Constable of France, and Companion-in-arms of Joan of Arc.

Panel: 16 x 9¾ inches.

LENT FROM THE COLLECTION OF WILLIAM GOLDMAN, NEW YORK.
COLLECTIONS: Duc de Langueville-Estouteville; Comte de Gaignières; Duc de Choiseul; and Gabeau d'Amboise.
EXHIBITIONS: The Louvre, Paris, 1904; Knoedler Galleries, New York, 1935.
BIBLIOGRAPHY: H. BOUCHOT: Catalogue de l'Exposition des Primitifs Francais au Palais du Louvre, Paris, 1904, No. 52; C. OULMONT: Un Portrait de Dunois, par Jehan Fouquet. Jn La Renaissance, May 1926, p. 299, Jllust.; W. R. VALENTINER: Unknown Masterpieces, 1930, No. 73, Jllust.; CATALOGUE of XV Century Portraits, Knoedler Galleries, New York, 1935, No. 4, Jllust.; C. STERLING: La Peinture française, Les Primitifs, p. 139, No. 183, Jllust.

FRAGONARD, JEAN HONORÉ

FRENCH, 1732-1806

Born at Grasse; in 1750 his family moved to Paris, where he entered Boucher's studio. In 1752 he gained the "prix de Rome." In 1756 he met Hubert Robert, and the Abbé St. Non, with whom he made a tour of South Italy and Sicily. In 1768 he painted the celebrated "Escarpolette," now in the Wallace Collection. In 1769 he married Marie Anne Gérard, the miniature painter, and was given an apartment in the Louvre, where he lived sumptuously. The Revolution ruined him, and in 1749 he fled to Grasse, where he finished the series of panels, originally begun for Madame du Barry, which are now in the Frick Gallery, New York. He returned to Paris, an obscure man, and died in 1806. Together with Watteau greatest French painter of the eighteenth century.

Le Billet Doux ('The Love Letter').

The Sitter represents the daughter of François Boucher, the noted French painter, before her marriage with M. de Cuviller, whose name appears on the letter which she is placing in the bouquet of flowers.

Canvas: 32¾ x 26⅜ inches.

LENT BY THE JULES S. BACHE COLLECTION, NEW YORK.

COLLECTIONS: Baron Feuillet de Conches; Madame Jäger-Schmidt; Ernest Cronier; Ernest Bardac; Wildenstein Galleries.

EXHIBITIONS: Palais de la Présidence du Corps Legislatifs, Paris, 1874; L'Ecole des Beaux-Arts, Paris, 1897; Galerie Georges Petit, Paris, 1907; Metropolitan Museum of Art, New York, 1920, and 1935; Royal Academy, London, 1932; San Francisco, 1934; Cleveland Museum, 1936; Paris, 1937.

BIBLIOGRAPHY: BARON R. PORTALÉS: Honoré Fragonard, sa vie et son œuvre, 1889, p. 272; A. ALEXANDRE: In "Les Arts", Nov. 1905, p. 7, Illust.; A. DAYOT ET L. VAILLAT: L'œuvre de Chardin et de Fragonard, Illust.; G. GRAPPE: Fragonard, 1913, p. 44, Illust.; P. DE NOLHAC: Fragonard, 1732-1806, 1918, Frontispiece in color; L. REAU: L'Art Francais aux Etats-Unis, 1926, p. 142; E. SINGLETON: Old World Masters, 1929, pp. 318-320, Illust.; W. R. VALENTINER: Unknown Masterpieces, 1930, No. 82, Illust.; H. TIETZE: Europaischer Malerei in Amerika, 1935, p. 261, Illust.; ANON: Catalogue of the Bache Collection, New York, 1938, No. 50, Illust.

FRAGONARD, JEAN HONORÉ
FRENCH, 1732 - 1806

118 L'Etude ('Study').

Pl. 83 Painted in 1769. Belongs to a series of decorative paintings representing allegorical subjects (imagination, music, etc.), for which various friends of Fragonard posed; unfortunately it is not known who sat for the present picture. Two paintings of the series have inscriptions on the backs saying that the pictures were painted in one hour.

Canvas: 32 x 25½ inches.

LENT BY THE MUSÉE DU LOUVRE, PARIS.

COLLECTION: Louis La Caze, 1869.

EXHIBITION: Three French Reigns, London, 1933.

BIBLIOGRAPHY: F. REISET: Catalogue La Caze, Musée impérial du Louvre, 1870, No. 198; BARON R. PORTALÉS: Honoré Fragonard, sa vie et son œuvre, 1889, p. 276; A. DAYOT: L'Image de la Femme, 1899, p. 227, Illust.; P. DE NOLHAC: J. H. Fragonard, 1732-1806, 1906, p. 90, Illust.; G. GRAPPE: Honoré Fragonard, 1913, p. 116, Illust. in color; G. BRIÈRE: Catalogue des Peintures, École Française, Musée National du Louvre, 1924, p. 103, No. 297, Illust.; R. H. WILENSKI: French Painting, 1931, p. 161; A. MAUROIS: Three French Reigns, Louis XIV-XVI, London, 1933, p. 65, No. 470, Illust.

FRAGONARD, JEAN HONORÉ
FRENCH, 1732 - 1806

119 The Repose of the Holy Family.

Painted about 1770-1775. This picture is closely connected with a large altarpiece painted by Fragonard now in St. Nizier at Troyes. An almost identical composition, also by Fragonard, is in the Jacobs collection of the Baltimore Museum.

Canvas, oval: 21⅜ x 17¾ inches.

COLLECTIONS: Charles Pillet; Mme. Oger de Bréarf; M. Chevallier; Mme. Richard Feuillet; Messrs. Wildenstein.
EXHIBITIONS: Gimpel and Wildenstein Galleries, New York, 1914; Chicago Art Institute, 1933.
BIBLIOGRAPHY: CATALOGUE des Tableaux dans le Collection Mme. Oger de Bréarf, 1886, No. 19; BARON R. PORTALIS: Honoré Fragonard, 1889, p. 287; P. DE NOLHAC: J. H. Fragonard, 1906, p. 166; D. C. RICH: Catalogue of Sculptures and Paintings, Chicago Art Inst., 1933, p. 33, No. 215.

FRAGONARD, JEAN HONORÉ

FRENCH, 1732-1806

L'Invocation à l'Amour ('The Invocation of Love').

Painted about 1780-1785.

Canvas: 20½ x 24¾ inches.

LENT BY MR. JOHN MORTIMER SCHIFF, NEW YORK.
COLLECTIONS: Duc de Rochefoucauld-Liancourt, 1827; Duc de Polignac; Duchesse de Polignac, née Crillon; M. L. Neumann; Jean Bartholoni; Mortimer L. Schiff.
EXHIBITIONS: Musée des Arts Decoratifs, Paris, 1921; Three French Reigns, London, 1933.
BIBLIOGRAPHY: G. WILDENSTEIN: Exposition d'oeuvres de Fragonard, Musée des Arts Decoratifs, Paris, 1921, p. 30, No. 65, Illust.; P. DORBEC: In Gaz. d. Beaux-Arts, July 1921, p. 26; L. REAU: Hist. de la Peinture Française, Vol. II, 1926, p. 29; IDEM: L'Art Française aux Etats-Unis, 1926, p. 149; Catalogue Three French Reigns, Louis XIV-XVI, 1933, No. 115, Illust.; E. SINGLETON: Old World Masters, 1929, p. 317, Illust.

FRAGONARD, JEAN HONORÉ

1732-1806

Mlle. Marie Madeleine Guimard.

Noted French dancer; born in Paris, 1743, and for twenty-five years was the star of the Paris Opera; she made herself even more famous by her love affairs, especially by her long romance with the Prince de Soubise. She retired in 1789, and married Jean Étienne Despréaux, celebrated playwright. She died in 1816.

Canvas, oval: 29 x 24 inches.

LENT BY MRS. I. D. LEVY, NEW YORK.
COLLECTIONS: Mlle. Guimard, in her residence in the Chaussée d'Autin, Paris; Sir Hugh Lane; Robert O'Neil; Wildenstein Galleries.
BIBLIOGRAPHY: LADY DILKE: French Painters of the Eighteenth Century, 1899, p. 63; H. MACFALL: The French Genius, 1911, p. 232.

FRANCESCO DI GIORGIO

SIENESE, 1439-1502

Pupil of Vecchietta, influenced by Pollaiuolo, Girolamo da Cremona and possibly

Botticelli; became a collaborator of Neroccio until 1476, after which he devoted himself partly to military architecture and engineering at the court of Urbino. His paintings are noted for their delicate refinement and perception of feminine grace, and he was one of the most versatile geniuses of Siena during the Quattrocento.

122 *Scenes from the Life of Tobias.*

A cassone panel; of the same dimensions, and painted apparently about the same period (1470) as the "Rape of Europa" in the Louvre.

Panel: 17 x 70 inches.

LENT BY THE WILLIAM RANDOLPH HEARST COLLECTION, NEW YORK.
COLLECTIONS: Palazzo Ducale, Urbino; Marczell von Nemes.
BIBLIOGRAPHY: P. SCHUBRING: Cassoni, 1923, Suppl., p. 5, No. 936, *Illust.*; A. VENTURI: Studi dal Vero, 1927, pp. 87-88, *Illust.*; L. VENTURI: Collection Marczell de Nemes, 1928, p. 6, No. 15, *Illust.*; R. VAN MARLE: Italian Schools, Vol. XVI, 1937, pp. 256, 286, 292, *Illust.*

FRENCH SCHOOL
BURGUNDIAN, FIRST HALF OF THE XV CENTURY

123 *Portrait of a Noble Lady.*

Presumed to be Michelle de France (1394-1422), daughter of Charles VI, King of France, and Isabella of Bavaria, and wife of Philip the Good, Duke of Burgundy, (1394-1422).

Panel: 10½ x 13½ inches.

LENT ANONYMOUSLY.

COLLECTIONS: George Salting; Messrs. Agnew; Baron W. von Bissing; Ernst Rosenfeld.
EXHIBITIONS: New Gallery, London, 1899-1900; Knoedler Galleries, New York, 1935.
BIBLIOGRAPHY: W. SCHMIDT: *In* Repertorium für Kunstw., 1900, p. 251; H. NASSE: *In* Münchener Jahrb., Vol. VI, 1911, pp. 94-118, 208-234; IDEM: *In* Revue Archéologique, 1912, pp. 406-412, *Illust.*; W. H. J. WEALE: Exhibition of Flemish Pictures, New Gallery, London, 1899-1900, No. 34; S. REINACH: Répertoire des Peintures, Vol. IV, 1918, p. 552, *Illust.*; S. DE RICCI: *In* Burl. Mag., Apr. 1922, p. 166, *Illust.*; ANON: Tableaux Anciens, Colln. Baron von Bissing, a La Haye, 1926, p. 3, No. 6, *Illust.*; ANON: Fifteenth Century Portraits, Knoedler Galleries, New York, 1935, No. 3, *Illust.*

FRENCH SCHOOL, NORTH
FIFTEENTH CENTURY

124 *Descent from the Cross.*

Painted about 1480. The execution of the figures in *grisaille* (with the exception of Christ) make it probable that the panel formed the outer part of a wing of a small altar.

Panel: 32 x 18 inches.

LENT BY THE EDWIN D. LEVINSON COLLECTION, NEW YORK.
COLLECTION: Wildenstein Galleries, Paris.

FRENCH SCHOOL, NORTH

5 *St. Lawrence and a Donor.*

Painted about 1520. Probably the wing of a triptych. The composition, strongly under Flemish (Antwerp) influence, shows a remarkably fine color-scheme.

Panel: 18¾ x 13 inches.

LENT BY MRS. LEON SCHINASI, NEW YORK.

COLLECTION: Van Diemen Gallery, Berlin.

FRENCH SCHOOL

SIXTEENTH CENTURY

Portrait of a Nobleman.

Closely in style to Corneille de Lyon (1520?-1574). Attributed by M. J. Fried-länder to a preëminent French Master of about 1540.

Panel: 15 x 12¾ inches.

LENT FROM THE WILLIAM GOLDMAN COLLECTION, NEW YORK.

COLLECTION: Gregoire, Count de Strogonoff; Paul Bottenwieser.

EXHIBITION: Art Institute of Chicago, 1933.

BIBLIOGRAPHY: D. C. RICH: Catalogue of Paintings, Art Inst. of Chicago, 1933, p. 3, No. 18.

FRENCH SCHOOL

PROVENCE, FIFTEENTH CENTURY (CIRCA 1440)

Saint Robertus of Molesmes.

This picture, the right wing of an Altarpiece, was probably painted for one of the Cistercian monasteries, founded by St. Robertus, or Robert, Abbot founder of the Cistercian Order in France. St. Robertus enjoined on his monks the wearing of a white habit, and directed that all the churches of his Order should be dedicated to the Virgin. After many times seeking to retire from the government of his monastery, St. Robertus died at the Abbey of Molesmes in 1108.

Panel: 24 x 13 inches.

LENT BY MRS. LILLIAN HENKEL HAASS, DETROIT.

EXHIBITIONS: Kleinberger Galleries, New York, 1927; Detroit Institute of Arts, 1928.

BIBLIOGRAPHY: Catalogue of French Primitives, Kleinberger Galleries, New York, 1927, p. 44, No. 14, *Illust.*; W. R. VALENTINER: French Gothic Art, Detroit Institute of Arts, 1928, No. 2, *Illust.*, IDEM: Unknown Masterpieces, 1930, No. 72, *Illust.*

GADDI, AGNOLO

FLORENTINE, 1333?-1396

Pupil and follower of his father, Taddeo Gaddi. In 1366 he worked with Jacopo del Casentino and Giovanni da Milano, and in 1367 he was painting in the Loggia della Piazza della Signoria, Florence. He went to Rome in 1369 and was occupied in the Vatican. He was again in Florence in 1370 and remained there until about 1390, when he went to Prato. He returned to Florence and died there two years afterwards. He was the last of the Giotto followers in the fourteenth century, influenced by Sienese and French art.

128 *The Coronation of the Virgin.*

Panel: 64 x 31 inches.

LENT BY MR. SAMUEL H. KRESS, NEW YORK.

COLLECTION: The Hon. W. Keith Rous.

GADDI, TADDEO

FLORENTINE, ACTIVE 1300-1366

Painter and architect, born in Florence. He studied under his father, Gaddo Gaddi, a mosaic worker, a friend of Cimabue, and afterwards assisted Giotto, his godfather. Between 1332-1338 he executed several frescoes in the Baroncelli Chapel in Santa Croce, Florence. In 1342 he painted at Pisa, and in 1349 he was noted as one of the best painters in Florence. The most important Florentine painter among the immediate followers of Giotto.

129 *The Madonna Enthroned.*

Pl. 1 This picture belongs to the master's later period, of which the most characteristic example is the dated altarpiece of 1355 in the Uffizi.

Panel: 33¾ x 20¾ inches.

LENT BY MR. MAITLAND F. GRIGGS, NEW YORK.

COLLECTION: J. Kerr-Lawson.

EXHIBITION:

BIBLIOGRAPHY: R. OFFNER: *In* L'Arte, Vol. XXIV, 1921, p. 116, *Illust.*, R. VAN MARLE: Ital. Schools of Painting, Vol. III, 1924, p. 342; R. OFFNER: Studies in Florentine Painting, 1927, p. 59 et seq, *Illust.*, ANON: *In* Connoisseur, Oct. 1931, p. 288, *Illust.*, B. BERENSON: Ital. Pictures, 1932, p. 215 (Ital. edn., 1936, p. 66, *Illust.*); L. VENTURI: Ital. Paintings in Amer., 1933, No. 50, *Illust.*

GAINSBOROUGH, R.A., THOMAS

ENGLISH, 1727-1788

Born at Sudbury, Suffolk, four years after the birth of Sir Joshua Reynolds. He went to London at the age of fifteen and studied under Gravelot and Hayman.

In 1745 he returned to Sudbury and set up a studio as a portrait painter, but soon moved to Ipswich, remaining there until 1760, when he went to Bath. In 1768 (excepting 1772-1776) he was a constant exhibitor at the Royal Academy; on account of a disagreement with the Council he sent nothing to the exhibitions after that year. He painted over 300 pictures, more than 220 being portraits. His celebrated "Blue Boy" is now in the Huntington Collection at Pasadena. He was the rival of Reynolds as a portrait painter and was regarded as the most brilliant landscape artist of his day.

Portrait of James Christie.

Painted in 1778 and presented by Gainsborough to the sitter. Founder of the firm of Christie, Manson and Woods, noted London auctioneers. Born at Perth, Scotland, 1730, became a midshipman in the Royal Navy, and later assistant to Annersley, auctioneer in London; about 1766 started his own business in Pall Mall. He died in 1803.

Canvas: 49½ x 39½ inches.

LENT BY MR. J. PAUL GETTY, NEW YORK.

COLLECTIONS: James Christie; James Archibald Christie, great-grandson of the sitter; P. and D. Colnaghi.

EXHIBITIONS: Royal Academy, London, 1778; South Kensington Museum, 1867; Royal Academy, 1891; Rijksmuseum, Amsterdam, 1936.

ENGRAVED in Mezzotint by G. Sanders.

BIBLIOGRAPHY: s. REDGRAVE: National Portraits Exhibition, South Kensington Museum, 1867, p. 171, No. 793; H. GRAVES: Engravings from the Works of Gainsborough, 1875, No. 39, *Illust.*, W. ROBERTS: Memorials of Christies, Vol. I, 1897, p. 11, *Illust.*, SIR W. ARMSTRONG: Gainsborough and his place in Eng. Art, 1898, p. 193; M. MENPES AND J. GREIG: Gainsborough, 1909, p. 123; W. T. WHITLEY: Art in England, 1800-1820, 1928, p. 66, *Illust.*, L. VAN PUYVELDE: *In Apollo*, Oct. 1936, p. 227, *Illust.*, ANON: Catalogus, Tentoonstelling van oude Kunst, Rijksmuseum, Amsterdam, 1936, p. 13, No. 51, *Illust.*

GAINSBOROUGH, R.A., THOMAS
ENGLISH, 1727-1788

The Harvest Waggon.

Painted in 1784. Signed T.G. The girl with her foot on the cartwheel is Gainsborough's eldest daughter, Mary, and the one in the background of the cart, with the large hat, is his youngest daughter, Margaret. The team of horses belonged to the painter's messenger, Walter Wiltshire.

Canvas: 48 x 59 inches.

LENT BY MR. FRANK P. WOOD, TORONTO, CANADA.

COLLECTIONS: Prince of Wales (afterwards George IV); Mrs. Fitzherbert; Col. H. G. Dawson Damer; John Gibbons; Thomas Gibbons; Rev. Benjamin Gibbons; Sir Lionel Phillips; Judge Elbert H. Gary.

EXHIBITIONS: British Institution, 1841; Royal Academy, London, 1870, and 1890; Agnew Galleries, London, 1895; New Gallery, London, 1899-1900; Art Gallery of Toronto, 1929.

66

BIBLIOGRAPHY: SIR W. ARMSTRONG: Gainsborough, 1898, p. 207, *Illust.*, W. T. WHITLEY: Artists and their Friends, Vol. II, 1928, pp. 63-66, *Illust.*, E. SINGLETON: Old World Masters, 1929, p. 391, *Illust.*

GAINSBOROUGH, R.A., THOMAS
ENGLISH, 1727-1788

132 *Sir John Edward Swinburne, Bart.*

Painted in 1785. Sir John Edward Swinburne, 6th Bart., F.R.S., F.S.A., eldest son of Sir Edward Swinburne, Bart. (1733-1786) and his wife Lady Christiana Dillon Swinburne, was born in 1762, and died in 1860; he married, 1787, Emilia Elizabeth Bennet (d. 1839) of Beckenham, niece of Frances, Duchess of Northumberland. His second son, Charles Henry, admiral R.N., was the father of Algernon Charles Swinburne (1837-1909), the celebrated English poet.

Canvas: 26½ x 25 inches.

LENT ANONYMOUSLY.

COLLECTIONS: Sir John Edward Swinburne, 6th Bart.; Sir John Swinburne, 7th Bart.
EXHIBITION: Royal Mining Exhibition, Newcastle-on-Tyne, 1887.

GAINSBOROUGH, R.A., THOMAS
ENGLISH, 1727-1788

133 *Mr. Edward Swinburne.*

Painted in 1785. Edward Swinburne, younger brother of Sir John Edward Swinburne, Bart., whose portrait is also included in this Exhibition, was born in 1765; the date of his death is not recorded.

Canvas: 27 x 23¼ inches.

LENT ANONYMOUSLY.

COLLECTIONS: Sir John Edward Swinburne, 6th Bart.; Sir John Swinburne, 7th Bart.
EXHIBITION: Royal Mining Exhibition, Newcastle-on-Tyne, 1887.

GAINSBOROUGH, R.A., THOMAS
ENGLISH, 1727-1788

134 *The Market Cart.*

Pl. 94   Painted about 1787. One of the masterpieces of landscape painting by the artist. Identical in composition with the picture of the same name in the National Gallery, London, which was inspired by the country around Lulworth Castle in Dorset.

Canvas: 48 x 40 inches.

LENT BY MR. AND MRS. CHARLES T. FISHER, DETROIT.

COLLECTIONS: Mrs. Thomas Gainsborough; William Neave; Sir Thomas Neave, Bart.; Lord Michelham.
EXHIBITIONS: British Institution, 1817; Detroit Institute of Arts, 1927; Howard Young Galleries, New York, 1928.
BIBLIOGRAPHY: ANON: Catalogue of Pictures by deceased British Artists, British Institution, London, 1917, p. 13, No. 72; G. W. FULCHER: Thomas Gainsborough, 1856, p. 200; W. HEIL: Old and Modern Masters, Detroit Institute of Arts, 1927, No. 56, *Illust.*, W. R. VALENTINER: Unknown Masterpieces, 1930, No. 97, *Illust.*

GAINSBOROUGH, R.A., THOMAS
ENGLISH, 1727-1788

Mrs. Alexander Champion.

Frances, daughter of William Hind, barrister-at-law, London, and his wife Elizabeth. Married Alexander Champion, Captain in the Bengal Army, 1758, Major, 1763, Lieut.-Colonel, 1774. He resigned in 1776, returned to England with his wife, settled at Bath, and died in 1793. She later married the Rev. Thomas Leman of Wenhaston House, Suffolk, Chancellor of Cloyne, and died in January 1818.

Canvas: 30 x 35 inches.

LENT BY MR. ANDRÉ DE COPPET, NEW YORK.

COLLECTIONS: Mrs. Alexander Champion; Miss Frances Conway; Charles Cobbe; Thomas Moberley Cobbe; Mrs. Daniel C. Jackling.
EXHIBITIONS: Dublin, 1872; California Palace of Legion of Honor, San Francisco, 1933.
BIBLIOGRAPHY: CATALOGUE of Paintings exhibited at the Dublin Gallery, 1872, No. 194; L. MEEHAN: Famous Houses of Bath and District, 1901, p. 164; W. HEIL: Exhibition of English Painting, Calif. Pal. of the Legion of Honor, San Francisco, 1933, p. 17, No. 9, *Illust.*, T. C. HOWE: *In* Fine Arts, July 1933, p. 12, *Illust.*

GAINSBOROUGH, R.A., THOMAS
ENGLISH, 1727-1788

Lieut.-Gen. Sir William Draper, K.B.

Born at Bristol, 1721; at one time aide-de-camp to the 2nd Duke of Marlborough; afterwards saw service in India and Manila. In 1770 he arrived at Charleston, North Carolina, journeyed through Maryland, and at New York during the same year married Susanna, daughter of Oliver De Lancey, brigadier-general of loyalist provincials during the American War of Independence. He died at Bath, England, in 1787.

Canvas: 50 x 40 inches.

LENT BY MRS. EDNA LEVINSON REPIN AND
MRS. EVELYN LEVINSON STEIN, NEW YORK.

COLLECTIONS: Sir Charles Brownlow; Mrs. Arthur Shirley; Mrs. Wilfred Brownlow; Miss Frances Shirley; John Levy Galleries.

EXHIBITION: Cincinnati Art Museum, 1931.
BIBLIOGRAPHY: w. h. siple: Exhibition of Paintings by Gainsborough, Cincinnati Art Museum, Ohio, 1931, p. 23, No. 8, *Illust.*; idem: *In* Art News, May 2, 1931, *Illust.*; w. heil: *In* Pantheon, Sept. 1931, p. 378, *Illust.*

GERMAN SCHOOL

COLOGNE, FIFTEENTH CENTURY

137 *Altar of the Adoration of the Magi.*

Pl. 39 Triptych, painted about 1410-1420. *Central Panel:* Adoration of the Magi; *Left Wing:* St. James and St. Philip; *Right Wing:* St. Severus and St. Walburga. Traditionally ascribed to Master Wilhelm of Cologne, but since this painter died before 1378 this attribution cannot be sustained. Stylistically related to the *Madonna with the Sweet-pea blossom* (Cologne), and to the *Madonna Enthroned with Saints* (Johnson Collection, Philadelphia).

Panels: 31¾ x 38 inches.

LENT BY THE DETROIT INSTITUTE OF ARTS.

COLLECTIONS: Freiin von Huene, Unkel; E. Hölscher, Mulheim; Camillo Castiglioni, Vienna.

EXHIBITION: Dusseldorf, 1904.

BIBLIOGRAPHY: e. firmenich-richartz: *In* Zeitschrift für Christliche Kunst, Vol. VIII, 1895, p. 342; *In* Cicerone, Vol. VIII, 1916, p. 451; anon: Collections Camillo Castiglioni de Vienne, 1925, p. 12, No. 38, *Illust.*, w. r. valentiner: *In* Detroit Inst. Bull., May 1926, pp. 87-89, *Illust.*, idem: Catalogue of Paintings, Detroit Inst. of Arts, 1930, No. 204, *Illust.*, c. h. kuhn: German Paintings in American Collections, 1936, p. 23, No. 2, *Illust.*

GERMAN SCHOOL

COLOGNE, FIFTEENTH CENTURY

138 *Bishop Anno and St. George.*

Pl. 40 Painted about 1460-80.

Panel: 31 x 28 inches.

LENT FROM THE WILLIAM GOLDMAN COLLECTION, NEW YORK.

COLLECTION: Paul Bottenwieser.

EXHIBITION: Bottenwieser Galleries, New York, 1928.

BIBLIOGRAPHY: h. comstock: *In* International Studio, Dec. 1928, p. 90, *Illust.*, c. l. kuhn: German Paintings in American Collections, 1936, pp. 23-24, No. 4, *Illust.*

GERMAN SCHOOL, SOUTH

FIFTEENTH CENTURY, C. 1480

9

Portrait of a Youth.

Represented at twenty-two years of age. Formerly attributed to Michael Wolgemuth, the master of Dürer.

Panel: 19½ x 13½ inches.

LENT BY MRS. STANLEY MORTIMER, NEW YORK.

GERMAN SCHOOL, SWABIAN

c. 1480

10

The Two Lovers.

By an artist related to Zeitblom, and it bears a very close resemblance to a picture by an unknown Ulm master, No. 35, in the Catalogue of the Staatsgalerie, Stuttgart. The Strassburg Museum possesses the reverse of the Cleveland panel, representing the lovers as skeletons, an interesting example of the macabre idea current in Germany at the end of the XV c.

Panel: 25½ x 15½ inches.

LENT BY THE CLEVELAND MUSEUM OF ART.

COLLECTIONS: H. Schnutzenberger, Mulhouse; Wildenstein Galleries, New York.
EXHIBITIONS: Brooklyn Museum, New York, 1936; Cleveland Museum of Art, 1936.
BIBLIOGRAPHY: H. SCHMITZ, and others: Die Deutsche Malerei, Vol. III, 1913; H. S. FRANCIS: In Cleveland Museum Bull., Oct. 1932; In Art Digest, Nov. 1, 1932, Illust., In Pantheon, Nov. 1932, p. 368, Illust., In Creative Art, Nov. 1932, p. 172, Illust. on cover, In Illustr. London News, Nov. 5, 1932, Illust., In Amer. Mag. of Art, Dec. 1932, p. 357, Illust., In Gaz. d. Beaux-Arts, Dec. 1932, p. 328; H. H. NEUMANN: Archives Alsaciennes, 1935, p. 61; H. TIETZE: Meisterwerke Europ. Malerei in Amer., 1935, p. 198, Illust., C. L. KUHN: German Paintings in Amer. Collns., 1936, p. 61, No. 244, Illust., ANON: Exhibition of European Art, 1450-1500, Brooklyn Museum, 1936, No. 38, Illust., H. S. FRANCIS: Exhn. of Paintings, Cleveland Museum, 1936, p. 80, No. 190, Illust.

GHIRLANDAIO, DOMENICO

FLORENTINE, 1449-1494

Called Ghirlandaio, "garland-maker", from his father's calling, was born in Florence; pupil of Baldovinetti. Influenced by Botticelli and Verrocchio. In 1475 he went to Rome, and after a lapse of a few years, which he spent around Florence, he returned there, in 1481, as Botticelli's assistant in the Sistine Chapel; he was back again in Florence in 1482, and painted frescoes in the Palazzo Vecchio, Santa Trinita, and Santa Maria Novella; in the latter he introduced many members of the Tornabuoni family. One of the greatest fresco painters of the Florentine School, excelling especially in portraiture.

141 *Francesco Sassetti and his Son Teodoro.*

Pl. 19   Sassetti, born in Florence, 1420, was a partner of Lorenzo de' Medici in his bank at Lyons, and died in 1491. In 1485 he gave Ghirlandajo a commission to execute a series of frescoes in Santa Trinita, Florence. In the same chapel he and his wife, Neri de Corsi, are buried in tombs made by Giuliano di San Gallo. In the National Museum, at Florence, there is a marble bust of Sassetti by Rossellino. His son was born in 1479, and is depicted about eight or ten years of age, which fixes the date of the picture as 1487-1489. Teodoro, who died in 1546, was grandfather of Filippo Sassetti, well-known traveller.

> Panel: 29½ x 20½ inches.

LENT BY THE JULES S. BACHE COLLECTION, NEW YORK.

COLLECTIONS: William Graham; Robert A. and Evelyn Benson; Lord Duveen of Millbank.
EXHIBITIONS: Royal Academy, London, 1875 and 1893; New Gallery, London, 1893-1894; Grafton Galleries, London, 1909-1910; Manchester Art Gallery, 1926; Paris, 1935.
BIBLIOGRAPHY: LIONEL CUST: *In* Les Arts, Oct. 1907, p. 26, *Illust.*, CROWE AND CAVALCASELLE: A History of Painting in Italy, Ed. by L. Douglas, Vol. IV, 1911, p. 336, Note 5; A. VENTURI: Storia dell'Arte Italiana, Vol. VII, Part I, 1911, p. 769; H. HAUVETTE: Ghirlandajo, N.d., p. 134; B. BERENSON: Florentine Painters, 1912, p. 138; ESTHER SINGLETON: Old World Masters, 1929, p. 72, *Illust.*, B. BERENSON: Italian Pictures, 1932, p. 225 (Ital. Edn., 1936, p. 194, *Illust.*); L. VENTURI: Italian Paintings in America, Vol. II, 1933, No. 268, *Illust.*, IDEM: Catalogue of the Bache Collection, New York, 1938, No. 7, *Illust.*

GHIRLANDAIO, DOMENICO
FLORENTINE, 1449 - 1494

142 *Portrait of a Young Man.*

> Panel: 13 x 9 inches.

LENT BY MR. AND MRS. ALFRED J. FISHER, DETROIT.

COLLECTIONS: Baron Hubert de Pourtales; Baron Arthur de Schickler; Lord Duveen of Millbank; Howard Young.
EXHIBITION: Detroit Institute of Arts, 1933.
BIBLIOGRAPHY: A. M. FRANKFURTER: *In* Antiquarian, Nov. 1931, p. 21, *Illust.*, W. R. VALENTINER: *In* Pantheon, Aug. 1933, p. 242, *Illust.*, IDEM: Italian Paintings of the XIV to XVI c, Detroit Inst. of Arts, 1933, No. 27, *Illust.*, A. M. FRANKFURTER: *In* Art News, Mar. 14, 1936, p. 6, *Illust.*

GHISLANDI, VITTORE
BERGAMO, 1655 - 1743

Giuseppe Ghislandi, called Fra Vittore or Fra Galgario, was born at Bergamo, and entered the Franciscan order at the Galgario monastery. He was a pupil of Bombelli and Bianchini. He went to Bologna in 1717 and became while there a member of

the Clementina Academy. He was one of the leading portrait painters in Italy
during the eighteenth century, his subjects being principally men and boys.

3 *Portrait of a Young Man.*

Canvas: 28 x 21¼ inches.

LENT BY MR. SAMUEL H. KRESS, NEW YORK.

EXHIBITIONS: Settecento, Venice, 1929; Twenty-four Art Museums in the U. S. A. from 1932
to 1935; Metropolitan Museum, New York, 1938; California Palace of the Legion of Honor, San
Francisco, 1938; Seattle, Washington, 1938; Portland, Oregon, 1938; Montgomery, Alabama, 1938.
BIBLIOGRAPHY: s. PICHETTO: An Exhibition of Italian Paintings: Samuel H. Kress Collection,
1934, p. 37, *Illust.*, H. B. WEHLE: Tiepolo and his Contemporaries, Met. Mus., N. Y., 1938, No. I,
Illust., ANON: Catalogo, Mostra del Settecento Italiano a Venezia, 1929, p. 48; W. HEIL: Exhi-
bition of Venetian Painting, Cal. Palace of the Legion of Honor, San Francisco, 1938, No. 27,
Illust.

GIORGIONE

VENETIAN, 1477-1510

Giorgione, known also as Giorgio Barbarelli, Zorzi, Zorzo, or Zorzon, of Castelfranco, was born at Castelfranco, near Treviso. It is not known when he first went
to Venice, but it is certain that he received his instruction in painting from Giovanni Bellini. By 1500 his reputation was established, and during that year he met
Leonardo da Vinci in Venice; in 1504 he painted the Constanzo altarpiece in the
Cathedral of Castelfranco; and in 1507 he, in company with other painters, including Titian, decorated the exterior of the Fondaco dei Tedeschi in Venice. He is
considered to be the inventor of the modern spirit of lyrical passion and romance
in pictorial art, and his mastery has never been equalled.

4 *The Holy Family.*

9 Painted during the master's early period, somewhat earlier than the famous 'Adoration of the Shepherds' until recently in the Collection of Lord Allendale.

Panel: 14 x 17 inches.

LENT ANONYMOUSLY.

COLLECTIONS: Allard von Everdingen (1621-1695), noted Dutch painter; afterwards in a
French collection; Henry Willett; Robert H. and Evelyn Benson.
EXHIBITIONS: New Gallery, London, 1894-1895; Burlington Fine Arts Club, London, 1905 and
1912; Grafton Galleries, London, 1909-1910; Manchester Art Gallery, 1929.
BIBLIOGRAPHY: B. BERENSON: Venetian Painters, 1894, p. 103; ANON: Venetian Art, New Gallery, London, 1894-5, p. 32, *Illust.*, G. GRONAU: *In* Gaz. d. B.-Arts, Mar. 1895, pp. 261-262, (Repeated in Rep. für Kunstw., Vol. XXXI, 1908, pp. 508 *et seq.*); S. REINACH: Rep. de Peintures, Vol.
I, 1905, p. 179, *Illust.*, H. F. COOK: Giorgione, 1907, p. 96, *Illust.*, SIR L. CUST: *In* Les Arts, Oct.
1907, p. 12; L. JUSTI: Giorgione, 1908, Vol. I, p. 120, *Illust.*, SIR C. J. HOLMES: *In* Burl. Mag.,
1909, p. 72; B. BERENSON: Study in Criticism, Vol. I, 1912, p. 133; ANON: Early Venetian Painting, Burl. F. A. Club, 1912, No. 57, *Illust.*, T. BORENIUS: *In* Rassegna d'Arte, Vol. XII, 1912,
p. 92; CROWE AND CAVALCASELLE: Hist. of Painting in N. Italy, Ed. by T. Borenius, Vol. III, 1912,
p. 11; T. BORENIUS: Catalogue of the Benson Colln., 1912, pp. 167-168, No. 83, *Illust.*, W. SUIDA:

In Gaz. des. B.-Arts, Aug. 1935, pp. 79-81, *Illust.,* L. JUSTI: Giorgione, 1936, Vol. I, pp. 86-88, No. 24, *Illust.,* G. M. RICHTER: Giorgio da Castelfranco, 1937, pp. 230-231, *Illust.,* D. PHILLIPS: Leadership of Giorgione, 1937, p. 37, *Illust.,* G. GRONAU: *In* Art in Amer., July, 1938, p. 101, *Illust.*

GIOTTO SCHOOL

FLORENTINE, FOURTEENTH CENTURY

Follower of Giotto, active about the middle of the fourteenth century, contemporary with Maso, by whom he was influenced. Unusually fine colorist and very passionate in the representation of tragic figures. He seems to have worked in Florence, but is also related to the schools of Siena and possibly of Rimini. Other works by him are a diptych (one part, a Pieta in the National Gallery, London, and the other, SS. John and Magdalen, in the Philip Lehman Collection, New York), and a Crucifixion in the Rasini Collection, Pisa.

145 *A Crucifixion.*

Dated 1351. *Inscribed:* HOC OP(VS) FE(IT) FIERI FRA(TER) LA(N)FRAN-CHINO (DE) VALE(N)ZANO, CVI OPE(RE) ATTVLIT D(OMI)NA MARCHA D(E) VGONIB(VS) MCCCLI (*This work was ordered by Frater Lanfranchino of Valenzano in 1351, whose work was supported by Donna Marcha de Ugonibus*).

Panel: 58½ x 24½ inches.

LENT BY THE DETROIT INSTITUTE OF ARTS.

COLLECTION: Private, Vienna.

BIBLIOGRAPHY: W. R. VALENTINER: Detroit Inst. Bulletin, May 1938, p. 70, *Illust.*

GIOVANNI DI PAOLO

SIENESE, 1430?-1482

Probably a pupil of Paolo di Giovanni Fei; a close follower of Sassetta, also an occasional assistant of Sano di Pietro. He is known as the 'Greco of the Quattrocento', and must have been in touch with contemporary Byzantine painting. He was on the roll of the Guild of St. Luke at Siena in 1428. His work displays unusual imagination and individuality, and he was also noted as an illuminator.

146 *The Madonna, and SS. Margaret and Catherine of Alexandria.*

Panel: 15¼ x 8 inches.

LENT BY THE DAN FELLOWS PLATT ESTATE,
ENGLEWOOD, NEW JERSEY.

COLLECTIONS: Chigi Gallery, Siena; Léon Somzée.

BIBLIOGRAPHY: E. BAES: Catalogue des Collections Somzée, 1904, p. 6, No. 286, *Illust.,*

J. BRECK: In Art in Amer., Vol. II, 1914, p. 285, Illust.; R. VAN MARLE: Ital. Schools, Vol. IX, 1927, p. 451; B. BERENSON: Ital. Pictures, 1932, p. 245; J. POPE-HENNESSY: Giovanni di Paolo, 1937, pp. 94, 112, 172, Illust.

GIOVANNI DI PAOLO

SIENESE, c. 1430-1482

St. Nicholas of Tolentino.

Painted about 1456. A vision of St. Augustine, above, waves over the Saint's head what appears to be an Augustinian scapular. This panel and the 'St. Nicholas appearing over the walls of a Town' in the Vienna Academy, and the 'Miraculous Appearance of St. Nicholas during a Storm' in the Johnson Collection, Philadelphia, probably formed part of a series of panels commissioned by an Augustinian community.

Panel: 10¾ x 16¾ inches.

LENT BY MR. ROBERT LEHMAN, NEW YORK.

BIBLIOGRAPHY: J. POPE-HENNESSY: Giovanni di Paolo, 1937, pp. 78, 108, 173.

GIOVANNI DI PAOLO

SIENESE, 1403?-1482

A Miracle of St. Clare.

Panel: 11¼ x 7¾ inches.

LENT BY MR. PERCY S. STRAUS, NEW YORK.

COLLECTIONS: Sir John Peter Boileau, Bart. of Ketteringham, Norfolk; Sir Frederick Raymond Boileau, Bart.; Henry Harris; Edward Hutton.

EXHIBITIONS: Manchester Art Treasures, 1857; Royal Academy, London, 1930.

BIBLIOGRAPHY: G. F. WAAGEN: Treasures of Art, Vol. III, 1854, p. 428 (as Sano di Pietro), G. SCHARF: Catalogue of Art Treasures, Manchester, 1857, p. 17, No. 60; CROWE AND CAVALCASELLE: Hist. of Painting in Italy, Ed. by T. Borenius, Vol. V, 1914, p. 173; B. BERENSON: Ital. Pictures, 1932, p. 246 (Ital. ed. 1936, p. 212); LORD BALNIEL AND K. CLARK: Ital. Art, Exhn. Cat., Royal Acad. London, 1930, p. 35, No. 104.

GIOVANNI DI PAOLO

SIENESE, 1430?-1482

The Death of Lucretia.

Evidently formed part of a cassone panel. The scene is from the story of Lucretia Romana, usually represented in Quattrocento cassoni in three or four scenes.

Panel: 17¾ x 12 inches.

LENT ANONYMOUSLY.

COLLECTION: Marczell von Nemes.

74

EXHIBITION: Detroit Institute of Arts, 1933.
BIBLIOGRAPHY: o. sirén: *Jn* Burl. Mag., June 1925, pp. 281-282; a. venturi: Studi dal Vero, 1927, pp. 83-84; w. r. valentiner: Catalogue of the Italian Exhn., Detroit Inst. of Arts, 1933, No. 50, *Jllust.*

GOYA, FRANCISCO DE

SPANISH, 1746-1828

Born at Fuentedos, near Saragossa. He was a noted etcher as well as a painter; among his works are portraits, satires, representations of bullfights, tapestry designs, etc. At the age of fourteen he went to Saragossa and entered the studio of José Martinez. In 1766 he went to Madrid and mixed in revolutionary agitations. In 1785 he became deputy-director of the San Fernando Academy, and in 1789 court-painter to Charles IV. Inspired by the horrors of the Napoleonic wars he produced his series of *Desastres,* which were pitiless in their imagination. At the end of his life the spirit of melancholy obsessed him, and he died at Bordeaux, his remains being taken to Madrid in 1900.

150 Don Manuel Osorio de Zuñiga.

Pl. 91 Inscribed: *El S. D. Manuel Osorio Manrrique de Zuñiga S. de-Gines nacio enab a JJ de 1784.*

Canvas: 50 x 40 inches.

LENT BY THE JULES S. BACHE COLLECTION, NEW YORK.

COLLECTIONS: Sénor Don Manuel Osorio de Zuñiga; Madame Henri Bernstein; Lord Duveen of Millbank.

EXHIBITIONS: This picture figured in a play by Henri Bernstein, entitled "La Galerie des Glaces," which was presented at the Théatre du Gymnase, Paris, for the first time, October 22, 1924; Metropolitan Museum of Art, New York, Spanish Exhibition, 1928; Brooklyn Museum, 1935; Baltimore Museum, 1937; Paris, 1937; Museum of Modern Art, Washington, D. C., 1938.

BIBLIOGRAPHY: h. stokes: Francisco Goya, 1914, pp. 156, 252; v. von loga: Francesco de Goya, 1921, p. 199, No. 290, *Jllust.*; l. mayer: Francesco de Goya, 1923, p. 197, No. 365; idem: In Pantheon, April 1928, p. 191, *Jllust.*, b. burroughs: Catalogue of Spanish Paintings from El Greco to Goya, Met. Mus. of Art, New York, 1928, No. 19, *Jllust.*; w. heil: *Jn* "The Art News," April 27, 1929, p. 19, *Jllust. in color*, w. r. valentiner: Unknown Masterpieces, 1930, No. 90, *Jllust.*, anon: Catalogue of the Bache Collection, New York, 1938, No. 42, *Jllust.*

GOYA, FRANCISCO

SPANISH, 1746-1828

151 Gossiping Women.

Pl. 90 Painted about 1787-1792.

Canvas: 23 x 57 inches.

LENT BY THE WADSWORTH ATHENEUM, HARTFORD, CONN.

COLLECTION: Private Collection, Madrid.

EXHIBITIONS: Springfield Museum, Mass., 1933; Brooklyn Museum, 1935; Metropolitan

Museum of Art, New York, 1936; Pennsylvania Museum, Philadelphia, 1937; California Palace of the Legion of Honor, San Francisco, 1937.
BIBLIOGRAPHY: A. L. MAYER: Goya, 1924, p. 179, No. 631, *Illust.*; T. H. PARKER: Springfield Museum Opening Exhibition Catalogue, 1933, p. 30, No. 97; F. A. SWEET: Exhn. of Spanish Painting, Brooklyn Museum, 1935, No. 26, *Illust.*; H. B. WEHLE: Francisco Goya, his paintings, etc., Met. Mus. of Art, 1936, No. 2, *Illust.*; W. HEIL: Paintings, etc., by F. Goya, San Francisco, 1937, p. 27, No. 6, *Illust.*

GOYA, FRANCESCO DE

SPANISH, 1746-1828

52 *Portrait of a Matador.*

Painted about 1788-1792.

Canvas: 29 x 24 inches.

LENT BY MR. AND MRS. ROBERT W. REFORD, MONTREAL, CANADA.
COLLECTIONS: Lord Paget, said to have been presented to him by the King of Spain; Croal Thompson.
EXHIBITION: California Palace of the Legion of Honor, San Francisco, 1937.
BIBLIOGRAPHY: W. HEIL: Catalogue of the Goya Exhn., California Pal. of the Legion of Honor, San Francisco, 1937, No. 13, *Illust.*; T. C. HOWE: *In* Art News, June 12, 1937, pp. 14-15, *Illust.*

GOYA, FRANCISCO DE

SPANISH, 1746-1828

53 *Marqués de Caballero.*

Painted in 1807. Joseph Antoine, Marqués de Caballero, Spanish Statesman, born at Sargossa in 1760, became Minister of Justice under Carlos IV, and occupied this position from 1798 until 1808; upon the accession of Ferdinand VII to the throne, he became Minister of Finance; and during the reign of Joseph Bonaparte he became State Councillor. During the Restoration he took refuge in France, but returned to Spain in 1820, where he died the following year at Salamanca.

LENT BY THE HON. OSCAR B. CINTAS, HAVANA, CUBA.
Canvas: 42½ x 33 inches.
COLLECTIONS: Marqués de Caballero; Doria Maria Mayano y Montoya; Marqués de Corvera; Boussot-Valadon; George Demotte; Knoedler Galleries, New York.
EXHIBITIONS: Bagatelle, Bois de Boulogne, Paris, 1911; Knoedler Galleries, New York, 1932 and 1934; Springfield Museum, Mass., 1933; Metropolitan Museum, New York.
BIBLIOGRAPHY: H. PELADAN: La Mode et les mœurs, Exposition de Bagatelle, Paris, 1911, No. 56; A. L. MAYER: Goya, 1923, p. 188, No. 217a, *Illust.*, (*Eng. Edn.*), 1924, p. 151, No. 217a, *Illust.*; ANON: Catalogue of Naval and Military Portraits, Knoedler Galleries, New York, 1932, No. 8; R. FLINT: *In* Art News, April 23, 1932, pp. 5-6, *Illust.*; T. H. PARKER: Catalogue of the Opening Exbn. Springfield Museum, 1933, p. 30, No. 94; E. S. SIPLE: *In* Burl. Mag., June 1934, p. 287, *Illust.*; H. B. WEHLE: Francisco Goya, Metrop. Mus., N. Y., 1936, No. 11, *Illust.*

GOYA, FRANCISCO

154 *Saint Peter Repentant.*

Pl. 90   Signed on right—*Goya*. Painted about 1820.

Canvas: 28¾ x 25¾ inches.

LENT BY THE PHILLIPS MEMORIAL GALLERY, WASHINGTON, D. C.

COLLECTIONS: Don Alejandro Pidal; Duc de Trévise; Newhouse Galleries, New York.

EXHIBITIONS: Ministerio de Instruccion publica, Madrid, 1900; Phillips Memorial Gallery, Washington, since 1936.

BIBLIOGRAPHY: ANON: Catalogo de las obras de Goya, Madrid, 1900; P. LAFOND: Goya, 1902, p. 104, No. 54; A. F. CALVERT: Goya, 1908, p. 171, No. 50, *Illust.*; A. DE BERUETE: Goya, composiciones, 1917, p. 170, No. 244; H. STOKES: Francisco Goya, 1914, p. 345, No. 386; V. VON LOGA: Francisco de Goya, 1921, p. 181, No. 53; A. L. MAYER: Francisco de Goya, 1924, p. 141, No. 66; F. ZAPATER Y GOMEZ: Don F. de Goya, *Edn. Calleja*, 1924, No. 215, *Illust.*, A. L. MAYER: A late Goya; *In Burl. Mag.*, Sept. 1937, p. 139, *Illust.*

GOYEN, JAN VAN

Born at Leyden; he formed his style under Esaias van de Velde in The Hague. He travelled in France and Belgium, lived in Leyden until 1631 and settled in The Hague in 1634 until his death. In 1640 he was elected a member of the Guild of Painters. His daughter Margaret married Jan Steen the painter. Together with Salomon van Ruisdael he shared the leadership of Dutch landscape painting of the Frans Hals period.

155 *Traffic on the Ice.*

Painted about 1630.

Panel: 9¼ x 10¼ inches.

LENT BY MR. H. E. TEN CATE, ALMELO, HOLLAND.

COLLECTIONS: H. M. Clark, London; D. Katz; Dr. Hans Schaeffer.

BIBLIOGRAPHY: C. HOFSTEDE DE GROOT: Catalogue Raisonné, Vol. VIII, 1927, p. 304, No. 1203.

GOYEN, JAN VAN

156 *View of Arnhem on the Rhine.*

Signed and dated 1646. One of the masterpieces of the artist's late period.

Panel: 38¾ x 53¼ inches.

LENT BY MR. H. E. TEN CATE, ALMELO, HOLLAND.

COLLECTION: Frank C. Stoop.

EXHIBITIONS: Royal Academy, London, 1929; Museum Boymans, Rotterdam, 1938.

BIBLIOGRAPHY: C. HOFSTEDE DE GROOT: Catalogue raisonné, Vol. VIII, 1927, p. 16, No. 13; H. SCHNEIDER AND W. G. CONSTABLE: Exhibition of Dutch Art, Royal Acad., Lond., 1929, p. 43, No.

205; D. HANNEMA: Meesterwerken uit vier eeuwen, 1400-1800, Museum Boymans, Rotterdam 1938, p. 21, No. 79, *Illust.*; A. M. FRANKFURTER: *In* Art News, Feb. 4, 1939, p. 21, *Illust.*

GOZZOLI, BENOZZO

FLORENTINE, 1420-1497

Born at Florence; assisted Fra Angelico at Rome, 1446, and Orvieto, 1447; in 1449-1455 he worked at Montefalco, and in 1456 at Perugia. He returned to Florence in 1459-1462. He was in S. Gimignano, 1463-1468, Pisa, 1469-1485. In 1497 he accompanied Cosimo Rosselli, Filippino Lippi, and Perugino to Florence, where he valued the frescoes of Baldovinetti in San. Trinita, and died the same year at Pistoia. His most famous frescoes are those in the Campo Santo in Pisa, and in the Medici chapel of the Palazzo Riccardi, Florence.

57

14

Madonna and Child with Cherubim.

Panel: 25½ x 20 inches.

LENT BY MR. AND MRS. EDSEL B. FORD, DETROIT.

COLLECTIONS: Baron H. von Tucher; Lord Duveen of Millbank.

EXHIBITION: Detroit Institute of Arts, 1933.

BIBLIOGRAPHY: B. BERENSON: Flor. Painters, 1909, p. 116; G. GRONAU: *In* Thieme-Becker's Lexikon, Vol. III, 1909, p. 348; A. VENTURI: Storia dell'Arte Ital., Vol. VII, 1, 1911, p. 430; R. VAN MARLE: Italian Schools, Vol. XI, 1929, p. 150, *Illust.*; L. VENTURI: Ital. Paintings in Amer., 1933, No. 215, *Illust.*; W. R. VALENTINER: Ital. Paintings of the XIV-XVIc., Detroit Inst. of Arts, 1933, No. 17, *Illust.*; IDEM: *In* Pantheon, Aug. 1933, p. 241, *Illust.*

GRECO, EL
(DOMENIKOS THEOTOKOPOULOS)

SPANISH, 1545-1614

Born at Candia, Crete. He was in Venice in 1570, mentioned as Titian's pupil; influenced by Tintoretto and Jacopo Bassano. He afterwards went to Rome; about 1575 went to Toledo, Spain, and worked in the Cathedral. The later works of the master have had considerable influence on modern art. After Spain, the United States now is the country richest in El Greco's paintings.

8

The Purification of the Temple.

Signed in Greek, K P H C. Painted between 1571-1576. The four men at the lower right are Titian, Michelangelo, Julio Clovio, and El Greco, or Raphael.

Canvas: 46 x 58 inches.

LENT BY THE MINNEAPOLIS INSTITUTE OF ARTS.

COLLECTIONS: Duke of Buckingham; Lord Yarborough.

EXHIBITIONS: British Institution, 1850; Grafton Galleries, London, 1913; Metropolitan Museum, New York, 1928; Brooklyn Museum, 1935.

BIBLIOGRAPHY: G. F. WAAGEN: Treasures of Art, Vol. II, 1854, p. 87, Vol. IV, 1857, p. 70; S. SANPERE Y MIGUEL: *In* 'Hispania', 1906, pp. 28, 29; M. B. COSSIO: El Greco, 1908, p. 77;

M. BARRES ET P. LAFOND: Le Greco, 1910, p. 38; W. B. BROCKWELL: Spanish Old Masters, Grafton Gallery, London, 1913, No. 118; A. L. MAYER: El Greco, 1926, p. 10, No. 50, *Illust.*, J. F. WIL-LUMSEN: La Jeunesse d'El Greco, Vol. II, 1927, p. 413, *Illust.*, B. BURROUGHS: Spanish Painting at the Met. Mus., New York, 1928, No. 28, *Illust.*, F. RUTTER: El Greco, 1930, pp. 16, 29; F. A. SWEET: Spanish Painting at the Brooklyn Museum, 1935, No. 27, *Illust.*, M. LEGENDRE and A. HARTMANN: Domenikos Theotokopoulos, 1937, p. 19, *Illust.*

GRECO, EL
(DOMENIKOS THEOTOKOPOULOS)

SPANISH, C. 1548-1625

159 *The Deposition.*

Pl. 85   Painted about 1590; signed. El Greco treated this subject three times, the two other versions being in the Henry E. Huntington (San Marino) and John G. Johnson (Philadelphia) Collections; the present composition is unique, no replica being known; it is one of the masterpieces of the artist.

Canvas: 47¼ x 57 inches.

LENT BY COMTESSE DE LA BÉRAUDIÈRE, PARIS.

COLLECTION: Yves Perdoux, Paris.

EXHIBITION: La Gazette des Beaux-Arts, Paris, 1937.

BIBLIOGRAPHY: A. L. MAYER: El Greco, 1923, p. 59; IDEM: El Greco, 1926, p. 17, No. 102, *Illust.*, IDEM: *In* Pantheon, Vol. I, 1928, p. 275; M. LEGENDRE ET A. HARTMANN: El Greco, 1937, Nos. 9-10, *Illust. in color;* R. FROST: *In* Art News, Aug. 14, 1937, p. 10, *Illust.*, A. RUBINSTEIN: El Greco; Exposition organisée par la "Gazette des Beaux-Arts", Paris, 1937, (Notes by A. L. Mayer), No. 20, and Foreword, *Illust.*

GRECO, EL
(DOMENIKOS THEOTOKOPOULOS)

SPANISH, 1545-1614

160 *Christ at Gethsemane.*

Signed in Greek: K P H C. Painted between 1590-1598. The composition is known in a number of adaptations usually upright in form.

Canvas: 41 x 45¾ inches.

LENT BY MR. ARTHUR SACHS, NEW YORK.

COLLECTION: Private, Madrid.

EXHIBITIONS: Metropolitan Museum of Art, New York, 1928; Wadsworth Atheneum, Hartford, Conn., 1930; Fogg Art Museum, Harvard University, Cambridge, Mass., 1932-33; Art Institute of Chicago, 1933.

BIBLIOGRAPHY: A. L. MAYER: El Greco, 1926, p. 10, No. 55, *Illust.*, B. BURROUGHS: Exhn. of Spanish Paintings, Met. Mus., N. Y., 1928, p. 4, No. 26, *Illust.*, A. L. MAYER: El Greco, 1931, p. 120, No. 10, *Illust.*, D. C. RICH: Catalogue of Paintings, Art Inst. of Chicago, 1933, p. 26, No. 167, *Illust.*

GRECO, EL
(DOMENIKOS THEOTOKOPOULOS)

SPANISH, 1545-1614

1 *The Penitent St. Peter.*

With St. Thomas, and an Angel in the Clouds. Signed in full; painted about 1596-1600.

Canvas: 48¼ x 40¼ inches.

LENT ANONYMOUSLY.

COLLECTIONS: José Maria de Zavala; Don Pedro and Don Antonio Verastegui, Vittoria.
EXHIBITION: Palacio Nazional, Barcelona, 1929.
BIBLIOGRAPHY: M. B. COSSIO: El Greco, 1908, p. 593, No. 277; A. L. MAYER: El Greco, 1926, No. 210a; ANON: Catálogo de la Exposición Palacio Nazional, Barcelona, 1929, pp. 443 and 408, *Illust.*

GRECO, EL
(DOMENIKOS THEOTOKOPOULOS)

SPANISH, C. 1548-1625

2 *Apparition of the Virgin to St. Dominic.*

86   Painted about 1597-1603; a smaller version of the same subject was exhibited at the Dresden Museum, 1928.

Canvas: 39¼ x 24 inches.

LENT BY THE MEMORIAL ART GALLERY, ROCHESTER, NEW YORK.

COLLECTIONS: Henri Rouart; J. Horace Harding.
EXHIBITIONS: Knoedler Galleries, New York, 1915; Metropolitan Museum of Art, New York, 1928; Albright Gallery, Buffalo, 1931; Knoedler Galleries, London, 1935; Brooklyn Museum, 1935; Dallas Museum of Fine Arts, 1936; Memorial Art Gallery, Rochester, 1938; Wadsworth Atheneum, Hartford, Conn.; Smith College, Northampton, Mass.
BIBLIOGRAPHY: A. ALEXANDER: Catalogue des Tableaux Anciens, Colln. Henri Rouart, 1912, p. 24, No. 93, *Illust.*, A. L. MAYER: El Greco, 1926, p. 38, No. 227a, *Illust.*, B. BURROUGHS: Exhn. of Spanish Paintings, Met. Mus., N. Y., 1928, No. 27, *Illust.*, ANON: Ten Masterpieces of Painting, Knoedler Galleries, London, 1935; F. A. SWEET: Exhn. of Spanish Paintings, Brooklyn Mus., N. Y., 1935, No. 32, *Illust.*, J. ST. L. O'TOOLE: The Collection of J. Horace Harding, n.d., p. 18, *Illust.*, In Art Digest, June 1, 1936, p. 9, *Illust.*, M. LEGENDRE et A. HARTMAN: El Greco, 1937, p. 363, *Illust.*, G. H. MOORE: Catalogue of the Memorial Art Gallery, Rochester, N. Y., 1938, No. 13, *Illust.*

GRECO, EL
(DOMENIKOS THEOTOKOPOULOS)

SPANISH, 1545-1614

3 *Christ in the House of Simon.*

86   Painted about 1604-1608. A slightly later version, with an open, arcaded back-

ground, is in the collection of Mr. Joseph Winterbotham, Burlington, Vermont. The composition was used by his son, Jorge Manuel Theotokopuli, for his Magdalen Altar at Toledo (1608).

Canvas: 58 x 40 inches.

LENT BY THE HON. OSCAR B. CINTAS, HAVANA, CUBA.

COLLECTIONS: José de Madrazo; Marqués de Salamanca; Ivan Stchoukine; Lord d'Abernon; C. Sedelmeyer; Paul Hess.

EXHIBITIONS: Grafton Galleries, London, 1909-10; 1913-14.

BIBLIOGRAPHY: ANON: Tableaux anciens, Collection Salamanca, 1875, p. 28, No. 16; M. B. COSSIO: El Greco, Vol. II, 1908, p. 64, No. 314, *Illust.*; H. COOK AND M. BROCKWELL: National Loan Exhibition, Grafton Gall., London, 1909-10, p. 49, No. 34; C. SEDELMEYER: Paintings by Old Masters, 1911, p. 78, No. 68, *Illust.*; M. BARRES et P. LAFOND: Le Greco, n.d., p. 191, No. 169, *Illust.*; A. L. MAYER: *In* Zeitsch. für Bild. Kunst, 1913, p. 71, *Illust.*, W. B. BROCKWELL: Exhn. of Spanish Old Masters, Grafton Gall., London, 1913-1914; A. DE BERUETE Y MORET: *In* Revue de l'Art, Jan. 1914, p. 68, *Illust.*, A. L. MAYER: *In* Art in America, Aug. 1916, p. 253; IDEM: Dom. Theotocopuli, El Greco, 1926, p. 9, No. 46, *Illust.*, F. RUTTER: El Greco, 1930, p. 100, No. 94; M. LEGENDRE ET A. HARTMANN: El Greco, 1937, p. 504, No. 170, *Illust.*, L. GOLDSCHEIDER: El Greco, 1938, No. 231, *Illust.*

GREUZE, JEAN BAPTISTE

FRENCH, 1725 - 1805

Born at Tournus, and apprenticed to an itinerant painter named Grondon, whom he served for eight years in the neighborhood of Lyons. In 1746 he went to Paris and studied under Natoire and Pigalle, and became an Associate of the Academy in 1758; in 1769 he became a Member, but sent no more pictures to the Academy until 1800. Broken by the Revolution he sank into oblivion. His subjects are inclined to be sentimental, and treated with a remarkable technical skill and a fine color sense. His work has influenced modern painters, such as Renoir.

164 *The Lazy Kitchen Maid* ('La Paresseuse').

Painted in 1757.

Canvas: 25½ x 19¼ inches.

LENT BY THE WADSWORTH ATHENEUM, HARTFORD, CONN.

COLLECTIONS: Boyer de Fonscolombe; Princess Radziwill-Branicki; Wildenstein Galleries.

ENGRAVED by P. E. Moiette (1722-1780).

EXHIBITIONS: Salon, Paris, 1757; Springfield Museum, Mass., 1933.

BIBLIOGRAPHY: LIVRET de Salon, Paris, 1757, No. 114; J. SMITH: Catalogue raisonné, Vol. VIII; E. AND J. DE GONCOURT: L'Art du 18me siècle, Vol. II, 1880, pp. 81, 89; R. PORTALIS et H. BERALDI: Graveurs du 18me siècle, Vol. III, 1880, p. 110, *Illust. by Moiette's engraving*, LADY DILKE: French Painters of the XVIIIc. 1899, p. 197; J. MARTIN: Catalogue raisonné, 1906, p. 15, No. 187; J. RIVERS: Greuze and his models, 1912, pp. 73, 126, 270; C. MAUCLAIR: Greuze et son temps, 1926, p. 81; T. H. PARKER: Springfield Museum Opening Exhibition Catalogue, 1933, p. 26, No. 52; G. WESTCOTT: *In* Wadsworth Atheneum Bulletin, Jan.-June, 1935, pp. 1-7, *Illust.*, M. VAUGHAN: *In* Parnassus, May 1939, p. 8, *Illust.*

GREUZE, JEAN BAPTISTE

FRENCH, 1725 - 1805

5 *L'Enfant Gâté* ('The Spoilt Child').

Canvas: 26¼ x 21¼ inches.

LENT BY MRS. SOSTHENES BEHN, NEW YORK.

COLLECTIONS: M. Duruey, 1797; Sénateur de Choiseul-Praslin, 1808; Prince Bezborodko; Prince Paskevitch-Erivansky; Musée de l'Ermitage, Petrograd.
ENGRAVED by Maloeuvre.
EXHIBITION: Salon du Louvre, Paris, 1795.
BIBLIOGRAPHY: J. SMITH: Catalogue Raisonné, Vol. VIII, 1837, p. 416, No. 58; L. REAU: Catalogue de l'Art Francais dans les Musées Russes, p. 30, No. 116; J. RIVERS: Greuze and his Models, 1912, p. 200; C. MAUCLAIR: Greuze et son temps, 1926, p. 183.

GRÜNEWALD, MATTHIAS

GERMAN, 1460? - 1527

Mathias Neithardt, alias Gothardt, called Mathias Grünewald, born about 1460 in Würzburg. He was in Aschaffenburg from 1485 to 1490, and had a workshop from 1501-1520 in Seligenstadt. From 1511-1525 he was painter at the court of the Archbishop of Mainz. In 1525 he became involved in the "peasant revolution" and fled to Frankfurt in 1526. In 1526 he moved to Halle, where he worked as engineer, and died in 1527. Next to Holbein and Dürer he was the greatest German painter of the sixteenth century, and one of the finest colorists in the whole history of painting. His compositions, especially his great altarpiece in Colmar, show a most extraordinary, eccentric imagination, and are greatly admired by painters of our time.

6 *The Madonna as Queen of Heaven.*

A drawing in black chalk with water-color washes. Probably the study for an altarpiece, now lost, by Grünewald which Joachim von Sandrart (1606-1688) had seen in the Mainz Cathedral.

Paper: 12¾ x 10½ inches.

LENT BY MR. FRANZ KOENIGS, AMSTERDAM, HOLLAND.

COLLECTIONS: von Savigny; Paul Cassirer, Amsterdam.
EXHIBITIONS: Haarlem, 1926-27; Berlin Museum, 1936; Museum Boymans, Rotterdam, 1938; Rijksmuseum, Amsterdam, 1939.
BIBLIOGRAPHY: M. J. FRIEDLÄNDER: Die Grünewaldzeichnungen der Sammlung von Savigny, Berlin, 1926, No. 7; IDEM: Die Zeichnungen von M. Grünewald, 1927, No. 17; R. GRAUL: Grünewalds Handzeichnungen, n.d., No. 13; A. BURCKHARD: Matthias Grünewald, 1936, p. 70, *Illust.*, W. FRAENGER: Matthias Grünewald, 1937, p. 145; D. HANNEMA: Meesterwerken uit vier eeuwen, 1400-1800, Museum Boymans, Rotterdam, 1938, pp. 67-68, No. 284, *Illust.*

GUARDI, FRANCESCO

VENETIAN, 1712-1793

Born of Austrian stock in Venice, and became the pupil of Antonio Canaleto. He painted the same class of subjects as his master, and his earlier works are in the style of Canaletto; later he developed a much freer technique, a more delicate design and a rare sense of atmosphere. His last years were spent in straitened circumstances, and he was obliged to sell his works for trifling sums. He was the greatest landscape painter of the later Venetian school.

167 *Campo San Zanipolo, Venice.*

Pl. 38   Painted about 1780. A Study for this work is in the Lampesti Collection, Milan.

Canvas: 14¾ x 12¼ inches.

LENT BY MR. SAMUEL H. KRESS, NEW YORK.

COLLECTION: Sir George Kane.

EXHIBITIONS: Twenty-four Art Museums in the U. S. A. from 1932 to 1935; Metropolitan Museum, New York, 1938; California Palace of the Legion of Honor, San Francisco, 1938; Seattle, Washington, 1938; Portland, Oregon, 1938; Montgomery, Alabama, 1938.

BIBLIOGRAPHY: s. PICHETTO: An Exhibition of Italian Paintings: Samuel H. Kress Collection, 1934, p. 55, *Illust.*, H. B. WEHLE: Tiepolo and his Contemporaries, Met. Museum, N. Y., 1938, No. 26, *Illust.*, W. HEIL: Exh. of Venetian Painting, Cal. Palace of the Legion of Honor, San Francisco, 1938, No. 31, *Illust.*

GUARDI, FRANCESCO

VENETIAN, 1712-1793

168 *View of Mestre, near Venice.*

Pl. 37   Canvas: 19 x 26 inches.

LENT BY MR. AND MRS. EDGAR B. WHITCOMB, DETROIT.

COLLECTION: Colin Agnew.

EXHIBITION: Detroit Institute of Arts, 1927.

BIBLIOGRAPHY: W. HEIL: Old and Modern Masters, Detroit Inst. of Arts, 1927, p. 18, No. 11, *Illust.*

GUARDI, FRANCESCO

VENETIAN, 1712-1793

169 *The Piazza San Marco, Venice.*

Canvas: 33 x 50⅜ inches.

LENT BY MR. AND MRS. CHARLES V. HICKOX, NEW YORK.

COLLECTIONS: Lady Margaret Charteris; Asher Wertheimer; J. Horace Harding.

EXHIBITION: California Palace of the Legion of Honor, San Francisco, 1938.

BIBLIOGRAPHY: L. VENTURI: Ital. Paintings in America, 1933, No. 611, *Illust.*, W. HEIL: Venetian Painting, Cal. Pal. of the Legion of Honor, San Francisco, 1938, No. 30, *Illust.*

GUARDI, FRANCESCO
VENETIAN, 1712-1793

0 *The Grand Canal, Venice.*

Canvas: 33 x 50⅜ inches.

LENT BY MR. AND MRS. CHARLES V. HICKOX, NEW YORK.

COLLECTIONS: Lady Mary Charteris; Asher Wertheimer; J. Horace Harding.

EXHIBITION: California Palace of the Legion of Honor, San Francisco, 1938.

BIBLIOGRAPHY: L. VENTURI: Ital. Paintings in America, 1933, No. 610, *Illust.*, W. HEIL: Venetian Painting, Cal. Palace of the Legion of Honor, San Francisco, 1938, No. 29, *Illust.*

GUARDI, FRANCESCO
VENETIAN, 1712-1793

1 *High Mass in Honor of Pius VI in SS. Giovanni e Paolo.*

Canvas: 20½ x 27 inches.

LENT BY MR. JAKOB GOLDSCHMIDT, NEW YORK.

EXHIBITION: California Palace of the Legion of Honor, San Francisco, 1938.

BIBLIOGRAPHY: W. HEIL: Venetian Painting, Cal. Pal. of Legion of Honor, San Fran., 1938, No. 35, *Illust.*

GUARDI, FRANCESCO
VENETIAN, 1712-1793

2 *Pius VI Received by the Doge in SS. Giovanni e Paolo.*

Canvas: 20½ x 27 inches.

LENT BY MR. JAKOB GOLDSCHMIDT, NEW YORK.

EXHIBITION: California Palace of the Legion of Honor, San Francisco, 1938.

BIBLIOGRAPHY: W. HEIL: Venetian Painting, Cal. Pal. of the Legion of Honor, San Francisco, 1938, No. 36, *Illust.*, A. M. FRANKFURTER: *In* Art News, July 16, 1938, p. 11, *Illust.*

GUARDI, FRANCESCO
VENETIAN, 1712-1793

3 *View of the Piazzetta, Venice.*

Canvas: 18 x 29¾ inches.

LENT BY THE WADSWORTH ATHENEUM, HARTFORD, CONN.

COLLECTION: Durlacher Galleries, New York.

EXHIBITIONS: City Art Museum, St. Louis, 1936; Springfield Museum of Fine Arts, Mass., 1937; William Rockhill Nelson Gallery, Kansas City, 1937; Colorado Springs Fine Arts Centre, 1938.

HALS, FRANS

Born at Antwerp, probably in 1585, his parents coming from Haarlem where he afterwards went; he probably studied under Karel van Mander, who died in 1604. His first known portraits can be dated 1610 and 1611. In 1616 he became a member of the Rhetorician's Club, and painted his first *doelen* picture. After 1620 he became a master of repute in his native city, which held him in esteem during his entire life. In the 'thirties the master reached the height of his renown, and received three new commissions for large 'shooting company' pictures (1633, 1637, and 1639), one of them from Amsterdam (1637). Also in the 'forties and 'fifties private and public commissions were frequent; his last group portraits were executed in 1664, two years before he died. Mostly on account of the general adverse conditions in Holland the artist became poor during his last years, but the city took care of him, so that he could live in rented quarters, and received since 1663 the considerable sum of 200 Carolus gulden yearly. The city accorded him the honor of being buried in St. Bavo, the principal church of Haarlem. He was the greatest master in Holland, of the first epoch of seventeenth century art.

174 *Claes Duyst van Voorhout.*

Proprietor of the Zwaan Brewery at Leyden (c. 1636). In conception, the person portrayed is related to the Willem van Heythuysen in the Liechtenstein Gallery, Vienna, and the Officer in the Goldman Collection, New York (compare No. 181). The picture belongs to the most excellent character portraits of the master's.

Canvas: 31¾ x 26 inches.

LENT BY THE JULES S. BACHE COLLECTION, NEW YORK.

COLLECTIONS: Earls of Egremont; Colonel Egremont Wyndham; Lord Leconfield; Lord Duveen of Millbank.

EXHIBITIONS: Royal Academy, Dutch Exhibition, London, 1929; Frans Hals Exhibition, Detroit, 1935; Haarlem, Holland, 1937.

BIBLIOGRAPHY: E. WYNDHAM: Catalogue of Paintings at Petworth, 1850, No. 383; G. F. WAAGEN: Treasures of Art in Great Britain, Vol. III, 1854, p. 36; W. VON BODE: Studien zur Geschichte der Holländischen Malerei, 1883, p. 153; E. W. MOES: Frans Hals, 1909, p. 101, No. 33; C. HOFSTEDE DE GROOT: Catalogue Raisonné, Vol. III, 1910, p. 55, No. 176; W. VON BODE, *Edr.*: Frans Hals, Vol. I, 1914, p. 40, No. 114, Plate 62; C. H. C. BAKER: Catalogue of Pictures in the Possession of Lord Leconfield, 1920, p. 53, No. 383, *Illust.*; W. R. VALENTINER: Frans Hals, (*Kl. der Kunst*), 1923, p. 154, *Illust.*; SIR R. WITT: The Dutch Exhn. at the R. A.; *In* "La Renaissance", March 1929, p. 130, *Illust.*; W. G. CONSTABLE and H. SCHNEIDER, *Edrs.*: Exhn. of Dutch Art, R. A., London, 1929, No. 367, *Illust.*; W. HEIL: The Jules Bache Collection, *In* The Art News, April 27, 1929, p. 27, *Illust. in color*; W. R. VALENTINER: F. Hals Paintings in Amer., 1936, No. 59, *Illust.*; ANON: Catalogue of the Bache Collection, New York, 1938, No. 34, *Illust.*

HALS, FRANS

DUTCH, 1585-1666

5 *The Young Violin Player.*

Painted about 1627. Of similar bravura of execution as the "Merry Lute Player", formerly in the Thompson Collection, Chicago, and like it painted on wood, a material especially well adapted to the sure and positive technique of the artist, lending an enamel-like brilliance to the surface. The hands in particular are drawn and painted in a masterly fashion.

Panel: 30 x 26½ inches.

LENT BY MR. L. M. FLESH, NEW YORK.

COLLECTIONS: C. Buys; Arthur Sulley; Carl Schoen; John Levy Galleries.

EXHIBITIONS: Detroit Institute of Arts, 1925 and 1935.

BIBLIOGRAPHY: C. HOFSTEDE DE GROOT: Catalogue raisonné, Vol. III, 1910, p. 25, No. 9a; W. R. VALENTINER: Frans Hals (Klas. der K.), 1923, No. 60, *Illust.*, F. DÜLBERG: Frans Hals, 1930, p. 78; W. R. VALENTINER: Fifty Paintings by Frans Hals, Detroit Inst. of Arts, 1935, No. 10, *Illust.*, IDEM: Frans Hals Paintings in America, 1936, No. 22, *Illust.*

HALS, FRANS

DUTCH, 1580-1666

6 *Arnoud Jansz van Druivesteyn.*

Painted in 1627. The artist here depicts the same model as the Colonel in the *Banquet of St. George's Shooting Company* in the Haarlem Museum, dated 1627; in the group portrait he holds a glass of wine in the right hand, while the left is invisible.

Canvas: 32 x 36 inches.

LENT BY THE HON. OSCAR B. CINTAS, HAVANA, CUBA.

COLLECTIONS: Haarlem, 1785; Jan Wubbels, 1792; John G. Johnson; Sir Hugh Lane; John Levy Galleries.

EXHIBITION: Detroit Institute, 1935.

BIBLIOGRAPHY: E. W. MOES: Frans Hals, 1909, p. 101, No. 52; C. HOFSTEDE DE GROOT: Catalogue raisonné, Vol. III, 1910, p. 55, No. 175; W. R. VALENTINER: Frans Hals (Kl. der Kunst), 1923, No. 62, *Illust.*, F. DÜLBERG: Frans Hals, 1930, p. 84; W. R. VALENTINER: Catalogue of Frans Hals Exhn., Detroit Inst. 1935, No. 8, *Illust.*, IDEM: Frans Hals Paintings in Amer., 1936, No. 19, *Illust.*

HALS, FRANS

DUTCH, 1585-1666

7 *Two Fisher Boys.*

Painted a bout 1630. One of the most excellent genre paintings of the artist's earlier period.

Canvas: 30 x 28 inches.

COLLECTIONS: Miss Laird, Brighton, England; Dr. Hans Schaeffer; D. Katz.
EXHIBITIONS: Gemeentelijk Museum, Haarlem, 1936; Rijksmuseum, Amsterdam, 1936;
Schaeffer Galleries, New York, 1936, and 1937; Frans Hals Museum, Haarlem, 1937; Arden Gallery, New York, 1937; California Palace of the Legion of Honor, San Francisco, 1938; Los Angeles Museum, 1938; Springfield Museum of Fine Arts, 1938; Museum of Art, Providence, R. I.
BIBLIOGRAPHY: ANON: Tentoonstelling van Oude Kunst, Rijksmuseum, 1936, p. 16, No. 67, *Illust.*, ANON: The Great Dutch Masters, Schaeffer Galleries, N. Y., 1936, No. 7, *Illust.*, G. D. GRATAMA: Frans Hals Tentoonstelling, Frans Hals Museum, Haarlem, 1937, p. 32, No. 8, *Illust.*, ANON: Paintings by Frans Hals, Schaeffer Gall., N. Y., 1937, No. 2; ANON: Paintings by Old Masters, Los Angeles Museum, 1938, No. 14, *Illust.*

HALS, FRANS

DUTCH, 1585-1666

178 *Portrait of a Gentleman in White.*

Painted about 1630-1632. The conception of the picture, and the costume with slit sleeves, are reminiscent of *The Laughing Cavalier* in the Wallace Collection, London, but the model is a more sympathetic one and the style more developed.

Canvas: 26½ x 22½ inches.

LENT BY MRS. SAMUEL P. ROTAN, CHESTNUT HILL, PA.

COLLECTIONS: Arthur Sulley; Andrew W. Mellon; Knoedler Galleries, New York.
EXHIBITION: Detroit Institute of Arts, 1935.
BIBLIOGRAPHY: W. R. VALENTINER: Frans Hals (Kl. der Kunst), 1923, p. 313, No. 106, *Illust.*, IDEM: Frans Hals Exhibition, Detroit Inst. of Arts, 1935, No. 20, *Illust.*, IDEM: Frans Hals Paintings in America, 1936, No. 38, *Illust.*

HALS, FRANS

DUTCH, 1585-1666

179 *Portrait of an Elderly Lady.*

Painted in 1633. Companion piece to the 'Portrait of an Elderly Gentleman' in the Frick Collection. One of the artist's most impressive women's portraits, in which the intelligent and good-natured expression of the woman with her prayer-book in her hand is excellently portrayed.

Canvas: 48 x 36 inches.

LENT BY THE NATIONAL GALLERY (MELLON COLLECTION),
WASHINGTON, D. C.

COLLECTIONS: M. Jurriaans, 1817; Comte de la Rupelle; James Simon; Lord Duveen of Millbank.
EXHIBITIONS: Sedelmeyer Gallery, Paris, 1905; Kaiser-Friedrich Museum, Berlin, 1906.
BIBLIOGRAPHY: C. SEDELMEYER: Paintings by Old Masters, 1905, No. 13, *Illust.*, W. VON BODE: Ausstell. von Werken alter Kunst, Kaiser Friedr. Mus. Berlin, 1906, p. 18, No. 49, *Illust.*, E. W. MOES: Frans Hals, 1909, No. 196; C. HOFSTEDE DE GROOT: Catalogue raisonné, Vol. III, 1910,

p. 108, No. 371; w. von bode: Frans Hals, Vol. I, 1914, No. 138, *Illust.*, w. r. valentiner: Frans Hals (Klas. der Kunst), 1923, No. 109, *Illust.*, f. dülberg: Frans Hals, 1930, p. 114; w. r. valentiner: Frans Hals Paintings in Amer., 1936, No. 41, *Illust.*

HALS, FRANS

DUTCH, 1585-1666

A Man with a Beer-keg, known also as "The Smuggler".

Painted about 1635. A brilliantly executed character study of the artist's middle period.

Canvas: 32½ x 26½ inches.

LENT BY MR. HENRY REICHHOLD, BIRMINGHAM, MICHIGAN.

COLLECTIONS: Miss Vera Bellingham; D. Katz.

EXHIBITIONS: Katz Galleries, Dieren, Holland, 1933; Arnheim Museum, 1934; Frans Hals Museum, Haarlem, 1934; Brussels, 1935; Detroit Institute of Arts, 1935; Smith College, Northampton, 1935; Rijksmuseum, Amsterdam, 1936; Schaeffer Galleries, New York, 1936; Gemeentelijk Museum, Haarlem, 1937.

BIBLIOGRAPHY: t. borenius: *In* Burl. Mag., Dec. 1932, p. 245, *Illust.*, w. r. valentiner: Catalogue of Paintings by Franz Hals, Detroit Institute of Arts, 1935, No. 27, *Illust.*, anon: Catalogus, Tentoonstelling Oude Kunst, Rijksmuseum, Amsterdam, 1936, p. 17, No. 68, *Illust.*, g. d. gratama: Frans Hals Tentoonstelling Catalogus, Haarlem, 1937, No. 83, *Illust.*

HALS, FRANS

DUTCH, 1585-1666

Portrait of an Officer.

Signed and dated 1637. One of the finest and most characteristic of the artist's works of the middle of the 'thirties; in style somewhat similar to the portrait of Willem Heythuysen in the Liechtenstein Gallery in Vienna. It shows the self-assurance and enjoyment of life of the sitter no less than of the successful artist, who at that period received more orders for portraits than at almost any other time of his life.

Canvas: 32¼ x 25¾ inches.

LENT BY MRS. HENRY GOLDMAN, NEW YORK.

COLLECTIONS: J. A. Töpfer; Francis Kleinberger; Arthur Sulley; Lord d'Aberon; Lord Duveen of Millbank.

EXHIBITION: Grafton Galleries, London, 1911.

BIBLIOGRAPHY: e. w. moes: Frans Hals, 1909, p. 106, No. 127; c. hofstede de groot: Catalogue raisonné, Vol. III, 1910, p. 275, No. 80; r. e. fry and m. w. brockwell: Catalogue of Old Masters, Grafton Galleries, London, 1911, p. 62, No. 65, *Illust.*, w. von bode: Frans Hals, 1914, No. 164, *Illust.*, f. j. mather: *In* Art in Amer., Vol. V, 1917, p. 58, *Illust.*, a. m. frankfurter: *In* Antiquarian, Sept. 1920, p. 34, *Illust.*, w. r. valentiner: Frans Hals (Kl. der Kunst), 1921, No. 154, *Illust.*, idem: The Henry Goldman Collection, 1922, No. 13, *Illust.*, f. dülberg: *Frans* Hals, 1930, p. 144; w. r. valentiner: Frans Hals Paintings in Amer., 1936, No. 62, *Illust.*

HALS, FRANS

DUTCH, 1585-1666

182 Portrait of Pieter Tjarck, known also as 'The Man with the Rose'.

Painted about 1638.

Canvas: 32½ x 26½ inches.

LENT BY SIR HARRY OAKES, BART., NASSAU, BAHAMAS.

COLLECTIONS: Comte d'Oultremont; Mon. Arnold and Tripp; Sir W. Cuthbert Quilter; Dowager Lady Quilter.

EXHIBITIONS: Brussels, 1882; International Exhibition, Paris, 1889; Royal Academy, London, 1891; Kunstring, The Hague, 1903; Gemeentelijk Museum, Haarlem.

BIBLIOGRAPHY: ANON: Catalogue de Tableaux, Colln. d'Oultremont, 1889, p. 11, No. 3; G. S. DAVIES: Frans Hals, 1902, pp. 136, 147, *Illust.*, IDEM: Frans Hals, 1908, p. 125, *Illust.*, E. MOES: Frans Hals, 1909, p. 104, No. 77; IDEM: *In* Iconographia Batava, No. 7993, Nos. 1-2; C. HOFSTEDE DE GROOT: Catalogue Raisonné, Vol. III, 1910, p. 69, No. 231; J. PELADAN: Frans Hals, 1912, p. 122, *Illust.*, W. VON BODE: Frans Hals, 1914, p. 9, No. 178, *Illust.*, W. R. VALENTINER: Frans Hals (Kl. der Kunst), 1923, p. 317, No. 172, *Illust.*, G. D. GRATAMA: Frans Hals Tentoon- stelling, Gemeentelij Mus., Haarlem, 1937; A. M. FRANKFURTER: *In* Art News, July 17, 1937; F. VAN THIENEN: *In* Pantheon, Sept. 1937, pp. 261, 269, *Illust.*, ANON: *In* Mag. of Art, Vol. XXX, 1937, p. 511, *Illust.*

HALS, FRANS

DUTCH, 1585-1666

183 Portrait of Hendrik Swalmius.

Pl. 67   Signed with the artist's monogram, and dated, *Aetat, 60, 1639, F.H.* The sitter was the Rector of Haarlem (d. 1649).

Panel: 10¾ x 8 inches.

LENT BY MR. H. E. TEN CATE, ALMELO, HOLLAND.

COLLECTIONS: Mrs. Brown Lindsay, Colstoun, Haddingtonshire; D. Katz, Dieren.

ENGRAVED (in reverse), by J. Suyderkof, from which the picture was known only until recently. (De Groot, 1910, mentions the picture as lost.)

EXHIBITIONS: Haarlem, 1936; Rijksmuseum, Amsterdam, 1936; Los Angeles Museum, 1937.

BIBLIOGRAPHY: E. W. MOES: Iconographia Batavia, No. 1720; IDEM: Frans Hals, 1909, No. 75; C. HOFSTEDE DE GROOT: Catalogue Raisonné, Vol. III, 1910, p. 69, No. 228; W. R. VALENTINER: Frans Hals (Kl. der Kunst), 1923, 230, *Illust.* with *Suyderkof's engraving*, ANON: Catalogus Tentoonstelling Oude Kunst, Rijksmuseum, Amsterdam, 1936, p. 17, No. 69, *Illust.*

HALS, FRANS

DUTCH, 1585-1666

184 Portrait of De Heer Bodolphe (Companion to No. 185).

Painted in 1643. Inscribed: AETAT SVAE 73. ANo. 1643. This picture and its companion are among the most accomplished portraits by the artist.

Canvas: 58½ x 38½ inches.

COLLECTIONS: James Odier; Count André Mniszech; J. Pierpont Morgan.
EXHIBITIONS: Agnew Galleries, London, 1906; Hudson Fulton, Metropolitan Museum of Art, New York, 1909; Century Club, New York, 1938.
BIBLIOGRAPHY: w. r. valentiner: Catalogue of Paintings by Dutch Masters, Hudson-Fulton Exhibition, Metropolitan Museum of Art, New York, 1909, No. 33, *Illust.*, e. w. moes: Frans Hals, 1909, p. 105, No. 105; c. hofstede de groot: Catalogue Raisonné, Vol. III, 1910, No. 157; w. von bode: Frans Hals, Vol. II, 1914, No. 208, *Illust.*, w. r. valentiner: *Frans Hals (Kl. der Kunst)*, 1923, p. 319, No. 204, *Illust.*, f. dülberg: Frans Hals, 1930, p. 171, *Illust.*, w. r. valentiner: Frans Hals Paintings in America, 1936, No. 72, *Illust.*, anon: Masters of Portraiture, The Century Club, New York, 1938, No. 3, *Illust.*

HALS, FRANS

DUTCH, 1585-1666

5 *Portrait of Mevrouw Bodolphe* (Companion to No. 184).

Painted in 1643. Inscribed: AETAT SVAE 72. ANo. 1643. F.H.

Canvas: 48½ x 38½ inches.

COLLECTIONS: James Odier; Count André Mniszech; J. Pierpont Morgan.
EXHIBITIONS: Agnew Galleries, London, 1906; Hudson Fulton, Metropolitan Museum of Art, New York, 1909; Century Club, New York, 1928.
BIBLIOGRAPHY: w. r. valentiner: Catalogue of Paintings by Dutch Masters, Hudson-Fulton Exhibition, Metropolitan Museum, New York, 1909, No. 34; e. w. moes: Frans Hals, 1909, p. 105, No. 106; c. hofstede de groot: Catalogue Raisonné, Vol. III, 1910, No. 158; w. von bode: Frans Hals, Vol. II, 1914, No. 209, *Illust.*, w. r. valentiner: Frans Hals (*Kl. der Kunst*), 1923, p. 319, No. 205, *Illust.*, f. dülberg: Frans Hals, 1930, p. 171, *Illust.*, w. r. valentiner: Frans Hals Paintings in America, 1936, No. 73, *Illust.*, anon: Masters of Portraiture, The Century Club, New York, 1938, No. 4, *Illust.*

HALS, FRANS

DUTCH, 1585-1666

6 *A Youth in a Feathered Hat.*

65 Signed with Monogram. Painted about 1645. This portrait and the one of the boy holding a skull, in Glenart Castle, have gone under the name of Hamlet, but it is more probable that the latter represents a *Vanitas* allegory, such as is depicted in the engraving of Lucas van Leyden. The present composition, apparently representing one of the artist's own children, is among the master's happiest inventions, and is of a rare richness and beauty of technique.

Canvas: 30 x 25 inches.

COLLECTIONS: William A. Coats; Lord Duveen of Millbank.
EXHIBITIONS: Lawrie Galleries, London, 1903; Rijksmuseum, Amsterdam, 1933; The Hague, 1903; Detroit Institute of Arts, 1935.
BIBLIOGRAPHY: ANON: Catalogue des Portraits Anciens, Cercle Artistique de La Haye, 1903, No. 40a; E. W. MOES: Frans Hals, 1909, No. 163; C. HOFSTEDE DE GROOT: Catalogue Raisonné, Vol. III, 1910, No. 103; W. VON BODE: Frans Hals, Vol. I, 1914, No. 63, Illust., W. R. VALENTINER: Frans Hals (Kl. der Kunst), 1923, p. 228, Illust., IDEM: Unknown Masterpieces; note by F. Schmidt-Degener, 1930, No. 49, Illust., IDEM: Fifty Paintings by Frans Hals, Detroit Inst. of Arts, 1935, No. 43, Illust., IDEM: Frans Hals Paintings in America, 1936, No. 86, Illust.

HALS, FRANS

DUTCH, 1585-1666

187 *Portrait of a Man.*

Painted about 1645-48. An outstanding example of the master's amiable, elegant conception; masterly in the easy brush-strokes and warm, brilliant colour scheme of the middle forties.

Canvas: 41½ x 31½ inches.

LENT BY THE CINCINNATI ART MUSEUM.

COLLECTIONS: Lord Talbot of Malahide, Dublin; Scott and Fowles; Charles P. Taft, Cincinnati.
EXHIBITIONS: Scott and Fowles Galleries, New York, 1909, and 1914.
BIBLIOGRAPHY: E. L. CARY: In Putnam's Mag., Vol. VII, 1910, p. 525; W. WALTON: In Burl. Mag., Vol. XVI, 1910, p. 368, Illust., A. HOEBER: In International Studio, Vol. XXXIX, 1910, p. 71; W. VON BODE: Frans Hals, Vol. II, 1914, No. 253, Illust., M. W. BROCKWELL: Catalogue of the Taft Colln., 1920, No. 27; W. R. VALENTINER: Frans Hals, (Klas. des K.) 1923, No. 238, Illust., IDEM: Frans Hals Paintings in America, 1936, No. 89, Illust.

HALS, FRANS

DUTCH, 1585-1666

188 *Self-Portrait.*

Pl. 67 Painted about 1648. A considerable number of contemporary copies are known, which suggests that the original had always been regarded as a self-portrait.

Canvas: 13 x 11 inches.

LENT BY DR. G. H. A. CLOWES, INDIANAPOLIS.

COLLECTION: The Dresden Gallery; recorded in the Inventory of 1710 as a Self-Portrait by Frans Hals; sold after 1900.
EXHIBITION: Detroit Institute of Arts, 1935; Gemeentelijk Museum, Haarlem, 1937.
BIBLIOGRAPHY: E. P. RICHARDSON: In Detroit Inst. Bulletin, Feb. 1935, pp. 50 and 59, Illust., W. R. VALENTINER: Catalogue of the F. Hals Exhbn. Detroit Inst., 1935, No. 49, Illust., IDEM: In Art News, Jan. 12, 1935; IDEM: In Art in America, June 1935, pp. 85-103, Illust., IDEM: Frans Hals Paintings in America, 1936, p. 88, Illust., G. D. GRATAMA: Frans Hals Tentoonstelling, Gemeent. Museum, Haarlem, 1937, p. 50, No. 98, Illust.

HALS, FRANS

DUTCH, 1585 - 1666

Joseph Coymans, Lord of Bruchem and Nieuwaal.

Born Aug. 1, 1591; died after 1649 and before 1677; married Nov. 21, 1616, to Dorothea Berck. Dated 1644 below the coat-of-arms. The portrait is characteristic of the artist's striving for elegance and dignity during the middle forties. Companion piece to the portrait of Dorothea Berck in the Baltimore Museum (Jacobs Collection).

Canvas: 33 x 27½ inches.

LENT BY MRS. VAN WIE WILLYS, NEW YORK.

COLLECTIONS: James Carnegie; Maurice Kann; Lord Duveen of Millbank; Reinhardt Galleries; John N. Willys.

EXHIBITION: Grafton Galleries, London, 1909.

BIBLIOGRAPHY: E. W. MOES: Frans Hals, 1909, p. 106, No. 146; ANON: Catalogue of the Grafton Galleries Exhib., London, 1909, No. 36; ANON: In Burl. Mag., No. 1909, pp. 109-110; C. HOFSTEDE DE GROOT: Catalogue Raisonné, Vol. III, 1910, No. 304; W. VON BODE: Frans Hals, Vol. II, 1914, No. 211, Illust., W. R. VALENTINER: Frans Hals, (Klas. der K.) 1921, p. 196, Illust., F. DÜLBERG: Frans Hals, 1930, p. 168; W. R. VALENTINER: Frans Hals Paintings in Amer., 1936, No. 75, Illust.

HEYDE, JAN VAN DER

DUTCH, 1637 - 1712

Born at Gorcum and died at Amsterdam. He travelled in Germany, Belgium, and England, painting in Cologne, Brussels, and London. Aside from being the finest Dutch painter of street-scenes, he was also an engineer, invented the fire-engine, and introduced the use of street lamps. He made several etched plates, and had a secret for printing pictures, which were stamped in oil colours and afterwards retouched.

View of Veere, Zeeland.

Signed: J. V. D. Heyde. The figures were painted by Adrian Van der Velde (1635-1672).

Canvas: 16½ x 21 inches.

LENT BY THE JOHN G. JOHNSON COLLECTION, PHILADELPHIA.

COLLECTION: David P. Sellar.

EXHIBITION: Royal Academy, London, 1885.

ENGRAVED by Teyssonnières.

BIBLIOGRAPHY: CATALOGUE of Old Masters, Royal Academy, London, 1885, p. 27, No. 123; CATALOGUE de Tableaux Anciens, Collection Sellar, 1889, p. 31, No. 41, Illust., W. R. VALENTINER: Flemish and Dutch Paintings in the John G. Johnson Collection, Phila., 1913, No. 596, Illust., C. HOFSTEDE DE GROOT: Catalogue raisonné, Vol. VIII, 1927, p. 364, No. 111.

HOBBEMA, MEINDERT

DUTCH, 1638-1709

Pupil of Jacob Ruisdael. His earliest paintings are dated 1658-1659; his most important compositions were executed during the 'sixties of the seventeenth century; he seems to have painted very rarely after 1670. The leading landscape painter in Holland next to Jacob Ruisdael and Cuyp.

191 *Landscape with Watermill.*

Pl. 76   Signed and dated 1664. One of the masterpieces of the artist.

Canvas: 37⅜ x 51¼ inches.

LENT BY MR. H. E. TEN CATE, ALMELO, HOLLAND.

COLLECTIONS: Louis Bernhard Coclers; G. Müller; Baron J. G. Verstolk van Soelen; Jones Loyd, afterwards Lord Overstone; Robert James Loyd-Lindsay, Baron Wantage; Lady Wantage; Earl of Crawford and Balcarres; D. Katz.

EXHIBITIONS: Royal Academy, 1870 and 1888; Guildhall, London, 1894; Jeu de Paume, Paris, 1921; Brussels Museum, 1935; Rijks-Museum, Amsterdam, 1936; Museum Boymans, Rotterdam, 1938.

BIBLIOGRAPHY: J. SMITH: Catalogue Raisonné, Vol. VI, 1835, No. 67; G. F. WAAGEN: Treasures of Art, Vol. IV, 1857, p. 141; SIR A. G. TEMPLE: Catalogue, Guildhall, London, 1894, p. 62, No. 74; F. T. KUGLER: Dutch Painters, 1898, p. 478; H. S. WANTAGE: Pictures in the Collection of Lord and Lady Wantage, 1902, pp. 69-70, No. 103, *Illust.*, C. HOFSTEDE DE GROOT: Catalogue Raisonné, Vol. IV, 1912, pp. 383-4, No. 86; BARONNE A. HOUTART: Cinq Siècles d'Art, Bruxelles, 1935, p. 172, No. 737; D. HANNEMA: Meesterwerken uit vier eeuwen, 1400-1800, Museum Boymans, Rotterdam, 1938, p. 23, No. 88, *Illust.*, G. BROULHIET: Meindert Hobbema, 1938, p. 380, No. 22, *Illust.*, p. 113; ANON: *In* American Magazine of Art, Jan. 1939, pp. 43-44, *Illust.*

HOBBEMA, MEINDERT

DUTCH, 1638-1709

192 *Forest Landscape, with Water and Boat.*

Signed in full in the centre foreground. From the artist's mature period. A similar landscape, but of slightly different dimensions, is in the John G. Johnson Collection, Philadelphia.

Panel: 12¾ x 14¾ inches.

LENT BY DR. C. J. K. VAN AALST, HOEVELAKEN, HOLLAND.

COLLECTIONS: Hendrik Muilman, Lord-banneret of Haamstede; Thomas Theodoor Cremer; M. Jurriaans; Jan Ancher; Thomas Baring, M.P.; Thomas George, first Earl of Northbrook; Francis George, second Earl of Northbrook.

BIBLIOGRAPHY: J. SMITH: Catalogue raisonné, Vol. VI, 1935, p. 126, No. 40; G. F. WAAGEN: Treasures of Art, Vol. II, 1854, p. 187; W. H. J. WEALE: Catalogue of Pictures belonging to the Earl of Northbrook, 1889, p. 49, No. 62; C. HOFSTEDE DE GROOT: Catalogue raisonné, Vol. IV, 1912, p. 437, No. 260; G. BROULHIET: Meindert Hobbema, 1938, p. 438, No. 456, *Illust.*, W. R. VALENTINER: Catalogue of Paintings in the Van Aalst Collection, 1939, p. 25, *Illust.*

HOBBEMA, MEINDERT

DUTCH, 1638 - 1709

A Watermill with a Red Roof.

Signed in full. One of the masterpieces of the artist's best period, about 1663-65.

Canvas: 31¾ x 43⅛ inches.

LENT BY THE ART INSTITUTE OF CHICAGO.

COLLECTIONS: J. Ellis; Lord Mount-Temple; Prince Anatoli Demidoff; Prince Paul Demidoff; Frank G. Logan.

BIBLIOGRAPHY: J. SMITH: Catalogue raisonné, Vol. VI, 1835, No. 105; C. HOFSTEDE DE GROOT: Catalogue raisonné, Vol. IV, 1912, No. 71; W. R. VALENTINER: *In* Art in America, Vol. II, 1914, p. 165; C. HOFSTEDE DE GROOT: *In* Thieme-Becker's Lexikon, Vol. XVII, 1924, p. 161; D. C. RICH: Catalogue of Paintings and Sculpture, Art Institute of Chicago, 1933, No. 66, *Illust.*, G. BROULHEIT: Meindert Hobbema, 1938, p. 378, No. 109, *Illust.*, A. GOLDSCHMIDT: *In* Art Quarterly, Winter, 1939, p. 11, *Illust.*

HOBBEMA, MEINDERT

DUTCH, 1638 - 1709

The Hamlet in the Wood.

Signed: M. Hobbema. Painted about 1665.

Canvas: 38¼ x 51¼ inches.

LENT BY MR. AND MRS. HORACE HAVEMEYER, NEW YORK.

COLLECTIONS: De Heer Van Winter; Six van Hillegom; Jan P. Six; P. H. Six van Vromade; Jan Six; Knoedler Galleries.

ENGRAVED in acquatint by M. C. Hoell Prestel (1744-1794).

EXHIBITION: Six Collection, Stedelijk Museum, Amsterdam, 1900.

BIBLIOGRAPHY: J. SMITH: Catalogue Raisonné, Vol. VI, 1835, No. 89; W. BÜRGER: *In* Gaz. d. B.A., Vol. IV, 1859, pp. 34-35; E. MICHEL: *In* L'Art, 1886, p. 262; IDEM: Hobbema, 1890, p. 49; G. LAFENESTRE ET E. RICHTENBERGER: La Hollande, n.d., p. 324; J. SIX: Catalogus der Schilderijen van P. H. Six van Vromade, Stedelijk Museum, Amsterdam, 1900, No. 44; A. V. WURZBACH: Niederl. Kunstl.-Lexikon, Vol. I, 1906, p. 691; C. HOFSTEDE DE GROOT: Catalogue Raisonné, Vol. IV, 1912, No. 145; W. GIBSON: *In* Apollo, Nov. 1928, pp. 239-240, *Illust.*, G. BROULHET: Meindert Hobbema, 1938, pp. 194 and 400, *Illust.*

HOGARTH, WILLIAM

ENGLISH, 1697 - 1764

Born in London. In 1712 he was apprenticed to Ellis Gamble, a silversmith, and turned his attention to engraving in 1718, but remained unknown until 1726 when he published his plates for "Hudibras". In 1729 he married the daughter of Sir James Thornhill, founder of an Academy to which he afterwards succeeded. In 1733 he published "The Harlot's Progress," which was soon followed by "The Rake's Progress." In later years he indulged in literary compositions, and wrote "The Analysis of Beauty." He also painted a number of excellent portraits.

195 *The Graham Children.*

Pl. 92 The four children of Robert Bontine Graham (d. 1797) of Gartmore, Scotland; William, his heir, is the boy playing the instrument in the picture, Nicol, and the infant at the left, became Maréchal-de-camp in the Austrian service. The picture was painted about 1742; it is one of the largest and most important paintings by the artist.

Canvas: 63½ x 71 inches.

LENT BY THE NATIONAL GALLERY, LONDON.

COLLECTIONS: R. R. Graham; Mr. Graham of Chelsea; William Segnier; George Watson-Taylor, M.P., Earl of Normanton; Lord Duveen of Millbank, who presented it to the National Gallery in 1934.

EXHIBITIONS: British Institution, 1814; Royal Academy, London, 1882 and 1908; The National Gallery, London, 1934.

BIBLIOGRAPHY: ANON: Catalogue of the British Institution Exhibition, 1814, No. 83; ANON: Catalogue of the Royal Academy Exhibitions, 1882, No. 275, and 1908, No. 105; A. DOBSON: William Hogarth, 1902, p. 180; M. ROLDIT: Pictures of the Earl of Normanton, *In* Burl. Mag., Dec. 1903, pp. 220-221, *Illust.*; W. C. LANE and N. E. BROWNE, Edrs.: American Library Assn. Portrait Index, 1906, p. 606; M. H. SPIELMANN: British Portrait Painting, Vol. I, 1910, pp. 40-41, *Illust.*; T. BORENIUS: Hogarth at the National Gallery. *In* Pantheon, Nov. 1934, p. 348, *Illust.*

HOLBEIN, AMBROSIUS

GERMAN, 1484?-1520?

Was a native of Augsburg, and brother of the more celebrated Hans Holbein the younger. He went to Basle in 1514, and it is almost certain that the two brothers worked together. In 1517 he was admitted to the guild 'zum Himmel', to which various artisans belonged. Soon after he must have gone away, or more probably have died.

196 *Portrait of a Young Girl.*

One of a group of similar portraits, two of which are in the Basle Museum.

Panel: 11½ x 8 inches.

LENT ANONYMOUSLY.

COLLECTION: Schloss Ambras, Innsbruck; Hapsburg Collection, Belvedere, Vienna.

BIBLIOGRAPHY: A. WOLTMANN: Holbein and his time, 1872, p. 108; W. HES: Ambrosius Holbein, 1911, pp. 124-125, *Illust.*

HOLBEIN THE YOUNGER, HANS

GERMAN, 1497-1543

Born at Augsburg. Taught by his father, and influenced by his fellow-citizen, Hans Burckmair. He went to Basle in 1514, the date of his earliest known picture, and matriculated in the Painters' Guild in 1519; he remained in that city until 1526, when he went to London. After staying for two years he returned to Basle, remaining there until 1532, when he was recalled to England, where he remained for the rest of his life. He received a great welcome from the German merchants of the Steelyard, and painted portraits of many of them. In 1536 he became court-painter to Henry VIII, and thence onward he was exclusively engaged in court circles. In 1538 he paid two short visits to the continent on the King's affairs. He died in London, apparently of the plague.

7 *Hermann Wedigh of Cologne.*

43 Painted in London in 1532. Signed H. H., and inscribed: HER. WID, on the book; and on the projecting paper: *Veritas odium parit* ('Truth brings hatred'); on the background: *Anno 1532, Aetatis Suae 29.* The sitter, born in 1503, was a member of a noted mercantile family of Germany which had long been active in the Hanseatic League, a powerful trading federation of North German towns, enjoying important privileges in England. Until the reign of Edward VI (1537-1553) the League was established at the "Steelyard", Cosin Lane, London, with a Guildhall, decorated by Holbein, in Thames Street, which was destroyed during the Great Fire in 1666. A portrait of the sitter's brother (?) Hildebrant Wedigh, dated 1533, is in the Berlin Museum.

Panel: 15¾ x 12¼ inches.

LENT BY MR. EDWARD S. HARKNESS, NEW YORK.

COLLECTIONS: Count von Schönborn-Buchheim; Frank D. Stout.
EXHIBITIONS: Art Institute of Chicago, 1924, and 1933.
BIBLIOGRAPHY: A. WOLTMANN: Holbein and his Time, 1872, p. 359; H. KNACKFUSS: Holbein, Trans. by C. Dodgson, 1899, p. 121, *Illust.*, G. S. DAVIES: Hans Holbein the Younger, 1903, p. 216; P. GANZ: Hans Holbein d.J. (Kl. der Kunst), 1912, p. 240, No. 97, *Illust.*, F. VON REBER and A. BAYERSDORFER: Klassicher Bilderschatz, Vol. VI, n.d, No. 94, *Illust.*, F. BENOIT: Holbein (*Les Maitres de l'Art*), n.d, p. 159; S. REINACH: Répértoire de Peintures, Vol. II, 1907, p. 317, *Illust.*, A. B. CHAMBERLAIN: Hans Holbein the Younger, Vol. II, 1913, pp. 15-16; W. STEIN: Holbein, 1929, pp. 226-227, *Illust.*, D. C. RICH: Catalogue of Paintings and Sculpture, Art. Inst. of Chicago, 1933, p. 4, No. 20, *Illust.*, IDEM: *In* Pantheon, Dec. 1933, p. 372, *Illust.*, C. L. KUHN: German Paintings in American Collections, 1936, p. 81, No. 360, *Illust.*

HOLBEIN THE YOUNGER, HANS
GERMAN, 1497-1543

8 *Dirk Berck of Cologne.*

44 A letter in the left hand bears his address: *Dem Ersame' u(n)d fromen Derick berk i. London upt. Stalhoff,* and the motto: *besad dz end* (To the honourable and noble Dirk Berck in London in the Steelyard — Consider the end); a small piece of paper lies on the table and bears the Latin sentence from Virgil: *Olim meminisse juvabit* (Hereafter I shall be remembered). Dated 1536. *See* reference under

No. 197 for particulars relating to the "Steel-yard".

Panel: 21 x 16¾ inches.

LENT BY THE JULES S. BACHE COLLECTION, NEW YORK.

COLLECTIONS: Earls of Egremont; Colonel Egremont Wyndham; Lord Leconfield; Lord Duveen of Millbank.

EXHIBITIONS: Royal Academy, London, 1880; Germanic Museum, Harvard University, 1936; Wadsworth Atheneum, Hartford, Conn., 1937.

BIBLIOGRAPHY: G. F. WAAGEN: Treasures of Art in Great Britain, Vol. III, 1854, p. 41; R. N. WORNUM: Hans Holbein, 1867, pp. 288-289; A. WOLTMANN: Holbein and his Time, 1872, p. 344; G. S. DAVIES: Hans Holbein the Younger, 1903, p. 219; P. GANZ: Jn Burl. Mag., Oct. 1911, p. 33, Jllust., IDEM: Hans Holbein d. J. (Kl. der Kunst), 1912, p. 107, Jllust., A. B. CHAMBER-LAIN: Hans Holbein the Younger, Vol. II, 1913, pp. 22-23, Plate 5; C. H. C. BAKER: Catalogue of Pictures in the possession of Lord Leconfield, 1920, No. 160, pp. 57-58, Jllust., U. CHRISTOFFEL: Hans Holbein d. J., 1927, p. 96; W. STEIN: Holbein, 1929, p. 235; H. TIETZE: Meisterwerke Europaïscher Malerei in Amerika, 1935, p. 216, Jllust., C. L. KUHN: German Paintings in American Collections, 1936, p. 82, No. 367, Jllust., A. E. AUSTIN: Forty-three Portraits, Wadsworth Museum, Hartford, Conn., 1937, No. 7, Jllust., ANON: Catalogue of the Bache Collection, New York, 1938, No. 30, Jllust.

HOLBEIN THE YOUNGER, HANS

GERMAN, 1497-1543

199 *A Merchant of the Hanseatic League.*

Pl. 44 *Jnscribed: Anno 1538 Aetatis Suae 33. See* reference under No. 197 for particulars relating to the Hanseatic League.

Panel: 19½ x 15½ inches.

LENT BY DR. A. HAMILTON RICE, NEW YORK.

COLLECTIONS: Royal Gallery of Poland, Warsaw; Count Kossakowski; Gabriel Faczycki; Lord Duveen of Millbank.

BIBLIOGRAPHY: A. L. MAYER: Jn Beiträge zur Geschichte der deutschen Kunst, Vol. I, 1924, p. 260; M. VAUGHAN: Holbein Portraits in America, Jn Inter. Studio, Nov. 1927, Jllust., W. STEIN: Holbein, 1929, p. 321; W. R. VALENTINER: Unknown Masterpieces, 1930, No. 69, Jllust., C. L. KUHN: German Paintings in American Collections, 1936, No. 369, Jllust.

HOLBEIN THE YOUNGER, HANS

GERMAN, 1497-1543

200 *Edward VJ, when Prince of Wales.*

Edward, Prince of Wales, born at Hampton Court, October 12, 1537, was Henry VIII's son by his third Queen, Jane Seymour. On January 21, 1547, four years after this portrait was painted, he succeeded his father. Edward died at Greenwich on July 6, 1553, probably from the effect of quack nostrums on his weak constitution. This portrait was painted in 1543, and is possibly the last work of the Master.

Panel: 12¾ diameter.

COLLECTIONS: Viscount Lee of Fareham; Lord Duveen of Millbank.

EXHIBITION: Kleinberger Galleries, New York, 1929.

BIBLIOGRAPHY: R. N. WORNUM: Hans Holbein, painter of Augsburg, 1867, p. 323; T. BORE-
NIUS: Pictures Collected by Viscount and Viscountess Lee of Fareham, 1923, pp. 44-45, *Illust.*;
P. GANZ: *In* Jahrb. für Kunst in der Schweiz, 1921-24, p. 294; IDEM: *In* Apollo, Dec. 1925, pp.
326-327, *Illust. in color*; R. R. TATLOCK: *In* The Art News, New York, April 14, 1928, *Illust. in
color*; W. STEIN: Holbein, 1929, p. 310; R. CORTISSOZ: *In* The Amer. Mag. of Art, Vol. XXI, 1930,
p. 259, *Illust.*; P. HENDY: Catalogue of the Gardner Museum, Boston, 1931, p. 186; O. GÖTZ: *In*
Staedel Jahrbuch, Vols. VII-VIII, 1932, p. 126; C. L. KUHN: German Paintings in American
Collections, 1936, p. 84, No. 379, *Illust.*; ANON: Catalogue of the Bache Collection, New York,
1938, No. 32, *Illust.*

HOOCH, PIETER DE

DUTCH, 1629-1683?

Born at Rotterdam. Pupil of Nicolaes Berchem and fellow pupil of Ochtervelt. Influenced by Carel Fabritius and Jan Vermeer. Between 1653-57 he was repeatedly
in Leyden and The Hague, and became a 'guest' of the Delft Guild during those
years. From 1667-83 he was at Amsterdam, where it is presumed he died. His best
works belong to the period he worked in Delft in rivalry with Jan Vermeer.

A Delft Courtyard.

Painted about 1656. A replica, with the addition of a second cavalier, is in the
Mellon Collection, National Gallery, Washington, D. C.

Canvas: 30¾ x 25½ inches.

COLLECTIONS: John Smith; William Wells of Redleaf; Jones Loyd, afterwards Lord Overstone; Robert James Loyd-Lindsay, Baron Wantage; Lady Wantage; Earl of Crawford and
Balcarres; D. Katz.

EXHIBITIONS: Royal Academy, London, 1871, and 1888; Guildhall, London, 1894; Burlington
Fine Arts Club, London, 1900; Tuileries, Paris, 1921; Mauritshuis, The Hague, 1921; Royal
Academy, London, 1929; Museum Boymans, Rotterdam, 1935, and 1938; Rhode Island School of
Design, 1938; Schaeffer Galleries, New York, 1939.

BIBLIOGRAPHY: J. SMITH: Catalogue raisonné, Vol. IV, 1833, p. 227, No. 30; G. F. WAAGEN:
Treasures of Art in Gt. Britain, Vol. IV, 1857, pp. 130-131; SIR A. G. TEMPLE: Catalogue of Pictures, Guildhall, London, 1894, p. 41, No. 50; H. S. WANTAGE: Pictures in the Collection of Lord
and Lady Wantage, 1902, p. 73, No. 108, *Illust.*; C. HOFSTEDE DE GROOT: Catalogue raisonné, Vol. I,
1907, p. 559, No. 297; L. BENEDITE: Exposition Hollandaise, Paris, 1921, No. 25; C. BRIÈRE-MISME:
In Gaz. des. B.-Arts, 1927, p. 63; H. SCHNEIDER and W. G. CONSTABLE: Dutch Art at the Royal
Academy, London, 1929, p. 62, No. 319; W. R. VALENTINER: Pieter de Hooch (Kl. de Kunst), n.d.,
pp. 271-272, No. 43, *Illust.*; D. HANNEMA: Meesterwerken uit vier eeuwen, Museum Boymans, Rotterdam, 1938, p. 24, No. 91, *Illust.*; A. M. FRANKFURTER: *In* Art News, Feb. 4, 1939, p. 10, *Illust.*

HOOCH, PIETER DE

DUTCH, 1629-1683?

202 *The Linen Cupboard,* known also as 'The Good Housewife'.

Pl. 75 Signed: *P. de Hoogh, 1663.* One of the best paintings of the artist's Amsterdam period. The technique and coloring of the house seen through the open doorway show Vermeer influence.

Canvas: 30 x 28 inches.

LENT BY THE RIJKSMUSEUM, AMSTERDAM, HOLLAND.

COLLECTIONS: Baron Lockhorst, Rotterdam, 1726; Joachim Randorp, Burgomaster of Amsterdam, 1794; a Scottish Collection; John Smith, 1828; Six van Hillegom, Amsterdam, 1833; Jan P. Six; P. H. Six de s'Graveland; Jan Six, 1928.

EXHIBITIONS: "Arti et Amicitiae", Amsterdam, 1872; Six Collection, Stedelijk Museum, Amsterdam, 1900.

BIBLIOGRAPHY: J. SMITH: Catalogue Raisonné, Vol. IV, 1833, p. 230; ANON: Katalogus, Tentoonstelling schilderijen van oude meesters, Amsterdam, 1872, No. 110; H. HAVARD: *In* Gaz. des B.-Arts, Nov. 1872, pp. 380-381; IDEM: *In* Les merveilles de l'Art hollandais, 1873, pp. 57, 123; C. HOFSTEDE DE GROOT: Catalogue Raisonné, Vol. I, 1907, p. 483, No. 25; C. BRIERE-MISME: *In* Gazette des B.-Arts, 1927, p. 72; ANON: Tableaux anciens, Collection Six, 1928, p. 4, No. 15, *Illust.,* W. R. VALENTINER: Pieter de Hooch (Kl. der Kunst), n.d., p. 275, No. 69, *Illust.*

HOOCH, PIETER DE (Attributed)

DUTCH, 1629-1683?

203 *The Terrace.*

W. R. Valentiner attributes this picture to Hendrik van den Burch (*compare* No. 30 in this Catalogue); D. Hannema to Carel Fabritius.

Canvas: 43¾ x 32¾ inches.

LENT BY THE MUSEUM OF ART, RHODE ISLAND SCHOOL OF DESIGN, PROVIDENCE.

COLLECTIONS: Duke George Nicolaivich de Leuchtenberg, Petrograd; Colnaghi Galleries, London; Leonard Gow, Glasgow; D. Katz, Dieren.

EXHIBITIONS: Museum Boymans, Rotterdam, 1935; Rhode Island School of Design, 1938.

BIBLIOGRAPHY: W. R. VALENTINER: Pieter de Hoogh (Kl. der Kunst), n.d., pp. 251, 296, *Illust.,* IDEM: *In* Pantheon, March 1929, p. 105, *Illust.,* D. HANNEMA: Vermeer Tentoonstelling, Museum Boymans, 1935, No. 39, *Illust.,* A. HEPPNER: *In* Pantheon, Aug. 1935, p. 260, *Illust.,* M. CHAMOT: *In* Apollo, Oct. 1935, p. 202, *Illust.,* W. STECHOW: Dutch Painting of the XVII c., Rhode Island Museum, 1938, No. 23, *Illust.,* ANON: *In* Pantheon, June 1939, p. 212, *Illust.*

HOPPNER, R.A., JOHN

ENGLISH, 1758-1810

Born at Whitechapel, London, of German parentage; when young he was one of the choristers in the Chapel Royal. He entered the Royal Academy Schools in 1775 at King George III's expense, and exhibited his first picture in 1780. In 1789 he was appointed Portrait Painter to the Prince of Wales. In 1795 he was elected a full member of the Academy. He was confessedly an imitator of Reynolds, and was regarded in his time as his 'most daring plagiarist'. He shared for some years the popularity of Sir Thomas Lawrence as a successful painter of women and children.

4 *Miss Selina Beresford.*

Painted about 1790. Selina, the younger daughter of Francis Beresford, of Ashbourne, Derbyshire, was born at Ashbourne in 1775, and married the Rev. Samuel Martin, for fifty years the Rector of Worksop, Nottinghamshire; she died June 2, 1847.

Canvas: 30 x 25 inches.

LENT BY MR. AND MRS. ROBERT W. REFORD, MONTREAL, CANADA.
COLLECTIONS: Rev. Samuel Martin, Rector of Worksop, Nottingham; Major William Martin; Marcus Trevelyan Martin; Lord Duveen of Millbank.
ENGRAVED in Mezzotint by J. B. Pratt, 1900.
EXHIBITIONS: Royal Academy, London, 1893; Detroit Institute of Arts, 1926; Wadsworth Atheneum, Hartford, Conn., 1928.
BIBLIOGRAPHY: ANON: Catalogue of Old Masters, Royal Acad., Lond., 1893, No. 23; SIR W. ARMSTRONG: Art in Great Britain, 1909, p. 196; W. MCKAY and W. ROBERTS: John Hoppner, R.A., 1914, p. 165, *Illust.*, W. R. VALENTINER: British Paintings of the XVIII and XIX c., Detroit Inst., 1926, No. 14, *Illust.*

JORDAENS, JACOB

FLEMISH, 1593-1678

Born in Antwerp. In 1607 he entered the studio of Adam van Noort, master of Rubens; in 1615 he became a member of the Guild as a tempera painter, and in 1621 was president of the Antwerp Guild. In 1635 he worked with Cornelis de Vos on the Triumphal Arch of Philip IV for the entry into Antwerp of the Cardinal Infant Ferdinand. From 1649-52 he was at The Hague. He frequently collaborated with other masters, putting in figures and backgrounds of still-life, etc., to their paintings. He excelled in humorous scenes of Flemish life, scriptural and mythological subjects. He is one of the outstanding Flemish masters of the XVII c.

5 *The Holy Family.*

An excellent work of the earlier period of the artist. A study for the Joseph is in the Van Aalst collection, Holland.

Canvas: 44 x 29 inches.

LENT BY MR. CLARENCE Y. PALITZ, NEW YORK.
COLLECTION: Count Potocki, Lwow, Poland.

KALF, WILLEM

DUTCH, 1622?-1693

Worked at Amsterdam, pupil of Hendrik Pot, a painter of historical subjects, and influenced by Leonard Bramer. In his earlier period he painted compositions of very small compass representing kitchen or stable interiors with still-lifes in the foreground. Since about 1655 he developed his mature style under the influence of Jan Vermeer. The strong contrast of light and shadows shows the impression Rembrandt's works made upon him, but his colors, especially the combination of blue and yellow, is nearer to Vermeer. He is rightly regarded as the greatest of all the Dutch still-life painters.

206 Still-Life, with Nautilus Cup.

Canvas: 31½ x 25⅝ inches.

LENT BY MR. H. E. TEN CATE, ALMELO, HOLLAND.

COLLECTIONS: Prince Alexis Orloff; Mme. M. Van Gelder; D. Katz.
EXHIBITIONS: Frederick Muller Galleries, Amsterdam, 1911; Royal Academy, London, 1929; Museum Boymans, Rotterdam, 1933 and 1938; Goudstikker Gallery, Amsterdam, 1933; Cinq Siècles, Bruxelles, 1935; Rijksmuseum, Amsterdam, 1936; Rhode Island School of Design, 1938; Schaeffer Galleries, 1939.
BIBLIOGRAPHY: H. SCHNEIDER and W. G. CONSTABLE: Dutch Art at the Royal Academy, London, 1929, p. 67, No. 299, Illust., BARONNE A. HOUTART: Cinq siècles d'Art, Bruxelles, 1935, p. 173, No. 739; D. HANNEMA: Meesterwerken uit vier eeuwen, 1400-1800, Museum Boymans, Rotterdam, 1938, p. 24, No. 92, Illust., A. P. VORENKAMP: In Art News, Dec. 10, 1938, p. 10, Illust., A. M. FRANKFURTER: In Art News, Feb. 4, 1939, p. 7, Illust.

KREMER, NICOLAS

GERMAN, 1500?-1553

The earliest recorded work is a drawing bearing Kremer's monogram and the date 1519, in the Stuttgart Museum. He became a citizen of Strassburg in 1521, married Christina von Han in 1522, took in a pupil in 1523, and in 1531 designed plans for the Cathedral; in 1545 he purchased the artistic effects of Hans Baldung Grien, in whose workshop it is almost certain that he worked. After marrying a second time he left Strassburg in 1547, and settled at Ottersweier in Baden, where he died.

207 Portrait of a Nobleman.

Signed with monogram and dated 1529.

Panel: 23 x 17 inches.

LENT BY THE RALPH HARMAN BOOTH COLLECTION, DETROIT.

COLLECTIONS: Baron Rechberg; Count von Leutzner.
BIBLIOGRAPHY: P. WESCHER: Nicolas Kremer of Strassburg. In Art Quarterly, Vol. I, 1938, pp. 204-209. Illust

LAWRENCE, P.R.A., SIR THOMAS
ENGLISH, 1769-1830

Born at Bristol, an innkeeper's son, and famed as a child for his recitations and portraits. At twelve he had his studio at Bath, at eighteen he entered as a student of the Royal Academy, in 1791 was elected A.R.A., and in 1794 R.A. In 1815 he was knighted, and in 1820 succeeded Sir Benjamin West as President. He was the favourite portrait-painter of his time.

B *Miss Farren, Countess of Derby.*

Painted in 1790 when Lawrence was twenty-one. Elizabeth Farren, born about 1759, was the daughter of a surgeon of Cork. A popular actress, she scored her first success at fifteen, and appeared at the Haymarket, London, in 1777 in "She Stoops to Conquer." Her greatest successes were in "The Provoked Husband", and in "The School for Scandal". She retired in 1797, and married Edward, twelfth Earl of Derby. She died in 1829.

Canvas: 57½ x 94 inches.

LENT BY MR. EDWARD S. HARKNESS, NEW YORK.

COLLECTIONS: Earl of Derby; Earl of Wilton; Ludwig Neumann; J. Pierpont Morgan.

ENGRAVED by F. Bartolozzi, and G. S. Shury.

EXHIBITIONS: Royal Academy, London, 1790; Art Treasures, Manchester, 1857; National Portraits, London, 1867; Leeds, 1868; Grafton Galleries, London, 1894; Royal Academy, London, 1904; Agnew's Galleries, London, 1806; Metropolitan Museum of Art, New York, 1913; Century Club, New York, 1931 and 1938.

BIBLIOGRAPHY: D. E. WILLIAMS: Sir Thomas Lawrence, Vol. I, 1831, pp. 124-125; LORD R. S. GOWER: Lawrence, 1900, p. 8, *Illust.*, A. DAYOT: Beautiful Women in Art, Vol. II, 1902, pp. 247-249, *Illust.*, E. LAYARD: Sir Thomas Lawrence's Letter Bag, 1906, pp. 11-15; W. ROBERTS: *In Connoisseur*, Feb. 1907, p. 73, *Illust.*, IDEM: Catalogue of the J. Pierpont Morgan Collection, 1907, *Illust. in color*, SIR W. ARMSTRONG: Lawrence, 1913, p. 131, *Illust.*, R. S. CLOUSTON: Sir Thomas Lawrence, No. 12, *Illust.*, E. SINGLETON: Old World Masters, 1929, p. 420, *Illust.*

LAWRENCE, P.R.A., SIR THOMAS
ENGLISH, 1769-1830

The Hon. Arthur Annesley ('The Red Boy').

Painted 1795. Not to be confused with Lord Durham's picture 'Master Lambton', also known as 'The Red Boy'. Arthur, tenth Viscount Valentia, born Nov. 30, 1785, succeeded to the title, with the Barony of Mountnorris, in 1844, on the death of his kinsman, George, second Earl of Mountnorris. He married, in 1808, Eleanor O'Brien of Blatherwycke Park, Northampton. He died in 1863 and was succeeded by his grandson.

Canvas: 30 x 25 inches.

LENT BY MR. AND MRS. CHARLES FINN WILLIAMS, CINCINNATI.

COLLECTIONS: Viscount Valentia; Howard Young.
EXHIBITION: Cincinnati Museum, 1937.
BIBLIOGRAPHY: F. W. ROBINSON: The C. F. Williams Collection, *In* Art News, Mar. 6, 1937, p. 10.

LAWRENCE, P.R.A., SIR THOMAS

ENGLISH, 1769-1830

210 *Lady Elizabeth Conyngham.*

Lady Elizabeth Henrietta Conyngham, eldest daughter of Henry, 3rd Baron and 1st Marquess Conyngham (1766-1832) and his wife, Elizabeth Denison (d. 1861). She married, as his first wife, 1826, Charles, 10th Marquess of Huntly (1792-1863), and died 1839, without issue. Lady Elizabeth's sister, Maria afterward Lady Athlumney, was also painted by Lawrence, and is in the same collection.

Canvas: 44¼ x 56¼ inches.

LENT BY THE ESTATE OF EDWARD T. STOTESBURY, PHILADELPHIA.

COLLECTION: Victor George, 1st Marquess of Conyngham, Slane Castle, Co. Meath, Ireland; Duveen Galleries, New York.
ENGRAVED in color by Richard Smythe; Reproduced in 'Town and Country' Feb. 17, 1917.
EXHIBITIONS: Duveen Galleries, New York, 1914; Detroit Institute of Arts, 1926; Pennsylvania Museum, Philadelphia, 1932.
BIBLIOGRAPHY: SIR W. ARMSTRONG: Lawrence, 1913, p. 123; ANON: Old Masters of the British School, Duveen Galleries, N. Y., 1914, No. 13, *Illust.*, W. R. VALENTINER: British Paintings of the late XVIII and early XIX Centuries, Detroit Inst., 1926, No. 20, *Illust.*, H. MARCEAU: *In* Pennsylvania Museum Bulletin, 1932, p. 23, *Illust.*

LE NAIN, ANTOINE

FRENCH, 1588-1648

Antoine Le Nain, the eldest of the three brothers Le Nain, was born in Laon and died in Paris two days after Louis (1593-1648). He founded a studio in which his two brothers joined him. In 1629 he obtained the title of Master-painter in Paris, and, with Louis, he was one of the first members of the Royal Academy, founded in 1648, a few months before their deaths. His realistic representations of beggars and children are of great charm.

211 *The Village Piper.*

Pl. 80 Signed—Le Nain ft. 1644.

Copper: 8½ x 11½ inches.

LENT BY THE DETROIT INSTITUTE OF ARTS.

COLLECTIONS: Marquess of Stafford; Duke of Sutherland.
ENGRAVED by Saint-Maurice.
EXHIBITIONS: British Institution, London, 1845; Burlington Fine Arts Club, London, 1910; California Palace of the Legion of Honor, San Francisco, 1934; Knoedler Galleries, New York, 1936.

BIBLIOGRAPHY: w. y. ottley: Engravings of the Marquis of Stafford's coll. of Pictures, 1818, No. 46, Plate 27; c. blanc: Jn Histoire des Peintres, Vol. I, 1865, pp. 6-8, No. 19, Jllust., sir r. c. witt: Pictures by the Brothers Le Nain, Burl. Fine Arts Club, London, 1910, No. 14, Jllust., a. valabiegue: Les frères Le Nain, 1904, p. 169; p. jamot: Les Le Nain, 1929, p. 31, note 4; w. heil and c. h. burroughs: Catalogue of Paintings, Detroit Inst. of Arts, 1930, No. 124, Jllust., r. h. wilenski: French Painting, 1931, p. 50, Jllust., p. fierens: Les Le Nain, 1933, p. 59, Jllust., w. heil: French Painting from the XV c., California Pal. of Legion of Honor, San Francisco, 1934, p. 33, No. 11; l. carré: Georges de La Tour and the Brothers Le Nain, Knoedler Galleries, New York, 1936, No. 9, Jllust.

LE NAIN, LOUIS

FRENCH, 1593-1648

Born at Laon, received his first artistic training under his elder brother Antoine (1588-1648), but he soon passed beyond the art of his elder, and his genius led him into a greater expression of Spirituality in his work. He went to Italy about 1629, and became influenced by the school of Caravaggio and the Bolognese, imitators of the realistic movement which made itself felt throughout Europe during the seventeenth century. Louis died two days before Antoine, and a third brother, Mathieu (1607-1677), another painter of this notable family of painters, survived them by twenty-nine years. Louis Le Nain is the most important painter of the family.

2 Peasants in a Landscape.

Canvas: 16⅛ x 21½ inches.

LENT BY THE WADSWORTH ATHENEUM, HARTFORD, CONN.

COLLECTIONS: George Wilbraham, M.P.; Durlacher Brothers.
EXHIBITIONS: British Institution, London, 1839; Wadsworth Atheneum, 1931; California Palace of the Legion of Honor, San Francisco, 1934; Musée de l'Orangerié, Paris, 1934; Knoedler Galleries, New York, 1936.
BIBLIOGRAPHY: anon: Catalogue of the British Institution, London, 1839, p. 14, No. 158; e. s. siple: Jn Burl. Mag., Feb. 1932, p. 115, Jllust., p. fierens: Les Le Nain, 1933, pp. 28, 30, 62, Jllust., p. w. cooley: Jn Wadsworth Atheneum Bulletin, Jan. 1933, p. 3, Jllust., c. sterling: L'Exposition des Peintures de la Realitè, Paris, 1934, p. 103, No. 68, Jllust., w. heil: French Painting, Cal. Palace of Legion of Honor, San Francisco, 1934, No. 12; l. carré: Georges de la Tour and the Brothers Le Nain, Knoedler Galleries, New York, 1936, No. 13, Jllust., w. george: Jn La Renaissance, May 1937, p. 17, Jllust.

LE NAIN, LOUIS

FRENCH, 1593-1648

3 A Blacksmith at his Forge.

Canvas: 27¼ x 22½ inches.

LENT BY THE MUSÉE DU LOUVRE, PARIS.

COLLECTIONS: Duc de Choiseul, 1772; Prince de Conti, 1777; King Louis XVI.
ENGRAVED by Levasseur, and Weisbrod.

104

EXHIBITIONS: Petit Palais, Paris, 1934; Musée de l'Orangerie, Paris, 1934; Knoedler Galleries, New York, 1936.

BIBLIOGRAPHY: F. VILLOT: Notice des Tableaux, Musée de Louvre, 1855, No. 375; J. H. CHAMPFLEURY: Documents positifs sur Le Nain, 1865, p. 45; C. BLANC: Jn Histoire des Peintres, Vol. I, 1865, p. 1, Jllust., A. VALABREGUE: Les frères Le Nain, 1904, pp. 79 and 159, Jllust., G. GEFFROY: Jn L'Art et les Artistes, Vol. II, 1905-6, p. 66; P. JAMOT: Jn Gaz. des B.-A., 1922 (1), p. 131, Jllust., L. SAMBON: Jn L'Illustration, Jan. 20, 1923; G. BRIÈRE: Catalogue des Peintures, École Française, Musée National du Louvre, 1924, p. 160, No. 540, Jllust., P. JAMOT: Jn Les Grands Artistes, 1929, p. 35, Jllust., P. MARCEL ET C. TERRASSE: La Peinture au Mus. du Louvre, s.d., p. 27, Jllust., P. JAMOT: Jn Gaz. des B.-A., 1930 (2), p. 228, Jllust., R. H. WILENSKI: French Painting, 1931, p. 49; P. FIERNES: Les Le Nain, 1933, p. 32, Jllust., G. BARNAUD: L'Exposition Le Nain, Petit Palais, Paris, 1934, No. 19; C. STERLING: Peintres de la Réalité, Mus. de l'Orangerie, Paris, 1934, p. 103, No. 69, Jllust., IDEM: Les Trésors de la Peinture Française, XVIIe siècle, 1935, Jllust. in color, L. CARRÉ: Georges de La Tour and the Brothers Le Nain, Knoedler Galleries, New York, 1936, No. 11, Jllust.

LEONARDO DA VINCI (and Assistants)

FLORENTINE, 1452-1519

Leonardo da Vinci was born in Vinci in 1452, pupil of Verrocchio in Florence, member of the guild in 1472; went to Milan in 1482 and stayed at the court of Lodovico Sforza (il Moro) until 1499; in Venice, Florence, and other parts of Italy from 1500 to 1507, in Milan from 1508 to 1513, in Rome from 1513 to 1515, in St. Cloud, near Paris, as painter to Francis I from 1516 to 1519. Earliest master of the Florentine High-Renaissance, who introduced *chiaroscuro* painting into art, and developed it to the highest degree. One of the greatest draughtsmen of all times, and the most versatile genius in all fields.

214 The Madonna and Child with a Cross.

Pl. 24 The composition exists in several versions of which the two best are the one in the collection of the Duke of Buccleuch, and the present one. E. Möller (Burl. Mag. 1926) believes the Buccleuch version the better of the two; W. Suida (Leonardo und sein Kreis, 1929), and others, consider the Reford picture the best one. Suida (*Racolta Vinciana*) procured x-rays and ultra-violet photographs and found (1) that a first sketch on the panel is somewhat different from the picture as finished, (2) that in the painting itself can be distinguished two different technical methods —the one (head of the child and part of the landscape) he believes by Leonardo himself; the remaining parts executed by a pupil, probably the same who painted the Buccleuch and the Schlichting examples. There is no doubt that the execution of the present picture is of unusual quality, much finer than the version mentioned before, or that in the Schlichting collection, or the one in the possession of Prince Rupprecht of Bavaria. Also the attributions to Sodoma (Frizzoni and Cust), or any other known pupil of Leonardo, are certainly erroneous. The painting gives an excellent idea of Leonardo's compositions during the second Florentine period in the marvellous color-scheme—a symphony in blue—as well as in the subtle gradation of light and shade. The composition seems to go back to the early Milan period, as the foreshortened hand of the Madonna appears similarly in the 'Vierge aux Rochers', and the Christchild's position must have been known to the artist who executed the Pala Sforzesca about 1495. On the other hand the Madonna type is related to the 'St. Anne' in the Louvre, and the landscape to the 'Mona Lisa'.

Canvas (transferred): 19 x 11 inches.

LENT BY MR. AND MRS. ROBERT W. REFORD, MONTREAL, CANADA.
COLLECTIONS: Marquis of Lansdowne; Lord Battersea; Wildenstein Galleries.
EXHIBITIONS: Royal Academy, London, 1880; New Gallery, London, 1893-94; Burlington Fine Arts Club, 1898; ("Attributed to Leonardo").
BIBLIOGRAPHY: R. H. H. CUST: Giovanni A. Bazzi, Sodoma ("attributed to Sodoma"), 1906, p. 359; G. BAPST: La Vierge du Leonard da Vinci; a monograph N.D.; E. MÖLLER: In Burl. Mag., August 1926, pp. 61-68, Illust., H. BODMER: Leonardo da Vinci (Kl. der Kunst), 1931, p. 372, No. 65, Illust., W. SUIDA: Leonardo und sein Kreis, 1929, p. 136; IDEM: Miscellanea di Studi Leonardeschi in onore di Ettore Verga, In Raccolta Vinciana, 1930-34; SIR H. F. COOK: Catalogue of the Milanese Exhib. Burl. F.A.C., 1898, No. 9; G. H. EDGELL: Hist. of Sienese Painting, 1932, p. 279, Illust., W. SUIDA: In Thieme-Becker's Lexikon, Vol. XXXI, 1937, p. 199.

LIPPI, FILIPPINO

FLORENTINE, 1457-1504

Son of Fra Filippo and Lucretia Buti, was born at Prato. As a boy he was instructed by Fra Diamante, his father's assistant, and in 1472 he entered Botticelli's studio. In 1482 he was at work in the Palazzo Publico at Florence, and from 1484 to 1485 in the Brancacci Chapel. From 1487 to 1502 he painted frescoes for the Strozzi Chapel of Santa Maria Novella, and during that time he was in Rome working in Santa Maria sopra Minerva. He was strongly influenced by Leonardo da Vinci and Botticelli, and shows the tendency of the later fifteenth century painters in Florence to exaggerate movements, and to give restlessness to his compositions.

5 *Portrait of the Artist and a Patron.*

An early work of the master. "By comparison with the portrait of Piero del Pugliese in the altar painting of the Badia in Florence, and with the self-portrait of Filippino himself in the frescoes of the Carmine, it appears very probable that here the artist represented himself in conversation with his patron, Piero del Pugliese" (*R. Longhi*).

Panel: 14¾ x 22¼ inches.

LENT BY SENATOR AND MRS. SIMON GUGGENHEIM, NEW YORK.
COLLECTION: Count Alessandro Contini-Bonacossi, Florence.
BIBLIOGRAPHY: M. VAUGHAN: In Parnassus, May 1939, p. 7, Illust.

LIPPI, FILIPPINO

FLORENTINE, 1457-1504

216 *The Madonna and Child.*

Painted about 1487. Known as 'The Strozzi Madonna', taking its title from the arms of the Strozzi—three crescents—which appear on the capital of the near column of the loggia. It is believed to have been painted on the occasion of the marriage of Filippini Strozzi to Selvaggia de' Gianfigliazzi.

Panel: 32 x 23½ inches.

LENT BY THE JULES S. BACHE COLLECTION, NEW YORK.

COLLECTIONS: The Strozzi Family; Dr. Marcello Massarenti; Prof. Götz Martius; Lord Duveen of Millbank.

EXHIBITION: Düsseldorf, 1904.

BIBLIOGRAPHY: ANON: Kunsthistorische Ausstellung Katalog, Düsseldorf, 1904, p. 108, No. 244; A. MARGUILLIER: *In* "Gaz. des Beaux-Arts", Oct. 1904, p. 285; G. FRIZZONI: *In* "Rassegna d'Arte", Jan. 1905, p. 6, *Illust.*; B. BERENSON: Florentine Painters, 1909, p. 148; A. VENTURI: Storia dell'Arte, Vol. VII, Part I, 1911, p. 674; CROWE AND CAVALCASELLE: History of Painting in Italy. Ed. by Langton Douglas, Vol. IV, 1911, p. 293; W. HEIL: *In* The Art News, April 27, 1929, p. 29, *Illust.*, ANON: Catalogue of the Bache Collection, 1929, No. 11, *Illust.*, G. GRONAU: *In* "Pantheon", Vol. VI, 1930, p. 512, *Illust.*; R. VAN MARLE: Italian Schools, Vol. XII, 1931, p. 318; G. SCHARF: *In* Art in Amer., Feb. 1931, p. 59; B. BERENSON: Italian Pictures, 1932, p. 286. (Ital. Edn. 1936, p. 246, *Illust.*); L. VENTURI: Ital. Paintings in Amer., 1933, No. 263, *Illust.*, G. SCHARF: Filippino Lippi, 1935, pp. 26, 31, 108, *Illust.*, K. B. NEILSON: Filippino Lippi, 1938, p. 68, No. 26, *Illust.*

LIPPI, FILIPPINO

FLORENTINE, 1457-1504

217 *The Crucifixion.*

Painted about 1490. A replica is in the Jarves collection, New Haven.

Panel: 11½ x 8¾ inches.

LENT BY SENATOR AND MRS. SIMON GUGGENHEIM, NEW YORK.

COLLECTION: Count Alessandro Contini-Bonacossi, Florence.

LIPPI, FRA FILIPPO

FLORENTINE, 1406?-1469

Fra Filippo Lippi, the son of a butcher, was born in Florence about 1406. In 1421 he took the vows in the Convent of Santa Maria del Carmino, where he remained until about 1437, and came under the influence of Masolino, Masaccio, and Fra Angelico. He painted subjects similar to those of Fra Angelico, but from a more worldly and realistic point of view. In 1456 he was made chaplain of Santa Margherita, Prato, from whence he abducted Lucrezia Buti, the mother of Filippino. One of the leading masters of the early Florentine Renaissance.

18 The Madonna and Child Enthroned.

The introduction of the rose in this picture is probably intended to represent the Madonna as the *Madonna del Fiore* — Our Lady of the Flower — to whom the Duomo at Florence was dedicated; the title is doubtlessly based on the verse in the Song of Solomon (II, i.) — "I am the rose of Sharon."

Panel: 48½ x 25 inches.

LENT BY THE JULES S. BACHE COLLECTION, NEW YORK.

COLLECTIONS: Dr. Adolf Schaeffer; Lord Duveen of Millbank.

EXHIBITIONS: L'Art Italien, Petit Palais, Paris, 1935.

BIBLIOGRAPHY: w. HEIL: Jn The Art News, April 27, 1929, p. 31, *Jllust.*, A. L. MAYER: Jn Pantheon, Vol. VI, 1930, pp. 540-541, *Jllust.*, B. BERENSON: Fra Angelico, Fra Filippo, e la chronologia, Jn Bolletino d'Arte, Vol. XXVI, 1932, p. 19, *Jllust.*, IDEM: Italian Pictures of the Renaissance, 1932, p. 288, (Ital. Edn., 1936, p. 247); L. VENTURI: Italian Paintings in America, Vol. II, 1933, No. 208, *Jllust.*, ANON: Catalogue of the Bache Collection, New York, 1938, No. 10, *Jllust.*

LIPPI, FRA FILIPPO

FLORENTINE, 1406?-1469

19 The Madonna and Child.

15 Of the earlier period of the master, and one of his finest and most expressive Madonna compositions.

Panel: 32⅝ x 24¾ inches.

LENT BY MRS. LEON SCHINASI, NEW YORK.

COLLECTIONS: The Monastery of the Carmine Brethren, Florence; Lord Duveen of Millbank; Carl W. Hamilton.

EXHIBITIONS: Duveen Galleries, New York, 1924; Montclair Art Museum, New Jersey, 1925-26; Buffalo Fine Arts Academy, Albright Art Gallery, 1926-27.

BIBLIOGRAPHY: w. R. VALENTINER: Catalogue of Early Italian Paintings, Duveen Galleries, New York, 1924, No. 7, *Jllust.*, ANON: Catalogue of the Loan Exhibition of Paintings, Montclair Art Museum, New Jersey, 1925-26, No. 92, *Jllust.*, M. VAUGHAN: Jn The Art News, April, 1929, *Jllust.*, B. BERENSON: Italian Pictures of the Renaissance, 1932, p. 288, (Ital. edn., 1936, p. 248).

LORENZETTI, AMBROGIO

SIENESE, ACTIVE 1319-1348

Younger brother of Pietro Lorenzetti, and perhaps the greater artist of the two, although Pietro is likewise one of the great masters of the Sienese school. A pupil of his brother and influenced by Giotto and the Pisani. First heard of in 1324, when he purchased some land; next in 1331 when he painted some frescoes in San Francesco, Siena. His "Annunciation" in the Academy at Siena bears the date 1344, and is the last dated work which we have from his hand. His greatest triumphs came to him as a mural painter, and his most important work is the large fresco in the Palazzo della Signoria at Siena. He died at Siena of the plague which also carried off his brother.

220 *The Crucifixion.*

Pl. 4 Painted about 1337-1342. A deeply expressive composition, remarkably rich in color-scheme.

Panel: 24 x 11⅜ inches.

LENT BY THE FOGG ART MUSEUM, CAMBRIDGE, MASS.

COLLECTIONS: C. Fairfax Murray; Paul J. Sachs.

EXHIBITION: Fogg Art Museum, 1921.

BIBLIOGRAPHY: F. M. PERKINS: *In* Art in Amer., Vol. VIII, 1920, p. 206; M. E. GILMAN, *Edr.: In* Fogg Art. Mus. Notes, Dec. 1921, pp. 9-16, *Illust.,* R. VAN MARLE: Italian Schools of Painting, Vol. II, 1924, p. 420, *Illust.,* L. VENTURI: Italian Paintings in America, 1933, No. 84, *Illust.,* B. BERENSON: Italian Pictures of the Renaissance, 1932, p. 290, (Ital. edn., 1936, p. 249); G. H. EDGELL: Hist. of Sienese Painting, 1932, p. 139, *Illust.*

LORENZETTI, PIETRO

SIENESE, ACTIVE 1305-1348

Pietro Lorenzetti, elder brother of Ambrogio, was born probably about 1280; he is first heard of in 1305-6 when he was working in the Sala dei Nove, in the Palazzo Pubblico, Siena. It is likely that he was a pupil of Duccio; influenced by Simone Martini, Giotto, and Giovanni Pisano. He was a prolific painter, both of fresco and panel paintings, and ranks very highly among the great masters of the Trecento in Siena. The last mention of Pietro is in the records of 1344, and he died, it is supposed, of plague, with his brother, in 1348.

221 *The Madonna, St. Catherine, and St. Mary Magdalen.*

Pl. 5 A Triptych. Painted about 1321.

Panels: 43½ x 63 inches, each.

LENT BY MRS. FELIX M. WARBURG, NEW YORK.

BIBLIOGRAPHY: E. T. DE WALD: Pietro Lorenzetti, *In* Art Studies, 1929, p. 162, *Illust.,* E. CECCHI: Pietro Lorenzetti, 1930, p. 37, *Illust.,* B. BERENSON: Italian Pictures of the Renaissance, 1932, p. 293, (Ital. Edn., 1936, p. 252).

LORENZO DI CREDI

FLORENTINE, 1456-1537

Born at Florence. A fellow pupil of Leonardo da Vinci and Pietro Perugino under Verrocchio: afterwards strongly influenced by Leonardo. A prolific painter of charming religious and mythological subjects. He was also an excellent portrait-painter, and may have been a sculptor since he was desired by Verrocchio in his will to take care of the completion of his colossal equestrian statue of Colleoni at Venice, which he left unfinished at his death.

2 *The Madonna and Child with St. John.*

Painted about 1495-1500.

Panel: 40 inches, diameter.

LENT BY MR. FREDERICK L. STEPHENS, NEW YORK.

EXHIBITION: National Gallery of New South Wales, Sydney, Australia, for several years.

LUCAS VAN LEYDEN

FLEMISH, 1494-1533

Lucas Jacobsz, known as Lucas van Leyden, was born at Leyden and studied under Cornelis Engelbrechtsen. He was influenced sometimes by Massys and Mabuse, and especially by Dürer. His paintings are rare; his most famous master-piece being 'The Last Judgment' at Leyden. His reputation rests chiefly on his skill as an engraver, no fewer than 174 plates being accounted for. He worked at Leyden, Middleburg, and Antwerp, and died young in his native town. He was the greatest Dutch master of the sixteenth century.

3 *Beheading of John the Baptist.*

58 A triptych, with inscribed wings. An early work of the artist, painted about 1515.

Panel: 11½ x 9 inches.

LENT BY THE JOHN G. JOHNSON COLLECTION, PHILADELPHIA.

COLLECTION: C. and G. Somzée.

EXHIBITION: Bruges, 1902.

BIBLIOGRAPHY: W. H. J. WEALE: Expos. des Primitifs flamands, Bruges, 1902, p. 104, No. 272; G. H. DE LOO: Catalogue Critique, Bruges, 1902, p. 72, No. 272; M. J. FRIEDLANDER: In Reper. für Kunstw., XXVI, 1903; W. R. VALENTINER: Flemish and Dutch Paintings in the John G. Johnson Colln., Phila., 1913, No. 413, Illust., P. WESCHER: In Thieme-Becker's Lexikon, Vol. XXIII, 1929, p. 169; M. J. FRIEDLANDER: Lucas van Leyden, 1932, p. 136, No. 129, Illust.

LUCAS VAN LEYDEN

FLEMISH, 1494-1533

4 *The Apostle St. Paul.*

8 Panel: 12¼ x 8⅝ inches.

LENT ANONYMOUSLY.

COLLECTIONS: D. H. Lijversberg; Dr. Paul Esch, Cologne; Silberman Galleries, New York.

EXHIBITIONS: Cologne, 1922; Dusseldorf, 1928; Boer Galleries, Amsterdam, 1936; Museum Boymans, Rotterdam, 1936.

BIBLIOGRAPHY: L. BALDASS: Lucas von Leyden, 1923, p. 31, Illust., P. WESCHER: In Thieme-Becker's Lexikon, Vol. XXIII, 1929, p. 169; M. VAUGHAN: In Parnassus, May 1939, p. 13, Illust.

LUINI, BERNARDINO

MILANESE, CIRCA 1475-1532

Born at Luino on the Lago Maggiore. Pupil of Stefano Scotto, probably influenced at first by Borgognone; afterwards by Bramantino; about 1510 came under the spell of Leonardo da Vinci. He approached the latter's style so closely that several of his best works were for a long time attributed to Leonardo himself. In the last period of his life, from about 1520 he developed a style of his own which led to the mural paintings in Santa Maria dei Miracola, Soronno (1526), and culminated in the grandiose Crucifixion in Santa Maria degli Angeli at Lugano (1529).

225 St. Catherine.

Panel: 28¼ x 20¼ inches.

LENT BY MR. AND MRS. FRED J. FISHER, DETROIT.

MABUSE, JAN GOSSÆRT, called

FLEMISH, 1472?-1535?

Born at Mabeuse in Hainaut, Netherlands. In 1503 he was in the Antwerp Guild. In 1508, in the train of Philip of Burgundy, he went to Rome where he became acquainted with the antique, and with the masters of the Italian High Renaissance. In 1509 the painter returned to Brussels with Philip of Burgundy. In 1515, he is supposed to have gone to Copenhagen to paint the King, Christopher II, and his bride; the portraits are at Copenhagen and Brussels. In 1517, the artist accompanied Philip to Utrecht. Together with Quentin Massys and Joos van Cleve, the greatest Flemish painter in the sixteenth century.

226 Henry III, Count of Nassau.

Pl. 56

Henry III, Count of Nassau, Marquis of Zeneta, friend of Charles V, was the second son of Jean V, Duke of Nassau. He was born in 1483, and inherited the possessions of his uncle, Englebert II, in the Netherlands. He was elected to the Order of the Golden Fleece at the Middleburg Chapter in 1505. His son, René de Chalons, inherited through his mother the Principality of Orange. Henry III died in 1538.

Panel: 21 x 17½ inches.

LENT BY MR. AND MRS. CHARLES V. HICKOX, NEW YORK.

COLLECTIONS: Alfred Charles de Rothschild; Almina, Countess of Carnarvon, Lord Duveen of Millbank; Ernst Rosenfeld.

EXHIBITIONS: Royal Academy, London, 1927; Kleinberger Galleries, New York, 1929.

BIBLIOGRAPHY: A. DE HÉVESY: Jacopo de Barbari, 1925, Pl. 39; T. BORENIUS: Picture section. In Catalogue of Flemish and Belgian Art, Royal Academy, London, 1927, p. 63, Illust. in color; M. J. FRIEDLÄNDER: In Der Cicerone, April 1927, p. 215, Illust. in color; IDEM: Jan Gossart, 1930, p. 159, Illust.; H. G. SPERLING: Catalogue of a Loan Exhibition of Flemish Primitives; Preface by

M. J. Friedländer, New York, 1929, No. 78, *Illust.*, R. VAN MARLE: Ital. Schools of Painting, Vol. XVIII, 1936, p. 476.

MABUSE, JAN GOSSÆRT, called

FLEMISH, 1472?-1535?

7 *Anne, Marquise de Veere.*

Anne de Berghes (1489-1541), daughter of Jean Seigneur de Berghes, became the wife of Adolphe de Bourgogne, Seigneur de Beveren et de Veere, who died 1540. A replica of this portrait is in the Gardner Museum, Boston.

Panel: 21½ x 16½ inches.

LENT BY GOVERNOR HERBERT H. LEHMAN, NEW YORK.

COLLECTIONS: Sir Abraham Hume, Bart.; Adelbert Wellington, Earl Brownlow; Lord Brownlow; Mrs. Stevenson Scott.

EXHIBITIONS: New Gallery, London, 1899-1900; Royal Academy, London, 1927.

BIBLIOGRAPHY: C. JUSTI: *In* Zeitsch. für Bild. Kunst, Vol. VI, 1895, pp. 161-168, 198-201, *Illust.*, W. H. J. WEALE: Flemish and British Schools, New Gallery, London, 1899-1900, p. 22, No. 97; H. FIERENS-GEVAERT: Les Primitifs Flamands, 1910, p. 211; SIR M. CONWAY: The Van Eycks and their followers, 1921, p. 374; A. SEGARD: Jean Gossart dit Mabuse, 1923, p. 180; SIR M. CONWAY: Flemish and Belgian Art, Royal Acad., London, 1927, pp. 81-82, No. 188, *Illust.*, M. J. FRIEDLÄNDER: Jan Gossart, 1930, pp. 61, 163, No. 76, *Illust.*, P. HENDY: Catalogue of the Gardner Museum, Boston, 1931, p. 213.

MABUSE, JAN GOSSÆRT, called

FLEMISH SCHOOL, 1472?-1535?

8 *Queen Eleanor of Austria.*

Eleanor, born at Ghent in 1498, was the daughter of Philip of Burgundy and Joanna, and sister of Emperor Charles V (1500-1558). She married in 1518, much against her will, as his third wife, Manuel of Portugal (1469-1521). In 1526, following the old Hapsburg practice of marriage as a means of alliance of influence, Charles V. made it a condition of the Treaty of Madrid that she should marry Francis I of France (1494-1547), in the hope that she would be an instrument of peace; the marriage, therefore, took place in 1530. She became a widow for the second time in 1547, and died, the same year as her Emperor-brother, in 1558. A double portrait of Eleanor and Francis I is at Hampton Court.

Panel: 15¼ x 12 inches.

LENT FROM THE WILLIAM GOLDMAN COLLECTION, NEW YORK.

COLLECTIONS: Probably from the gallery of Charles V, and afterwards in an Italian collection; August Berg.

EXHIBITION: Kleinberger Galleries, New York, 1929.

BIBLIOGRAPHY: H. G. SPERLING: Exhibition of Flemish Primitives, New York, 1929, with preface by M. J. Friedländer, p. 238, No. 84, *Illust.*, M. J. FRIEDLÄNDER: Jan Gossart u. B. van Orley, 1930, p. 163, No. 74, *Illust.*

MAES, NICOLAES

DUTCH, 1632-1693

Nicolaes Maes, painter of genre subjects and later almost exclusively of portraits, was born at Dordrecht; about 1650 he became a pupil of Rembrandt at Amsterdam; from 1654 to 1673 he lived at Dordrecht, where it is said Reijnier Covijn was his pupil; he then went to Amsterdam and remained there until his death. Leading genre painter among the Rembrandt pupils. The portraits of his later period show French influence.

229 *An Old Woman Spinning.*

Signed at the right. One of the finest compositions of the artist, executed about 1655.

Canvas: 24 x 21¼ inches.

LENT BY THE RIJKS-MUSEUM, AMSTERDAM.

COLLECTIONS: P. Beelaerts van Blokland; J. Rombouts; L. Dupper.
ENGRAVED by W. Unger, and L. Löwenstam.
BIBLIOGRAPHY: J. SMITH: Catalogue raisonné, Supplement, 1842, p. 577, No. 6; G. LAFE-NESTRE et E. RICHTENBERGER: La Hollande, 1900, p. 257, No. 882; K. VOLL: Die Meisterw. des Rijks-Museum, Amsterdam, 1903, p. 91, *Illust.*, B. W. F. VAN RIEMSDIJK: Catalogue des Tableaux, Rijks-Museum, Amsterdam, 1911, No. 1504; C. HOFSTEDE DE GROOT: Catalogue raisonné, Vol. VI, 1916, pp. 491-492, No. 58; W. R. VALENTINER: Nicolaes Maes, 1924, p. 45, No. 32, *Illust.*

MAGNASCO, ALESSANDRO

GENOESE, 1667-1749

Painter of monastic scenes, battles, and grotesques, was born in Genoa. He was the son of Stefano Magnasco, also a painter, and studied in Milan under Filippo Abbiati, whose manner he imitated. He worked in various towns of Italy, notably in Florence, where he was sponsored by the Grand Duke Giovanni Gastone de' Medici. He returned to Genoa in 1735, and died there fourteen years afterward. In his impressionistic technique and his fantastic compositions the artist appears to be remarkably modern.

230 *The Synagogue.*

Painted about 1730.

Canvas: 48 x 58½ inches.

LENT BY THE CLEVELAND MUSEUM OF ART.

COLLECTION: Italico Brass, Venice.
EXHIBITIONS: Venice, 1929; Cleveland Museum of Art, 1936.
BIBLIOGRAPHY: U. OGETTI: Catalogo del Settecento Italiano, 1929, p. 66, *Illust.*, G. FIOCCO:

Revista della Citta de Venezia, 1929, p. 501, *Illust.*, G. DELOGU: Pittore minori lugiri, etc., 1931, p. 128; U. OGETTI, Edr.: Il Settecento Italiano, 1932, No. 85, *Illust.*; L. VENTURI: Ital. Paintings in America, 1933, No. 50, *Illust.*, H. TIETZE: Meisterw. Europäischer Malerei in Amer., 1935, p. 116, *Illust.*, M. W. MILLIKEN: Catalogue of the Art Exhibit, Cleveland Museum, 1936, No. 158, *Illust.*

MALER ZU SCHWAZ, HANS

GERMAN, ACTIVE 1510-1530

Born at Schwaz in the Tirol. Active in Swabia, mostly in Ulm, also in Innsbruck and Vienna. Painted portraits for Ferdinand of Hapsburg, the Emperor Maximilian, and Maria of Burgundy. One of the leading South German portrait painters at the time of the Renaissance.

1 *Portrait of Sebastian Andorffer.*

45 Painted in 1517. Inscribed: *Da man 1517 zalt Sebastian was Ich 48 Jar alt Anndorfeer* (Trans: 'When we counted 1517 I was 48 years old, Sebastian Andorffer'). Another portrait of the sitter, with a beard, is in the Metropolitan Museum, Friedsam Collection.

Panel: 14 x 17 inches.

LENT BY MRS. CHARLES R. HENSCHEL, NEW YORK.
COLLECTION: Count Toggenburg, Bolzano, Tirol; A. S. Drey.
EXHIBITION: Doll and Richards Gallery, Boston, 1926.
BIBLIOGRAPHY: O. BENESCH: *In* Berlin Jahrbuch, Vol. LIV, 1933, pp. 245-247, *Illust.*, C. L. KUHN: German Paintings in America, 1936, p. 64, No. 263.

MANTEGNA, ANDREA

PADUAN, 1431-1506

Born at Vicenza, a pupil and adopted son of Squarcione; influenced by his father-in-law Jacopo Bellini, Donatello and Pizzolo, and possibly by Uccello, Castagno and Fra Filippo Lippi. In Padua till 1460 when he settled in Mantua where he died; in Verona 1463, Florence 1466, and Rome 1488-90. His most important frescoes are in Padua (Eremitani), and in Mantua Castle. The greatest North Italian master of the fifteenth century. His influence was irresistible, not only in Padua and Mantua, but in Venice, and other parts of Italy.

2 *Judith with the Head of Holofernes.*

21 According to A. Van der Doort (d. 1640) this picture was given by Prince Charles to Lord Pembroke in exchange for two pictures by Bellini and Parmigianino.

Panel: 12 x 7⅛ inches.

LENT BY MR. JOSEPH E. WIDENER, ELKINS PARK, PENNSYLVANIA.
COLLECTIONS: Prince Charles of England, afterwards Charles I; Earl of Pembroke and Montgomery; Lord Duveen of Millbank.

114

EXHIBITIONS: Manchester Art Treasures, 1857; New Gallery, London, 1894-5; Grosvenor Galleries, London, 1913-14; Duveen Galleries, New York, 1924; Royal Academy, London, 1930; California Palace of the Legion of Honor, San Francisco, 1938.

BIBLIOGRAPHY: R. COWDRY: Pictures at the Earl of Pembroke's House at Wilton, 1751, p. 74; G. VENTUE: Catalogue and desc. of King Charles I's Collections, 1757, pp. 4, 5, 7 (after Van der Doort's MSS.); R. VON PASSAVANT: A German Artist in England, Vol. I, 1836, p. 306; G. F. WAAGEN: Treasures of Art, Vol. III, 1854, p. 151; G. SCHARF: Art Treasures, Manchester, 1857, p. 20, No. 96; CROWE AND CAVALCASELLE: Hist. of Painting in N. Italy, Vol. I, 1871, p. 404; B. BERENSON: Study and Criticism, 1901, pp. 97-98; P. KRISTELLE: Mant egna, 1901, pp. 375, 453; C. YRIARTE: Mantegna, 1901, pp. 204, 208; B. BERENSON: N. Ital. Painters, 1907, p. 255; N. R. WILKINSON: Wilton House Pictures, 1907, p. 184; F. HOWARD: Woman and Child in Art, Grosvenor Gallery, London, 1913-1914, No. 41a, Illust., A. VENTURI: Storia dell'Arte, Vol. VIII, 3, 1914, p. 247, Illust., B. BERENSON: In Art in Amer., Vol. VI, 1918, pp. 127-128, Illust., F. KNAPP: Mantegna (Kl. d. Kunst), n.d. p. 182, No. 128, Illust., W. R. VALENTINER: Early Ital. Paintings, Duveen Galleries, 1924 (1936), No. 40, Illust., A. M. FRANKFURTER: In Antiquarian, Vol. XIII, 1929, p. 96, Illust., LORD BALNIEL and K. CLARK: Ital. Art, Royal Acad., London, 1930, p. 64, No. 187; B. BERENSON, AND OTHERS: Pictures in the Colln. of Joseph Widener, 1931, p. 34, Illust., B. BERENSON: Ital. Pictures, 1932, p. 328; L. VENTURI: Ital. Paintings in Amer., 1933, No. 340, Illust., H. TIETZE: Meisterw. Europäisher, 1935, No. 65, Illust., R. VAN MARLE: Ital. Painting, Vol. XVII, 1935, pp. 105-107, Illust., G. FIOCCO: Mantegna, 1936, p. 68, No. 115, Illust., W. HEIL: Venetian Painting, Cal. Palace of the Legion of Honor, San Fran., 1938, No. 42, Illust., A. M. FRANKFURTER: In Art News, July 16, 1938, p. 7; Feb. 25, 1939, p. 99, Illust.

MANTEGNA, ANDREA

PADUAN, 1431-1506

233 Portrait of Janus Pannonius (Presumed)

Painted about 1470. Janus Pannonius, Hungarian poet and scholar, studied in Italy, and belonged to the Humanist circle in Verona, 1457-58; he was a personal friend of Mantegna. The re-discovery of this portrait means an important addition to the work of the artist since only a very limited number of portraits on panel are known by him. Attributed to Mantegna by B. Berenson, L. Venturi and others.

Canvas, transferred: 9½ x 7½ inches.

LENT ANONYMOUSLY.

COLLECTION: Ludwig Kelemen, Budapest.

MANTEGNA, ANDREA

PADUAN, 1431-1506

234 Judith (Companion to No. 235).

Painted during the late period of the artist. Monochrome of gold and brown on a marble ground. Belongs to the same series of 'Heroines' as the 'Lucia' and 'Sophonisba' in the National Gallery, London. According to an inventory of 1452 (d'Arco; Arti e Artefici di Mantova, II, 134), it is possible that it was this series which was at that time in the study of Isabella d'Este at Mantua.

Canvas: 25½ x 11¾ inches.

COLLECTIONS: Ducal Palace, Mantua; John Edward Taylor, London.

BIBLIOGRAPHY: p. kristeller: Mantegna, 1901, p. 373; c. yriarte: Mantegna, 1901, p. 210, *Illust.*, f. knapp: Mantegna, 1910, p. 135; r. schwabe: *In* Burl. Mag., Dec. 1919, p. 215, *Illust.*, anon: Catalogue of the Art Association, Montreal, 1930, p. 64; l. venturi: Italian Paintings in America, 1933, No. 342, *Illust.*, h. tietze: *In* Pantheon, June 1936, pp. 180 and 185, *Illust.*, g. fiocco: Mantegna, 1937, p. 68, *Illust.*

MANTEGNA, ANDREA

PADUAN, 1431-1506

5 *Dido* (Companion to No. 234).

Refer to remarks in preceding entry.

Canvas: 25½ x 11¾ inches.

MARMION, SIMON

FRENCH, C. 1420-1489

Born probably at Amiens, where he was still in 1453. In 1454 he went to Lille, and from 1458 to 1468 he was in Valenciennes, where in 1460 he was recorded as being one of the founders of the Lucas Guild. In 1468 he attained the rank of Master at Tournai. He was in the service of Philip the Good, Duke of Burgundy, and painted an Altar-piece for the Abbey of St. Bertin at St. Omer. He was also celebrated as an illuminator.

6 *St. George and the Dragon.*

Painted about 1480. The composition is influenced by the painting by Roger van der Weyden in the Collection of Lady Evelyn Mason.

Panel: 20½ x 14⅝ inches.

COLLECTIONS: Henri Haro; Mr. and Mrs. Otto H. Kahn.

EXHIBITIONS: Pavillon de Marsan, Paris, 1904; Gainsborough Galleries, New York, 1926; Kleinberger Galleries, New York, 1927; Royal Academy, London, 1932.

BIBLIOGRAPHY: h. bouchot: Catalogue, Exposition Primitifs Francais, 1904, No. 93, *Illust.*, anon: Catal. Exhn. French Primitives, Kleinberger Gall., N. Y., 1927, No. 20, *Illust.*, w. g. constable, edr.: Commemorative Catal., Exhibition of French Art, Royal Acad., London, 1932, p. 11, No. 31, *Illust.*

MARMION, SIMON

FRENCH, C. 1420-1489

236a *St. Benedict, St. Maurus and St. Placidus.*

Pl. 78   The scene depicts St. Placidus being rescued by St. Maurus when the former falls into a lake while drawing water. St. Benedict, founder of the Benedictine order, having had a revelation of his disciple's danger, while praying in his cell, sends St. Maurus to rescue him, which he did by treading on the water as if it had been dry land.

Panel: 37 x 31 inches.

LENT ANONYMOUSLY.

BIBLIOGRAPHY: F. WINKLER: *In* Pantheon, March 1934, p. 65, *Illust.*

MARTINI, SIMONE

SIENESE, 1285?-1344

Born in Siena, pupil of Duccio, influenced by Giovanni Pisano and Giotto. His first known work was the 'Majestas' for the Palazzo Publico of Siena. He was in Naples in 1317, Pisa 1320, Siena 1321-1322, and afterwards for some time in Assisi. In 1339 he represented Siena at the papal court of Avignon, where he died five years later. Greatest Sienese painter in the fourteenth century, next to Duccio and the Lorenzetti.

237 *St. John the Evangelist.*

Pl. 2   Painted during the early period of the master, circa 1315.

Panel: 37 x 17½ inches.

LENT BY MR. MAITLAND F. GRIGGS, NEW YORK.

COLLECTIONS: Commandatore Giulio Sterbini; Mrs. Benjamin Thaw; Lord Duveen of Millbank.

EXHIBITION: Kleinberger Galleries, 1917.

BIBLIOGRAPHY: A. VENTURI: *In* L'Arte, Vol. VIII, 1905, p. 426, *Illust.*, IDEM: La Galleria Sterbini in Roma, 1906, pp. 22-25, No. 3; O. SIREN and M. W. BROCKWELL: Italian Primitives, Kleinberger Galleries, 1917, p. 126, No. 47, *Illust.*, R. VAN MARLE: Simone Martini, 1920, p. 24; L. VENTURI: Italian Paintings in America, 1933, No. 70, *Illust.*, B. BERENSON: Italian Pictures, 1932, p. 534, (Ital. Edn., 1936, p. 459); A. M. FRANKFURTER: *In* Art News, May 1, 1937, p. 44, *Illust.*, H. COMSTOCK: *In* Connoisseur, May 1939, p. 276, *Illust.*

MARTINI, SIMONE

SIENESE, 1285?-1344

238 *St. Philip* (Companion to No. 239).

Inscribed: *Sanctus Phylippus.* This panel, together with its companion picture of St. Matthew, also with three others in the Lehman Collection, four in the Maitland

Griggs Collection, one in the Stocklet Collection, Brussels, and two others which have disappeared, twelve in all, have been attributed to Lippo Memmi by Cavalcaselle and L. Venturi. They probably formed the predella of a great polyptych. These pictures are similar in many respects to the prophets in the altarpiece by Simone in the Seminario at Pisa.

Panel: 11½ x 8½ inches.

LENT BY MR. ROBERT LEHMAN, NEW YORK.

COLLECTIONS: Jean A. Ramboux; Wallraf-Richartz Museum, Cologne; Philip Lehman.
BIBLIOGRAPHY: J. NIESSEN: Verzeichniss der Gemälde-Sammlung des Mus. Wallraf-Richartz, 1877, pp. 91-92, No. 748; CROWE AND CAVALCASELLE: Painting in Italy, Ed. by L. Douglas, Vol. III, 1908, p. 76; A. VENTURI: Storia dell'Arte Ital., Vol. V, 1907, p. 667; B. BERENSON: Central Ital. Painters, 1909, p. 202; R. LEHMAN: The Philip Lehman Colln., 1928, Nos. 21 and 23, Illust., B. BERENSON: Ital. Pictures, 1932, p. 534 (Ital. Edn., 1936, p. 459); L. VENTURI: Ital. Paintings in Amer., 1933, Nos. 76 and 77, Illust.

MARTINI, SIMONE

SIENESE, 1285?-1344

St. Matthew (Companion to No. 238).

Inscribed: S(an)c(tu)s Matheus. Refer to remarks in previous entry in this Catalogue.

Panel: 11½ x 8½ inches.

LENT BY MR. ROBERT LEHMAN, NEW YORK.

MASO DI BANCO

FLORENTINE, FIRST HALF OF THE XIV CENTURY

Maso is perhaps the most powerful painter among the immediate followers of Giotto in Florence. His frescoes in Santa Croce (Bardi Chapel) are most impressive and original in conception. Ghiberti spoke highly of his work, calling it "perfect". Maso is mentioned from 1341-1346. In his later phase he is strongly influenced by the Lorenzetti.

St. Anthony of Padua.

The painting originally formed a wing of an altarpiece of which the Madonna and two Saints are in the Berlin Museum.

Panel: 28¾ x 15¼ inches.

LENT BY MR. MAITLAND F. GRIGGS, NEW YORK.

COLLECTIONS: Edward Solly; Kaiser Friedrich Museum, Berlin; Uffizi Gallery, Florence, 1937.
BIBLIOGRAPHY: G. F. WAAGEN: Gemälde-Sammlung des Königl. Museum zu Berlin, 1837, pp. 269 and 284; R. OFFNER: In Burl. Mag., May 1929, p. 224, Illust., L. VENTURI: Italian Paintings in America, 1933, No. 35, Illust., B. BERENSON: Italian Pictures of the Renaissance, 1932, p. 337; A. M. FRANKFURTER: In Art News, May 1937, p. 29, Illust., ANON: Mostra Giottesca, Palazzo degli Uffizi, Firenze, 1937, p. 54, No. 152, Illust.

MASTER MICHIEL

FLEMISH XV - XVI C.

One of a group of painters developing around Memling in the last quarter of the XV century, of whom a number were attracted to the Spanish court of Isabella of Castile. Michiel was there from 1492 onward, and possibly as early as 1480. After the death of Isabella (1504) he went to the court of Margaret of Austria. In 1514 he visited Denmark; from 1515 until about 1520 he was again in Flanders in the service of Margaret, and of her nephew, the future Charles V.

241 *Young Man in a Red Cap.*

Pl. 55   Painted about 1512.

Panel: 6½ x 5 inches.

LENT BY MRS. LILLIAN HENKEL HAASS, DETROIT, MICHIGAN.
COLLECTION: Paul Bottenwieser.
BIBLIOGRAPHY: M. J. FRIEDLÄNDER: Jan Gossart u B. van Orley, 1930, p. 162, No. 67, *Illust.*, and Nachträge, 1937, p. 112, No. 67; E. P. RICHARDSON: *In* Art Quarterly, Spring 1939, pp. 107-108, *Illust.*

MASTER OF ALKMAAR

DUTCH, ACTIVE C. 1504

A provisional name given by M. J. Friedländer to an anonymous master whose chief works are in the Church of St. Lawrence, Alkmaar; there are seven panels by him in the Rijksmuseum, Amsterdam.

242 *SS. Ursula, Godelieva, Catherine, and Agnes.*

Painted about 1500. Two companion panels were until recently also in the Northbrook Collection.

Panel: 14½ x 9½ inches each.

LENT BY MR. AND MRS. SOLOMON R. GUGGENHEIM, NEW YORK.
BIBLIOGRAPHY: M. J. FRIEDLÄNDER: Die Altniederländische Malerei, Vol. X, 1932, p. 39, No. 24, *Illust.*

MASTER OF FLÉMALLE

FLEMISH, XV CENTURY

So called after the parts from a large altarpiece in the Frankfort Museum, supposedly from the Abbey of Flémalle near Liège, executed before 1430. Other important works by the same hand are the Merode-Altar (c.1428), the Nativity in Dijon (c.1428), the Werl Altar in the Prado (1438). The artist was identified at one time with Jacques Daret, later with Robert Campin. It is, however, not impossible that the right identification is with Roger van der Weyden. If this is the case, the works given to the Master of Flémalle represent an early phase of Roger's activity. (1425-1445).

3 *Portrait of a Noblewoman.*

It is supposed that this is a portrait of Marie of Savoy, who married Filippo Maria Visconti, Duke of Milan, and upon his death in 1447 became a nun. The style of the portrait, however, points to an earlier date, to the epoch when Roger painted the Escorial Deposition from the Cross (compare the hands of the Magdalen), about 1430.

Panel: 19½ x 14 inches.

LENT BY THE DUMBARTON OAKS COLLECTION, WASHINGTON, D. C.

COLLECTIONS: Henri Cernuschi; René Boylesve; Wildenstein Galleries.

EXHIBITIONS: Princeton University, 1937; Worcester Art Museum, 1939; Philadelphia Museum of Art, 1939.

BIBLIOGRAPHY: L. ROGER-MILES: Catalogue des Tableaux Anciens, Colln. Henri Cernuschi, Paris, 1900, p. 73, No. 143, *Illust.*; M. J. FRIEDLÄNDER: Rogier v.d. Weyden u. der Meister von Flémalle, 1924, p. 109, No. 57, *Illust.*; H. MARCEAU, and others: The Worcester-Philadelphia Exhbn. of Flemish Painting, 1939, p. 19, No. 3, *Illust.*

MASTER OF MOULINS

FRENCH, ACTIVE C. 1480 - C. 1520

An unidentified painter named from the noted Triptych in the Cathedral of Moulins, Dep. de l'Allier, France. Also known as 'The Painter of the Bourbons' from the portraits of the Bourbon family in the Triptych. Recently identified convincingly with Jean Perréal who was patronized by Pierre de Bourbon, Louis XII and Francis I.

4 *Portrait of a Young Lady.*

Painted about 1480.

Panel: 10½ x 8½ inches.

LENT BY MR. SOLOMON R. GUGGENHEIM, NEW YORK.

COLLECTIONS: Victoria, Empress Frederick of Germany; Privy-Councillor Dr. von Frericks; A. S. Drey.

MASTER OF SANTA CECILIA

FLORENTINE, XIII - XIV CENTURIES

Contemporary of Giotto, named after the painting in the Uffizi representing the Life of St. Cecilia. He executed several frescoes from the Life of St. Francis in the Upper Church of San Francesco at Assisi. Active at the end of the XIII and the first decades of the XIV c. He has been identified with Buffalmaco, whom Vasari describes as an independent and versatile artist of the same epoch as Giotto. "Of all the Florentine artists who belonged to the same generation as Giotto and worked more or less independently at his side, none is more interesting than the so-called Cecilia-Master" (Sirén).

245 St. Catherine of Alexandria,
and Twelve Scenes from her Legend.

Left: St. Catherine and her mother visiting the hermit; Apparition of the Madonna; Baptism of the young Catherine by the hermit; Her mystic marriage; Her dispute with the Grammarians; Her prayer for the Grammarians. *Right:* St. Catherine in prison; The Empress visiting St. Catherine; Christ and Angels comforting St. Catherine; Her Martyrdom; Decapitation of Porphyrus; Decapitation of St. Catherine.

Panel: 43 x 68¼ inches.

LENT BY MR. WILLIAM RANDOLPH HEARST, NEW YORK.

COLLECTIONS: Chigi-Saracini Chapel, Siena; Georges Wildenstein.

EXHIBITION: Palazzo Uffizi, Florence, 1937.

BIBLIOGRAPHY: o. SIREN: *Jn* Burl. Mag., June 1924, pp. 273-277, *Jllust.*, ANON: Mostra Giottesca, Catalogo delle opere, Palazzo degli Uffizi, Firenze, 1927, p. 47, No. 124, *Jllust.*, (*As in the 'maniera del Maestro della S. Cecilia'.*)

MASTER OF THE CODEX OF SAN GIORGIO

AVIGNONESE, XIV. CENTURY

The identity of this painter has not been established, but judging from the Miniatures of the "Codex of S. Giorgio", after which he is named, and which he painted for Cardinal Stefaneschi, in the Capitolare in St. Peter's, Rome, he was a master-illuminator, active in Avignon apparently between 1320 and 1350. His works reveal him as a follower of Simone Martini, who also worked in Avignon.

246 The Crucifixion, and The Entombment.

These paintings, now forming a diptych, are probably part of a small polyptych of which the central part is in the Louvre, and two others in the Bargello Museum, Florence.

Panels: Each 15½ x 10½ inches.

LENT BY MR. AND MRS. JOHN D. ROCKEFELLER, JR., NEW YORK.

COLLECTIONS: Henry G. Bohn; Charles Butler; Robert and Evelyn Benson; Lord Duveen of Millbank.

EXHIBITIONS: New Gallery, London, 1893-1894; Royal Academy, London, 1896; Burlington Fine Arts Club, London, 1904.

BIBLIOGRAPHY: J. P. RICHTER: *Jn* Repertor. für Kunstw., Vol. XVII, 1894, pp. 236-238; SIR L. CUST: *Jn* Les Arts, Oct. 1907, p. 24, *Jllust.*, R. LANGDON-DOUGLAS: Sienese Exhibition, Burl. F. A. Club, 1904, pp. 55-56, *Jllust.*, S. REINACH: Repértoire, Vol. I, 1905, p. 413, *Jllust.*, A. VENTURI: Storia dell'Arte Ital., Vol. V, 1907, pp 631 and 1030, CROWE AND CAVALCASELLE: Hist. of Painting in Italy, Vol. III, 1908, p. 69; G. NICOLA: *Jn* L'Arte, Vol. XI, 1908, p. 385; T. BORENIUS: Catalogue of the Benson Col., 1914, pp. 9-10, Nos. 6-7, *Jllust.*, R. VAN MARLE: Le Maitre du Codex de St. Georges, *Jn* Gaz. d. B.A., Jan. 1931, pp. 9-10, *Jllust.*, B. BERENSON: Italian Pictures, 1932, p. 346, (Ital. Edn., 1936, p. 282).

MATTEO DI GIOVANNI

SIENESE, c. 1435-1495

The son of a tradesman from Borgo San Sepolcro, who settled in Siena. His first master was probably the Umbrian painter Piero della Francesca, and he was influenced by Domenico di Bartolo and Vecchietta, and, later, by Pollaiuolo and Girolamo da Cremona. The leading painter in Siena during the second half of the fifteenth century.

7 *The Madonna and Child.*

Panel: 26 x 18 inches.

LENT BY MR. RICHARD M. HURD, NEW YORK.

COLLECTION: Count Palmieri-Nuti, Siena.

EXHIBITION: Newhouse Galleries, New York, 1937.

BIBLIOGRAPHY: B. BERENSON: Italian Pictures of the Renaissance, 1932, p. 351, (Ital. edn., 1936, p. 302); S. BOURGEOIS: Italian Primitives in the Collection of Richard M. Hurd, 1937, No. 15, *Illust.*

MATTEO DI GIOVANNI

SIENESE, C. 1435-1495

8
9 *The Marriage of the Blessed Virgin* (Companion to No. 249).

An early work of the master. Part of a predella from the same altarpiece as the companion picture. The two figures in the foreground, at the left, are presumed to be portraits of L. B. Alberti and Donatello.

Panel: 9 x 17½ inches.

LENT BY THE JOHN G. JOHNSON COLLECTION, PHILADELPHIA.

COLLECTION: F. Kleinberger.

EXHIBITION: Kleinberger Galleries, Paris, 1911.

BIBLIOGRAPHY: A. VENTURI: Storia dell'Arte Ital., Vol. VII, 1, 1911, p. 474, *Illust.*, B. BERENSON: Ital. Paintings in the John G. Johnson Colln., 1913, p. 58, No. 107, *Illust.*, CROWE AND CAVALCASELLE: Painting in Italy, Vol. V, 1914, p. 153; B. BERENSON: Italian Pictures, 1932, p. 352 (Ital. Edn., 1936, p. 302); R. VAN MARLE: Ital. Schools, Vol. XVI, 1937, pp. 246 and 362.

MATTEO DI GIOVANNI

SIENESE, C. 1435-1495

9 *The Visitation* (Companion to No. 248).

Panel: 9 x 17½ inches.

LENT BY THE JOHN G. JOHNSON COLLECTION, PHILADELPHIA.

COLLECTION: F. Kleinberger.

EXHIBITION: Kleinberger Galleries, Paris, 1911.

BIBLIOGRAPHY: A. VENTURI: Storia dell'Arte Ital., Vol. VII (1), 1911, p. 474, *Illust.*, B. BER-

ENSON: Ital. Paintings in the John G. Johnson Collection, 1913, p. 58, No. 108, *Illust.*, CROWE AND CAVALCASELLE: Painting in Italy, Vol. V, 1914, p. 153; B. BERENSON: Italian Pictures, 1932, p. 352 (Ital. edn., 1936, p. 302); R. VAN MARLE: Italian Schools, Vol. XVI, 1937, pp. 246 and 362.

MEMLING, HANS

FLEMISH, 1430?-1494

German by birth, from the Mainz diocese; born possibly in Mömlingen near Mainz. Studied probably in Cologne, and later at Brussels under Roger van der Weyden. About 1465 he settled in Bruges. In 1478 he painted the Erckhout altarpiece, now at Turin, and in 1479, the "Adoration of the Kings", in the St. John's Hospital, Bruges. In 1480 he completed the large "Light of the World", now at Munich, and in 1484 finished the Morcel Triptych, now in the Bruges Museum. By 1489 the famous Shrine of St. Ursula, in the St. John's Hospital, was completed. He is regarded as the most poetical and tender of the masters of the Netherlandish School. He died at Bruges, and was buried in St. Giles.

250 *The Madonna and Child.*

Pl. 53   Panel: 9½ x 7 inches.

LENT BY THE JULES S. BACHE COLLECTION, NEW YORK.

COLLECTIONS: René Della Faille de Waerloos; Caspar Bourgeois; Richard von Kaufmann; Lord Duveen of Millbank.

EXHIBITIONS: Düsseldorf, 1904; Royal Academy, London, 1927; Princeton University, 1937.

BIBLIOGRAPHY: ANON: Catalogue de la Collection René della Faille de Waerloos à Anvers, 1903, p. 4, No. 3, *Illust.*, M. J. FRIEDLÄNDER: *In* L'Art Flamand et Hollandais, Vol. VI, 1906, p. 31; S. REINACH: Répertoire de Peintures, Vol. II, 1907, p. 140, *Illust.*, M. J. FRIEDLÄNDER: Die Sammlung Richard von Kaufmann, Berlin, 1917, p. 142, No. 70, *Illust.*, IDEM: Memling und Gerard David, 1928, p. 126, No. 53; SIR M. CONWAY: Catalogue of Flemish and Belgian Art, Royal Academy, London, 1927, No. 48, Plate XXVII; R. CORTISSOZ: *In* The American Mag. of Art, Vol. XXI, 1930, p. 251, *Illust.*, ANON: Exhn. of Belgian Medieval Art, Princeton, 1937, No. 2; ANON: Catalogue of the Bache Collection, New York, 1938, No. 23, *Illust.*

MEMLING, HANS

FLEMISH, 1430?-1494

251 *A Young Man with Folded Hands.*

Painted about 1470.

Panel: 15⅜ x 11¾ inches.

LENT FROM THE WILLIAM GOLDMAN COLLECTION, NEW YORK.

COLLECTION: Duke of Anhalt-Dessau.

EXHIBITION: L'Art Flamand, Antwerp, 1930.

BIBLIOGRAPHY: D. GOLDSCHMIDT: L'Exposition d'Art Flamand Ancien, Antwerp, 1930, pp. 77-78, No. 195; P. LAMBOTTE: *In* Apollo, July 1930, p. 17, *Illust.*, A. M. FRANKFURTER: *In* Fine Arts, March 1932, p. 21, *Illust.*

MEMLING, HANS

FLEMISH, 1430-1494

2 *The Blessing Christ.*

Dated 1478 upon the original frame, which has been replaced by a modern one. At this time the artist was at the height of his activity in Bruges; in 1479 he executed the famous Floreins-altar and the large St. John altarpiece, both in the Hospital at Bruges, and in 1480 the panel representing the life of the Virgin, in the Munich Pinakothek.

Panel: 14½ x 10½ inches.

LENT BY DR. A. HAMILTON RICE, NEW YORK.

COLLECTIONS: Don Manoel, King of Portugal; Lord Duveen of Millbank.
EXHIBITIONS: Royal Academy, London, 1927; Kleinberger Galleries, New York, 1929.
BIBLIOGRAPHY: J. O. KRONIG: *In* Les Arts, Mar. 1910, p. 28, *Jllust.*, M. J. FRIEDLÄNDER: *In* Der Cicerone, 1927, p. 212; T. BORENIUS: Catalogue of Flemish and Belgium Art, Royal Academy, London, 1927, No. 62, *Jllust.*, M. J. FRIEDLÄNDER: Memling u. Gerard David, 1928, No. 39, *Jllust.*, IDEM: Flemish Primitives, Kleinberger Galleries, New York, 1929, No. 23, *Jllust.*

MEMLING, HANS

FLEMISH, 1430?-1494

3 *Portrait of a Lady of Quality.*

49 Painted before 1480. According to Dr. Friedländer, this panel apparently comes from the same altarpiece as the one recently in the Cardon Collection, Brussels, in which are two horses in a landscape, and, according to Dr. Winkler, probably formed the back of the panel. The lady is probably a donatrice, her portrait having occupied the left wing of a triptych, with her husband at the right.

Panel: 17 x 17¼ inches.

LENT BY THE JULES S. BACHE COLLECTION, NEW YORK.

COLLECTIONS: Heinrich Vieweg; Dr. Wilhelm von Bode; Signor Gabbida.
EXHIBITION: Kleinberger Galleries, New York, 1929, No. 21; Princeton University, 1937.
BIBLIOGRAPHY: F. WINKLER: *Jn* Apollo, Jan. 1928, pp. 9-12, *Jllust.*, M. J. FRIEDLÄNDER: Memling and Gerard David, 1928, p. 119, No. 16b, *Jllust.*, H. G. SPERLING: Catalogue of Flemish Primitives, New York, 1929, p. 76, No. 21, *Jllust.*, H. VOLLMER: *Jn* Thieme-Becker's Lexikon, Vol. XXIV, 1930, p. 376; ANON: Exhn. of Belgian Medieval Art, Princeton, 1937, No. 3; ANON: Catalogue of the Bache Collection, New York, 1938, No. 24, *Jllust.*

MEMLING, HANS

FLEMISH, 1430?-1494

4 *Portrait of a Man with a Pink.*

Panel: 14¾ x 8 inches.

LENT BY MR. J. PIERPONT MORGAN, NEW YORK.

COLLECTIONS: Charles du Bourg de Perreux; Rodolphe Kann; Lord Duveen of Millbank.

EXHIBITIONS: Pavillon de Marsan, Louvre, Paris, 1904; Metropolitan Museum, 1913; Knoedler Galleries, 1935; Cleveland Museum, 1935; Knoedler Galleries, London, 1935; Wadsworth Atheneum, 1937; Worcester Art Museum, 1938.

BIBLIOGRAPHY: H. BOUCHOT, and others: Exposition des Primitifs français, Paris, 1904, No. 59; W. VON BODE: Catalogue of the R. Kahn Colln., Vol. II, No. 106, *Illust.*, M. J. FRIEDLÄNDER: *In* Art in Amer., Apr. 1920, p. 108, *Illust.*, SIR M. CONWAY: The Van Eycks and their followers, 1921, p. 238; M. J. FRIEDLÄNDER: Memling u. Gerard David, 1928, p. 131, No. 83; A. M. FRANK-FURTER: *In* Fine Arts, Mar. 1932, p. 22; F. WATSON: *In* Amer. Mag. of Art, May 1935, pp. 285-286, *Illust.*, H. FURST: *In* Apollo, June 1935, p. 365, *Illust.*

MEMLING, HANS

FLEMISH, 1430?-1494

255 *Portrait of a Youth.*

Pl. 52 One of the most delightful portraits of the master, in an unusually fine state of preservation.

Panel: 13½ x 9 inches.

LENT BY MRS. VAN WIE WILLYS, NEW YORK.

COLLECTIONS: John Edward Taylor; Julius Böhler; John N. Willys.

EXHIBITIONS: Toledo Museum, 1926; Kleinberger Galleries, New York, 1929; Reinhardt Galleries, New York, 1929; Chicago Art Institute, 1933.

BIBLIOGRAPHY: M. J. FRIEDLANDER: *In* Art in Amer., Apr. 1920, p. 108, *Illust.*, IDEM: Memling u. Gerard David, 1928, p. 131, No. 80; E. SINGLETON: Old World Masters, 1929, p. 175, *Illust.*, H. G. SPERLING: Flemish Primitives, Kleinberger Galleries, New York, 1929, No. 20, *Illust.*, D. C. RICH: Exhibition of Paintings, etc., Art Inst. of Chicago, 1933, p. 8, No. 51.

MEMMI, LIPPO

SIENESE, 1290-1357

Assistant and follower of his brother-in-law Simone Martini, and a pupil probably of Duccio, influenced by Pietro and Ambrogio Lorenzetti. His most important work is the fresco of the "Majestas" in the town hall at San Gimignano. His signed altarpieces are found in the Church of the Servi at Siena, the Duomo of Orvieto, the Uffizi, and the Berlin Museum. In lyrical quality his compositions are very near to those of Simone Martini, but he is less emotional and imaginative. In refinement of execution his paintings are unsurpassed in the Sienese school.

256 *The Madonna and Child, with St. John the Baptist,*
Pl. 4 *St. Francis, and Angels; Predella, small saints.*

Painted about 1340.

Panel: 26 x 12¼ inches.

LENT BY MR. MAITLAND F. GRIGGS, NEW YORK.

COLLECTIONS: Martin T. Smith; R. E. Norton; Lord Duveen of Millbank.

EXHIBITION: Early Italian Paintings, Duveen Galleries, New York, 1924.
BIBLIOGRAPHY: R. OFFNER: *In* The Arts, May 1924, p. 241, *Illust.*, W. R. VALENTINER: Catalogue of Early Italian Paintings, Duveen Galleries, New York, 1926, No. 27, *Illust.*, L. VENTURI: Italian Paintings in America, 1933, No. 73, *Illust.*, B. BERENSON: Italian Pictures, 1932, p. 360, (Ital. edn., 1936, p. 309); A. M. FRANKFURTER: *In* The Art News, May 1, 1937, p. 155, *Illust.*

MEMMI, LIPPO

SIENESE, 1290-1357

Madonna and Child, with SS. Francis, Clare, and Two Angels.

Panel: 16 x 6¾ inches.

LENT BY MR. PERCY S. STRAUS, NEW YORK.

COLLECTIONS: Private collection in Scotland; Edward Hutton.

MORONI, GIAMBATTISTA

BRESCIAN, 1520-1578

Born at Bondo in Bergamo, and studied under Moretto da Brescia, influenced later by Lorenzo Lotto and Titian; his dated works appear between 1545-77. One of his most noted portraits is that known as 'Titian's Schoolmaster' in the Widener Collection, Philadelphia, another is 'The Tailor', in the National Gallery, London. There is a tradition that Titian, when asked to paint the portrait of a nobleman at Bergamo, recommended Moroni to him. The cool, silvery colors of his compositions, differing from the warm, glowing tones of the Venetian masters, are characteristic of the school of Bergamo.

A Gentleman adoring the Madonna.

Painted about 1560.

Canvas: 23½ x 25½ inches.

LENT BY MR. SAMUEL H. KRESS, NEW YORK.

COLLECTION: Casa Grimani, Venice.

EXHIBITION: Petit Palais, Paris, 1935.

BIBLIOGRAPHY: H. TIETZE: Meisterw. Europä.-Malerei in Amer., 1935, No. 96, *Illust.*, EXPOSITION de l'Art Ital. de Cimabue a Tiepolo, Petit Palais, Paris, 1935, p. 145, No. 322; B. BERENSON: Pitture Ital., 1936, p. ?18.

MURILLO, BARTOLOMÉ ESTEBAN

SPANISH, 1617-1682

Born in Seville. Studied under Juan del Castillo; became an independent painter at twenty-three, and sold his pictures at the fairs in Seville. In 1642 he went to

Madrid and improved his art under Velazquez's supervision. In 1660 he established an academy in Seville from which date his most brilliant period was established. After 1675 he executed a large number of paintings for the Capucin convents, both in Seville and Cadiz. He is regarded as the most popular painter of Spain.

259 *A Girl lifting her Veil.*

Pl. 89   Painted about 1670.

Canvas: 20½ x 15 inches.

LENT BY DR. JAKOB GOLDSCHMIDT, NEW YORK.

COLLECTIONS: Sir Thomas Baring; Robert Stayner Holford; Sir George Lindsay Holford.
EXHIBITIONS: British Institution, London, 1837, 1844, and 1852; New Gallery, London, 1895-96; Grafton Gallery, London.
BIBLIOGRAPHY: ANON: Catalogues of the British Institution, London, 1837, No. 100; 1844, No. 101; 1852, No. 33; SIR E. HEAD: Spanish Painting, 1848, p. 185; G. F. WAAGEN: Art Treasures in Great Britain, Vol. II, 1854, p. 199; C. B. CURTIS: Velazquez and Murillo, 1883, p. 283, No. 430; L. C. LINDSAY: Exhib. of Spanish Art, New Gallery, Lond., 1895-96, p. 6, No. 20; A. L. MAYER: Murillo (Kl. der Kunst), 1913, p. 210, *Illust.*, M. W. BROCKWELL: Exhib. of Spanish Old Masters, Grafton Gallery, Lond., 1914, pp. 105-106, No. 106, *Illust.*, R. BENSON: The Holford Collection, Westonbirt, 1924, p. 84, No. 103, *Illust.*, S. DE RICCI: *In* Gazette des B.-Arts, Jan. 1925, p. 42.

MURILLO, BARTOLOME ESTEBAN

SPANISH, 1617 - 1682

260 *St. Giles in Ecstacy.*

Pl. 87   Painted about 1645-50. The scene depicts St. Giles the Franciscan standing in a transport of religious ecstasy before Pope Gregory IX (1227-41); the latter had gone to Perugia to consult the saint who in return was filled with a miraculous love and faith. The picture is one of a series of scenes in the lives of Franciscan saints, which the painter executed for the monastery of that order in Seville; they were removed by the French troops in 1810 and eventually dispersed.

Canvas: 65 x 74 inches.

LENT ANONYMOUSLY.

COLLECTIONS: San Francisco Monastery, Seville; Baron Mathieu de Faviers (1812); Vicomte Aguado, Marquis de Las Marismas (1843); William Buchanan (1846); Philip S. Miles; John Miles; Thomas Harris.
ENGRAVED by Tavernier.
EXHIBITION: Art Treasures, Manchester, 1857.
BIBLIOGRAPHY: ANON: Collection Baron Mathieu de Faviers, Intendant Général des Armées, 1837, No. 165; ANON: Tableaux anciens, Collection Vicomte Agnado, 1843, No. 33, *Illust. with Tavernier's engraving*, G. SCHARF: Art Treasures, Manchester, 1857, p. 50, No. 620; C. B. CURTIS: Velazquez and Murillo, 1883, p. 242, No. 309; A. F. CALVERT: Murillo, 1907, p. 172; A. L. MAYER: Murillo (Kl. der Kunst), 1913, p. 9, *Illust.*, A. JAMESON: Sacred and Legendary Art, Vol. II, 1895, p. 754.

MURILLO, BARTOLOME ESTEBAN

SPANISH, 1617-1682

1 The Madonna and Child.

Painted about 1670-1682.

Canvas: 49 x 37 inches.

LENT BY MR. C. STILLMAN AND MRS. LANGBOURNE M. WILLIAMS,

JNR., NEW YORK.

COLLECTIONS: James Stillman; C. C. Stillman.

EXHIBITION: Metropolitan Museum of Art, 1921-1926.

BIBLIOGRAPHY: A. L. MAYER: Murillo (Kl. der Kunst), 1913, p. 172, *Illust.*, ANON: Paintings by Old and Modern Masters, Stillman Collection, 1927, No. 24, *Illust.*

NATTIER, JEAN MARC

FRENCH, 1685-1766

Born in Paris. He obtained the *grand prix* at the Academy in 1700, travelled to Holland and Russia, and painted the portraits of Peter the Great and Catherine I, and afterwards copied the Rubens pictures in the Luxembourg for the purposes of engraving. He became a member of the Academy in 1718, and a professor in 1752. He is the most representative portrait painter in France during the time of Louis XV.

2 Madame Bonier de la Mosson.

Represented as Diana. Signed and dated 1742. Wife of M. Bonier de la Mosson (died 1745) noted member of XVIII c. Parisian society, *capitaine des chasses*, naturalist, and friend of Comte de Buffon, author of the *Histoire Naturelle* (1749-1804). Her *salon* in the rue St. Dominique, Paris, was the *rendez-vous* of the most noted personages of her day.

Canvas: 51 x 38 inches.

LENT BY MRS. SOSTHENES BEHN, NEW YORK.

COLLECTIONS: Capt. Bonier de la Mosson; Dr. Debatz, Reims; M. Tamvaco, Cairo; Henry E. Huntington, Los Angeles; Knoedler Galleries, New York; Edward J. Berwind.

EXHIBITION: Salon du Louvre, Paris, 1742.

BIBLIOGRAPHY: ANON: Livret de Salon de l'Académie Royale, Paris, 1742, p. 20, No. 64; LADY DILKE: French Painters of the XVIII c., 1899, p. 205; P. DE NOLHAC: In Les Arts, Jan. 1910, p. 2, *Illust.*, IDEM: Nattier, peintre de la cour de Louis XV, 1925, pp. 170, 101, 248, *Illust.*, E. SINGLETON: Old World Masters, 1929, p. 287, *Illust.*, L. DIMIER: Les Peintres Français du XVIII e siecle, Vol. II, 1930, p. 123, No. 123.

NATTIER, JEAN-MARC

263 *Portrait of Louis XV, King of France.*

Painted about 1744. Great-grandson of Louis XIV, whom he succeeded in 1715. At fifteen he married Marie Leczinska, daughter of Stanislas, dethroned king of Poland. After the peace of Aix-la-Chapelle in 1748, he came under the influence of Madame de Pompadour, and later Madame du Barry, and their combined extravagance brought about the ruin of the French constitution, culminating in the Revolution during the reign of his successor, Louis XVI. He died in 1774.

Canvas: 31 x 24 inches.

LENT BY MR. CARL M. LOEB, NEW YORK.

COLLECTION: M. de Buttet, Alais, Gard, France; Wildenstein Galleries, New York.
BIBLIOGRAPHY: P. DE NOLHAC: Nattier, 1905, p. 145, *Illust.* p. 70; L. DUMONT-WILDEN: Le Portrait en France, 1909, p. 226.

NATTIER, JEAN MARC

264 *Mme. de la Porte, née Caumartin.*

Signed and dated 1759. Inscribed: Mme. de Caumartin, femme de M. de la Porte, Conseiller d'Etat.

Canvas: 47¼ x 37¼ inches.

LENT BY MR. JAMES SPEYER, NEW YORK.

COLLECTION: Comte de Lariboisière; Charles Sedelmeyer; Count A. Trotti.
EXHIBITIONS: Cent Portraits de Femme, Galerie Georges Petit, Paris, 1909; Sedelmeyer Gallery, 1911.
BIBLIOGRAPHY: A. DAYOT: L'Image de la Femme, 1899, p. 181, *Illust.*, L. DUMONT-WILDEN: Le Portrait en France, 1909, p. 226; L. DIMIER: Les Peintres français du XVIII siècle, n.d., p. 126, No. 96; L. VAILLAT ET R. DELL: Cent Portraits de Femmes, 1910, p. 82, *Illust.*, C. SEDELMEYER: Paintings by Old Masters, 1911, p. 100, No. 83, *Illust.*, P. DE NOLHAC: J.-M. Nattier, 1926, p. 259, *Illust. in large edn.*

NEROCCIO DE' LANDI

Born in Siena, was one of the leading painters and sculptors in that city during the late quattrocento. He was a pupil of Sassetta and Vecchietta; he afterwards became a partner of Francesco di Giorgio. He married twice, and a son, by his second marriage, in 1493, also became a painter. He is noted for his refinement of drawing, unequalled by any other Sienese painter of his time.

265 *The Madonna and Child,*
Pl. 6 *with SS. John the Baptist and Mary Magdalen.*

With the escutcheons of the Chigi-Saracini families, respectively, in the upper corners.

Panel: 28 x 20 inches.

LENT BY DR. G. H. A. CLOWES, INDIANAPOLIS.

COLLECTIONS: Chigi-Saracini family, Siena; Count Ladislaus Karolyi, Budapest; Silbermann Galleries.

EXHIBITION: Budapest Museum (Loan).

BIBLIOGRAPHY: M. L. BERENSON: Jn Rassegna d'Arte, May 1913, p. 73, Jllust., L. DAMI: Jn Rassegna d'Arte, Oct. 1913, p. 164, Jllust., CROWE AND CAVALCASELLE: Hist. of Painting in Italy, Ed. by T. Borenius, Vol. V, 1914, p. 159; C. CHLEDOWSKI: Siena, Vol. II, 1923, p. 225; S. SCHUBRING: Jn Thieme-Becker's Lexikon, Vol. XXII, 1923, p. 295; B. BERENSON: Ital. Pictures, 1932, p. 389, (Ital. Edn., 1936, p. 335), as in the Budapest Museum, (Palffy Bequest).

NEROCCIO DE LANDI

SIENESE, 1447 - 1500

Madonna and Child.

Panel: 15¾ x 9¼ inches.

LENT BY SENATOR AND MRS. SIMON GUGGENHEIM, NEW YORK.

COLLECTION: Edward Hutton.

OLIVER, ISAAC

ENGLISH, 1562? - 1617

Born at Rouen, and went to London as a child about 1568; he studied under Zucchero who was in England c. 1581-1583; in 1596 he was working in Venice, and in 1598 was again in England with Hilliard, the miniature painter. In 1602 he married three times, his first wife being Sarah Gheeraerts, a daughter of the noted painter. In 1606 he became a naturalized citizen of London, where he was employed by James I, and died there eleven years afterwards. One of the greatest miniature painters of the English School.

Sir Anthony Mildmay, Knight of Apethorpe.

Painted about 1596. Sir Anthony Mildmay, born about 1555, was the eldest son of Sir Walter Mildmay (1520-1589), Chancellor of the Exchequer. He was educated at Peter House, Cambridge, entered at Gray's Inn 1579, Knighted 1596, Ambassador to Henry IV of France 1596-7, and died 1617. His daughter and heiress, Mary, married Francis, 1st Earl of Westmorland, and their grandson, Henry Fane, married Anne, daughter of John Wynn, D.D., Bishop of Bath and Wells; and their daughter married Sir Thomas Stapleton Bart. of Henley, London.

Panel: 9¼ x 7 inches.

LENT BY THE CLEVELAND MUSEUM OF ART.

COLLECTION: Sir Miles Stapleton, Bart., Descendant of Sir Anthony.

EXHIBITION: J. H. Wade Fund, Cleveland Museum, 1929.
BIBLIOGRAPHY: w. m. milliken: A Miniature by Isaac Oliver, *In* Cleveland Museum Bulletin, Feb. 1927, p. 19, *Illust.*, *In* International Studio, Apr. 1929, p. 82, *Illust.*

ORLEY, BAREND VAN

FLEMISH, C. 1492-1542

Born at Brussels; pupil of his father, Valentin, further trained under Italian influence, especially that of Raphael, whom he is said to have met in Rome about 1509. In 1514 he was a Master painter in Brussels. In 1518 he was made official painter to Margaret of Austria. In 1520 Dürer visited Brussels and was welcomed by Van Orley; in 1521 he was again there and painted the Flemish master. Besides being a painter he was also known as a tapestry weaver, and in the field of applied arts he was one of the most influential craftsmen of the Flemish school.

268 *Portrait of a Young Man.*

Pl. 55 Painted between 1515-20. The smallest known portrait of the master, and perhaps his best.

Panel: 5⅜ x 4¼ inches.

LENT BY THE DETROIT INSTITUTE OF ARTS.

BIBLIOGRAPHY: w. r. valentiner: *In* Detroit Inst. of Arts Bulletin, Nov. 1934, p. 18, *Illust.*, anon: *In* Art News, Mar. 30, 1935, p. 9, *Illust.*

OSTADE, ADRIAEN VAN

DUTCH, 1610-1685

Born in Haarlem, where he lived all his life. About 1627 he and Adriaen Brouwer were pupils together under Frans Hals, but his work reflects little of that influence, and in their choice of subjects the pupils became closely related. His earliest dated painting is 1631. Towards the end of the 'thirties the cool colours became warmer under Rembrandt's influence. After 1650 the local colours became stronger again, and the restlessness in his compositions is replaced by a calmer mood. After 1670 his paintings are lighter in key, and over-rich in colour. His last painting is dated 1683. He produced several excellent etchings, which, as well as his paintings, represent the life of the Dutch bourgeoisie in a most pleasing manner.

269 *Still-life in a Courtyard.*

The unusual composition belongs to the best period of the artist, about 1650-60.

Panel: 17½ x 14 inches.

LENT BY MR. H. E. TEN CATE, ALMELO, HOLLAND.

COLLECTIONS: Baron Dominique Vivant-Denon, Director of the French Imperial Museum (1825); Thomas Emmerson; William Wells of Redleaf; Jones Loyd, afterwards Lord Overstone; Robert James Loyd-Lindsay, Baron Wantage; Lady Wantage; Earl of Crawford and Balcarres; D. Katz.

EXHIBITIONS: Manchester Art Treasures, 1857; Royal Academy, London, 1871 and 1888; Kleykamp Galleries, The Hague, 1927; Brussels, 1935; Museum Boymans, Rotterdam, 1938.
BIBLIOGRAPHY: A. N. PERIGNON: Le Cabinet de M. le Baron V. Denon, 1826, p. 47, No. 100; J. SMITH: Catalogue raisonné, Vol. I, 1829, p. 155, No. 174; G. F. WAAGEN: Art Treasures, Vol. IV, 1857, p. 143; G. SCHARF: Art Treasures at Manchester, 1857, p. 56, No. 740; W. BURGER: Trésors d'Art à Manchester, 1857, p. 314; C. BLANC: Le Trésor de la Curiosité, Vol. II, 1858, p. 362; H. S. WANTAGE: Pictures in the Collection of Lord and Lady Wantage, 1902, p. 105, No. 169, Illust., C. HOFSTEDE DE GROOT: Catalogue raisonné, Vol. III, 1910, pp. 423-424, No. 916; H. P. BREMMER: In Beeldende Kunst, Feb. 1928, p. 30, Illust., BARONNE A. HOUTART: Cinq siècles d'Art, Bruxelles, 1935, p. 179, No. 753; D. HANNEMA: Meesterwerken uit vier eeuween, 1400-1800, Museum Boymans, 1938, p. 29, No. 118, Illust.

OSTADE, ADRIAEN VAN

DUTCH, 1610-1685

Woman Selling Fish. Known also as 'The Fish Market'.

Signed and dated, 1672. A similar composition by Ostade is in the Budapest Museum.

Canvas: 14¼ x 15¾ inches.

LENT BY THE RIJKSMUSEUM, AMSTERDAM.

COLLECTIONS: Gerard Braamkamp; P. de Smeth van Alphen; De Heer van Winter; Six van Hillegom; Jan P. Six; P. H. Six van s'Graveland; Jan Six; Sir Henry Deterding.
ENGRAVED by Johann Willem Kaiser.
EXHIBITIONS: Royal Academy, London, 1929; Six Collection, Stedelijk Museum, Amsterdam, 1900.
BIBLIOGRAPHY: G. HOET: Catalogus of Naamlyst (Kabinet Braamkamp), 1752, p. 507; J. SMITH: Catalogue Raisonné, Vol. I, 1829, p. 119, No. 42; Supp., 1842, p. 117, No. 126; J. SIX: Catalogus der Schilderijen van P. H. Six van Vromade, Stedelijk Museum, Amsterdam, 1900, No. 104; C. HOFSTEDE DE GROOT: Catalogue Raisonné, Vol. III, 1910, No. 130; ANON: Tableaux Anciens, Collection Six, 1928; SCHNEIDER AND CONSTABLE: Exhibition of Dutch Art, Royal Acad., Lond., 1929, p. 84, No. 174, Illust. in 'Souvenir'.

PAOLO VERONESE

VENETIAN, 1528-1588

Born in Verona and first studied under Antonio Badile of that city; he was strongly influenced by Brusasorci, Parmigianino, and Primaticcio, to which may be added Lotto, Moretto, Romanino, and Titian. About 1547 he went to Mantua to work for Cardinal Gonzaga. In 1555 he went to Venice and painted a 'Coronation of the Virgin' in S. Sebastiano. From about 1562 he produced his great Supper pieces. Many of his decorations in the Ducal Palace were destroyed by fire in 1576, and he was commissioned to paint a new series. From 1578 until his death he was occupied in decorating churches in the neighborhood of Venice. Together with Titian and Tintoretto he was the leading painter in Venice in the sixteenth century.

The Mystic Marriage of St. Catherine.

Belongs to the early period of the artist.

Canvas: 23 x 35¾ inches.

LENT BY MR. AND MRS. CHARLES V. HICKOX, NEW YORK.

COLLECTION: Prince Liechtenstein.

EXHIBITIONS: Chicago Art Institute, 1927 and 1933; Van Diemen Galleries, New York, 1931.
BIBLIOGRAPHY: J. FALKE: Katalog der Fürstlich Liechtensteinschen Bildgalerie, 1873, No.
610; G. FIOCCO: Paolo Veronese, 1928, pp. 23-24, *Illust.*; L. VENTURI: Ital. Paintings in America,
1933, No. 565, *Illust.*; D. C. RICH: Catalogue of Paintings and Sculpture, Art. Inst. of Chicago,
1933, No. 142.

PAOLO VERONESE

VENETIAN, 1528-1588

272 *Rest on the Flight into Egypt.*

Signed: Pauli Caliari Veronesi faciebat. Painted about 1570.

Canvas: 92¾ x 63¼ inches.

LENT BY THE JOHN AND MABEL RINGLING MUSEUM, SARASOTA.

COLLECTIONS: Electoral Gallery, Düsseldorf; Castle Schleissheim; Alte Pinakothek, Munich;
Julius Böhler.
EXHIBITIONS: Reinhardt Galleries, New York, 1928; Chicago Art Institute, 1933.
BIBLIOGRAPHY: G. KARSH: Designation des Peintures a Düsseldorf, 1719; J. VON GOOL: De
nieuwe Schönburg, s'Gravenhage, Vol. II, 1751, p. 5; N. DE PIGAGE: La Galerie Electorale de
Düsseldorf, 1778, No. 116, *Illust.*; ANON: Galerie Schleissheim, Katalog, 1905, No. 517; ANON:
Katalog der alten Pinakothek München, 1925, No. 921; A. VENTURI: Paolo Veronese, 1928, p. 16;
W. R. VALENTINER: Unknown Masterpieces (Note by Hadeln), 1930, No. 30, *Illust.*; B. BERENSON:
Italian Pictures, 1932, p. 425; D. C. RICH: Catalogue of Paintings and Sculpture, Art. Inst. of
Chicago, 1933, No. 143, *Illust.*

PAOLO VERONESE

VENETIAN, 1528-1588

273 *Christ and the Centurion.*

Painted about 1570-1580.

Canvas: 56 x 82 inches.

LENT BY THE KANSAS CITY ART MUSEUM.

COLLECTIONS: Arthur Sulley; William Rockhill Nelson.
EXHIBITION: Sulley Galleries, London, 1930.
BIBLIOGRAPHY: L. VENTURI: *In* L'Arte, May 1930, pp. 292-299, *Illust.*; B. BERENSON: Italian
Pictures, 1932, p. 422; L. VENTURI: Italian Paintings in America, 1933, No. 578, *Illust.*

PAOLO VERONESE

VENETIAN, 1528-1588

274 *Rebecca and Jacob at the Well.*

PL. 35   Canvas: 32 x 40 inches.

LENT ANONYMOUSLY.

COLLECTION: Earl of Lovelace.

PATER, JEAN-BAPTISTE JOSEPH

5 *Pastoral Pleasures.*

Born at Valenciennes. While still young he became a pupil of Watteau. In 1728 he was received into the Academy. His feverish industry, caused by an ever-haunting fear of poverty, led him to stint himself to provide for his latter days. His health gave way, and he died before he could enjoy the comfortable competency which he had laid up. Like Watteau and Fragonard, he was noted as a painter of *fêtes galantes.*

Canvas: 31½ x 38 inches.

LENT BY MRS. WILLIAM R. TIMKEN, NEW YORK.

COLLECTIONS: Comte Daupias; James Saloschin; Charles Sedelmeyer; Edward R. Bacon; Frank T. Sabin.

EXHIBITIONS: L'Art Français, Brussels, 1904; Sedelmeyer Gallery, Paris, 1905; Art Institute, Chicago, 1933.

BIBLIOGRAPHY: J. MALVAUX: Catalogue de l'Exposition de l'Art Français, Brussels, 1904, No. 54, *Illust.*, L. DUMONT-WILDEN: *In* Revue de l'Art, March 1904, p. 233, *Illust.*, C. SEDELMEYER: Paintings by Old Masters, 1904, p. 90, No. 71, *Illust.*; J. B. TOWNSEND and W. S. HOWARD: Memorial Catalogue, Edward R. Bacon Collection, New York, 1919, p. 82, No. 97, *Illust.*, F. INGERSOLL-SMOUSE: Pater, 1928, p. 41, No. 42; D. C. RICH: Exhibition of Paintings and Sculptures, Art Inst. of Chicago, 1933, p. 34, No. 224.

PATINIR, JOACHIM

Born at Dinant; became a member of the Guild at Antwerp, in 1515. His second marriage took place in 1521, and Albrecht Dürer was present and drew his portrait. He is considered the first master who painted landscape for its own sake, making it the motive of a picture.

Repose on the Flight into Egypt.

Panel: 17½ x 22¾ inches.

LENT BY THE JOHN G. JOHNSON COLLECTION, PHILADELPHIA.

EXHIBITIONS: Worcester Art Museum, 1939; Philadelphia Museum of Art, 1939.

BIBLIOGRAPHY: W. R. VALENTINER: Flemish and Dutch Paintings in the John G. Johnson Collection, Philadelphia, 1913, No. 377, *Illust.*; M. J. FRIEDLÄNDER: Joachim Patenier, 1931, p. 157, No. 234; H. MARCEAU, and others: The Worcester-Philadelphia Exhn. of Flemish Painting, 1939; p. 41, No. 61.

PERUGINO (PIETRO VANNUCCI)

Pietro Vannucci, called 'Il Perugino' from his long residence in Perugia, was born at Castello della Pieve. He was probably a pupil of Fiorenzo di Lorenzo, and developed under the influence of Melozzo da Forli and Verrocchio. In 1481 he was in

Rome with Signorelli, Cosimo Rosselli, D. Ghirlandajo, and Botticelli, at work on the decorations of the Sixtine Chapel. His most important frescoes are those in the Cambio at Perugia (1499) on which he was possibly assisted by Raphael, his celebrated pupil. In his art he is a master of well-balanced space composition, of an expression of a sweet religious sentiment, and of deep, glowing color schemes.

277 *Portrait of Pietro de' Medici.*

Pietro, born 1471, was the eldest son of Lorenzo de' Medici, called 'The Magnificent' (1449-1492), celebrated Florentine statesman. He succeeded his father as the governor of Florence but his rule lasted only two years, when he was deposed by the citizens for having yielded to the French under Charles VIII. He died from drowning in the Garigliano in 1503.

Panel: 15¾ x 11¾ inches.

LENT ANONYMOUSLY.

EXHIBITION: Detroit Institute of Arts, 1927.
BIBLIOGRAPHY: w. HEIL: Catalogue of Old Masters, Detroit Inst. of Arts, 1927, No. 16.

PERUGINO (PIETRO VANNUCCI)
UMBRIAN, 1445-1523

278 *Madonna and Child with Two Saints.*

Painted about 1490-95. According to R. van Marle, A. Morassi, A. Venturi, and W. Suida, the work may be compared with the similar composition in the Louvre, in which, however, St. Catherine occupies the place given to the young cleric.

Panel: 35 x 24 inches.

LENT ANONYMOUSLY.

PERUGINO (PIETRO VANNUCCI)
UMBRIAN, 1445-1523

279 *Madonna and Child.*

Pl. 20   Painted about 1495, during the master's second Florentine period.

Panel: 23¼ x 19¼ inches.

LENT BY MR. JOHN BASS, NEW YORK.

COLLECTIONS: Mauthner von Markhofschen; Joseph Engelhart.
BIBLIOGRAPHY: T. VON FRIMMEL: Lexikon der Wiener Gemäldesammlungen, Vol. I, 1913, p. 310, No. 57, *Illust.*, w. BOMBE: Perugino (Klas. der Kunst), 1914, p. 236, No. 35, *Illust.*, U. GNOLI: Pietro Perugino, 1923, p. 69; R. VAN MARLE: Italian Schools, Vol. XIV, 1933, p. 341.

PESELLINO, FRANCESCO
FLORENTINE, 1422-1457

Francesco Pesello, called Pesellino, was born in Florence, the grandson of Giuliano d'Arrigo Giuochi. He was a close follower of Fra Filippo Lippi, and influenced by Fra Angelico, Masaccio, and Domenico Veneziano. He is noted chiefly for his small panels of religious subjects, and as a decorator of cassoni; he was a refined colorist and one of the most delicate and charming of Florentine painters.

The Madonna and Child, with Infant Baptist and Angels.

The composition, influenced by Fra Filippo Lippi, has been imitated greatly by contemporary Florentine masters.

Panel: 28½ x 22 inches.

LENT BY MR. AND MRS. HAROLD I. PRATT, NEW YORK.

COLLECTIONS: William Graham; Oscar Hainauer; Lord Duveen of Millbank; Robert Hoe; Theron J. Blakeslee.

EXHIBITIONS: Kaiser Friedrich Museum, Berlin, 1898; Duveen Galleries, New York, 1924; Fogg Art Museum, Cambridge, 1927.

BIBLIOGRAPHY: W. VON BODE: Die Sammlung Oscar Hainauer, 1897, pp. 14-15, 67; H. MACKOWSKY: Die Florentiner. In Werk über die Renaissance-Austellung, Berlin, 1898, p. 36, Illust., M. LOGAN (Mrs. B. Berenson); In Gaz. des B.-Arts, July 1901, p. 34; W. WEISBACH: Francesco Pesellino, 1901, p. 114; F. J. MATHER: In Burl. Mag., Aug. 1910, p. 315; A. F. JACCACI: Catalogue of the Robert Hoe Collection, 1911, No. 97, Illust., E. W. FORBES: Mediaeval and Renaissance Paintings, Fogg Art. Mus., 1919, p. 71; W. R. VALENTINER: Early Ital. Paintings, Duveen Galleries, New York, 1926, No. 10, Illust., P. H. HENDY: Pesellino. In Burl. Mag., Aug. 1928, pp. 68-73, Illust., R. VAN MARLE: Italian Schools, Vol. XIII, 1931, p. 447; B. BERENSON: Ital. Pictures, 1932, p. 443, (Ital. Edn., 1936, p. 381); IDEM: Quadri senza casa. In Dedalo, Sept. 1932, p. 671, Illust., L. VENTURI: Ital. Paintings in America, Vol. II, 1933, No. 227, Illust.

PIAZZETTA, GIOVANNI BATTISTA

VENETIAN, 1682-1754

Born in Venice. He worked as apprentice to his father, and later with Antonio Molinari. He studied with Giovanni Maria Crespi in Bologna from 1703 until 1711, when he returned to Venice, where he spent the rest of his life painting monumental altarpieces and genre scenes. In the strong contrast of light and shadows he shows the influence of the Caravaggio school, combining it with a Correggiesque *sfumato* which he learned from Crespi. His greatest follower was Giovanni Battista Tiepolo.

The Sleeping Shepherdess.

Canvas: 31¼ x 24 inches.

LENT BY MR. SAMUEL H. KRESS, NEW YORK.

COLLECTION: Contessa Giustiniani, Genoa.

EXHIBITIONS: Petit Palais, Paris, 1935; City Art Museum, St. Louis, 1936; Knoedler Galleries, New York, 1936.

BIBLIOGRAPHY: A. M. FRANKFURTER: In Fine Arts, Dec. 1932, pp. 7-10, Illust., S. DE RICCI: Exposition de l'Art Italien, Petit Palais, Paris, 1935, p. 361, No. 362; M. R. ROGERS: In Art News,

Feb. 1936, p. 7, *Illust.*, IDEM: *In* St. Louis Museum Bulletin, Mar. 1936, p. 30, No. 31, *Illust.*, ANON: Venetian Painting of the XVIII c., Knoedler Galleries, New York, 1936, No. 20.

PIERO DELLA FRANCESCA

UMBRO - FLORENTINE, 1416? - 1492

Born at Borgo San Sepolcro. He was a pupil of Domenico Veneziano, at Perugia and Florence, and influenced by Paolo Uccello. His earliest known work dates from 1445 when he was working in his native town. Between 1447 and 1451 he was in Rome. In 1451 he painted in fresco in the chapel in San Francisco at Rimini the portrait of Sigismondo Malatesta and his patron saint. Between 1454 and 1464 he executed his most extensive extant frescoes in the choir of San Francesco at Arezzo, and about 1465 he worked for Federigo, the Duke of Urbino. For his originality and invention as a colorist and painter of light and atmosphere Piero ranks with the greatest Italian masters of the early Renaissance.

282 *St. Apollonia of Alexandria.*

A late work of the master, probably contemporary with the Urbino 'Madonna'. One of the panels of a polyptych, two others of which are in the Liechtenstein Gallery, Vienna.

Panel: 16¼ x 11 inches.

LENT BY MR. ROBERT LEHMAN, NEW YORK.

COLLECTIONS: Giuseppe Marini-Francheschi, Borgo San Sepolcro, descendant of the artist; Philip Lehman.
BIBLIOGRAPHY: G. VASARI: (1511-1574) Le Vite de' piu eccellenti pittori (*Edn.* H. Lemonnier, Vol. IV, 1848, pp. 13-14; *Edn.* G. Milanesi, Vol. II, 1878, p. 488); G. MANCINI: *In* Giornale Arcadico di Roma, 1826; IDEM: Istruzione storico-pittorica di Città di Castello, 1832, Appendice, p. 340; CROWE AND CAVALCASELLE: Hist. of Painting, Vol. V, 1914, p. 26; A. VENTURI: *In* L'Arte, Vol. XXIV, 1921, pp. 152-154; IDEM: Piero della Francesca, 1922, No. 60-61, *Illust.*, R. LEHMAN: The Philip Lehman Colln., 1928, No. 68, *Illust.*, B. BERENSON: Ital. Pictures, 1932, p. 455 (Ital. Edn., 1936, p. 391); L. VENTURI: Ital. Paintings in Amer., 1933, No. 204, *Illust.*

PIERO DI COSIMO

FLORENTINE, 1462 - 1521

Pupil of Cosimo Rosselli, influenced by Leonardo. In 1480 he went with Rosselli to Rome to decorate Sixtine Chapel in the Vatican. He afterwards returned to Florence, where his most noted works were executed. He was considerably impressed by the Portinari altarpiece by Hugo Van der Goes, which was set up in Florence in 1482. In his art he is inclined to be fantastic and original. In his tendency towards strange and sombre color combinations he had a considerable influence on the following generation of artists in Florence.

3 *The Finding of Vulcan.*

Painted about 1485-1490. For several years known and catalogued as "Hylas and the Nymphs."

Canvas: 61¼ x 68½ inches.

LENT BY THE WADSWORTH ATHENEUM, HARTFORD, CONN.

COLLECTIONS: William Graham, London; Robert H. and Evelyn Benson; Lord Duveen of Millbank.

EXHIBITIONS: Burlington Fine Arts Club, London, 1893; New Gallery, London, 1893-94; Grafton Galleries, London, 1911; Manchester Art Gallery, 1927; Knoedler Galleries, New York, 1929; Royal Academy, London, 1930; Schaeffer Galleries, New York, 1938.

BIBLIOGRAPHY: c. f. foulkes: *In* Archivio storico dell'Arte, Vol. VII, 1894, p. 168; h. ulmann: *In* Berlin Jahrbuch, Vol. XVII, 1896, pp. 120 *et seq., Illust.,* f. knapp: Piero di Cosimo, 1899, pp. 32 *et seq., Illust.,* h. p. horne: *In* Architectural Review, Vol. XII, 1902, p. 61, *Illust.,* s. reinach: Repértoire, Vol. I, 1905, p. 637, *Illust.,* sir l. cust: *In* Les Arts, Oct. 1907, p. 26; r. fry and m. w. brockwell: Old Masters, Grafton Gall., London, 1911, p. 25, No. 23, *Illust.,* a. venturi: Storia dell'Arte Ital., Vol. VII, I, 1911, p. 712; b. berenson: Flor. Painters, 1912, p. 164; t. borenius: Catalogue of the Benson Colln., 1914, pp. 55-56, No. 29, *Illust.,* p. schubring: Cassoni, 1923, No. 411; f. rutter: *In* International Studio, Dec. 1929, p. 82, *Illust.,* balniel and clark: Exhn. of Ital. Art, Royal Academy, London, 1930, p. 101, No. 294; anon: *In* Art Digest, Feb. 15, 1932, p. 8, *Illust.,* l. venturi: Ital. Paintings in Amer., 1933, No. 285, *Illust.,* b. berenson: Pitture Italiane, 1936, p. 390; I Pittori Ital., 1936, p. 113, *Illust.,* c. gamba: *In* Bolletino d'Arte, Aug. 1936, p. 54, *Illust.,* e. panofsky: *In* Jour. of the Warburg Inst., July 1937, p. 12, *Illust.,* a. m. frankfurter: Piero di Cosimo Exhn., Schaeffer Galleries, N. Y., 1938, No. 3, *Illust.,* h. devree: *In* Amer. Mag. of Art, Dec. 1938, p. 686, *Illust.,* j. w. lane: *In* Apollo, Jan. 1939, p. 34, *Illust.*

PIERO DI COSIMO

FLORENTINE, 1462-1521

4 *The Visitation of the Virgin.*

27 Painted about 1487 for the Chapel of Gino Capponi in the Church of San Spirito, Florence. The original pen-sketch for the two principal figures in this picture is in the Uffizi, Florence.

Panel: 71 x 73 inches.

LENT BY MR. SAMUEL H. KRESS, NEW YORK.

COLLECTIONS: Marchese Gaetano Capponi; Colonel W. Cornwallis-West; Lord Duveen of Millbank.

EXHIBITIONS: Royal Academy, London, 1891; Detroit Institute of Arts, 1933.

BIBLIOGRAPHY: anon: Catalogue of Old Masters, Royal Academy, London, 1891, No. 154; f. knapp: Piero di Cosimo, 1899, pp. 35-39, *Illust.,* h. haberfeld: Piero di Cosimo, 1900, pp. 54-57; b. berenson: Flor. Painters of the Renais, 1909, p. 165; idem: Drawings of the Flor. Painters, Vol. I, p. 131; Vol. II, p. 130, No. 1853 (1938 Edn. Vol. I, p. 153; Vol. II, p. 257, No. 1853, Fig. 431); a. venturi: Storia dell'Arte Ital., Vol. VII, 1, 1911, p. 706; g. vasari: Lives of the Most Eminent Painters, Vol. IV, p. 126, 1914 Edition; crowe and cavalcaselle: Hist. of Painting in Italy, Vol. VI, London, 1914, p. 48; t. borenius: "The Salutation" by Piero di Cosimo (A. Monograph), 1919, pp. 8-10; R. VAN MARLE: Italian Schools, Vol. XIII, 1931, p. 350; W. R. VALENTINER: Ital. Paintings from the XIV to the XVI Century, Detroit Inst., 1933, No. 40, *Illust.*; L. VENTURI: Ital. Paintings in America, Vol. II, 1933, No. 287, *Illust.*, B. DEGEN-HART: *In* Thieme-Becker's Lexikon, Vol. XXVII, 1933, p. 15.

PIERO DI COSIMO

FLORENTINE, 1462-1521

285 St. John the Evangelist.

Painted about 1505; considered to be a pendant to the *St. Mary Magdalen* in the Palazzo Corsini, Rome, formerly in the Baracco collection.

Panel: 33 x 23½ inches.

LENT BY MR. AND MRS. HAROLD I. PRATT, NEW YORK.

COLLECTIONS: Joseph Augustin Brentano; Charles Sedelmeyer; T. Humphry Ward; Klein-berger Galleries.

EXHIBITIONS: Sedelmeyer Gallery, Paris, 1913; Kleinberger Galleries, New York, 1917; Schaeffer Galleries, New York, 1938.

BIBLIOGRAPHY: ANON: Cabinet de Tableaux de Joseph Augustin Brentano, Amsterdam, 1822, p. 110, No. 361; F. KNAPP: Piero di Cosimo, pp. 59-60, *Illust. Corsini picture*, C. SEDEL-MEYER: Paintings by Old Masters, 1913, p. 58, No. 36, *Illust.*, O. SIREN and M. W. BROCKWELL: Exhibition of Italian Primitifs, Kleinberger Gal., New York, 1917, p. 94, No. 34, *Illust.*, L. VENTURI: Ital. Paintings in America, 1933, No. 289, *Illust.*, B. BERENSON: Ital. Pictures, 1932, p. 454, (Ital. Edn., 1936, p. 390), A. M. FRANKFURTER: Piero di Cosimo, Schaeffer Galleries, New York, 1939, No. 2, *Illust.*

PIERO DI COSIMO

FLORENTINE, 1462-1521

286 Portrait of a Lady.

Attributed to Mainardi (Borenius), and Davide Ghirlandajo (Francovich and Van Marle); to Piero di Cosimo by L. Venturi.

Panel: 27 x 18½ inches.

LENT BY MRS. CHARLES PAYSON, NEW YORK.

COLLECTIONS: Friedrich William IV, King of Prussia; Count Ingenheim, Silesia; A. S. Drey; Colnaghi Galleries, London; Knoedler Galleries, New York.

EXHIBITIONS: Toronto Art Gallery, Canada, 1929; Knoedler Galleries, New York, 1929.

BIBLIOGRAPHY: T. BORENIUS: *In* Apollo, Jan. 1927, *Illust. in color*, ANON: *In* Pantheon, April 1929, p. 191, *Illust.*, F. E. W. FREUND: *In* Cicerone, Vol. XXI, 1929, p. 193, *Illust.*, G. DE FRANCO-VICH: *In* Dedalo, Aug. 1930, p. 144, *Illust.*, R. VAN MARLE: Ital. Schools, 1931, p. 156, *Illust.*, A. M. FRANKFURTER: *In* Art News, May 16, 1931, p. 3, *Illust.*, L. VENTURI: Ital. Paintings in Amer., 1933, No. 286, *Illust.*

PONTORMO, JACOPO CARRUCCI

FLORENTINE, 1494-1556

Jacopo Carucci da Pontormo, so-called from his birthplace near Empoli, was a pupil to Andrea del Sarto in 1512, and greatly influenced by Michelangelo. His most important frescoes are those in Poggio a Cajano, in the Certosa di Galluzzo, and formerly in San Lorenzo, for which many drawings are still extant. He also painted portraits for the Medici family. He was the master of Angelo Bronzino, who assisted him in many of his works.

The Halberdier.

Painted about 1530. Two drawings by Pontormo for this portrait are in the Louvre (No. 958) and the Uffizi (No. 463F) respectively. Not to be confused with the portrait of "Francesco Guardi", painted during the Siege of Florence, 1529-30 (*vide* Vasari, p. 275), which is still missing, and believed to be of smaller dimensions.

Canvas: 37½ x 29 inches.

LENT BY MR. CHAUNCEY DEVEREUX STILLMAN, NEW YORK.

COLLECTIONS: Cardinal Fesch; Leroy d'Étiolles; Princess Mathilde Bonaparte; James Stillman; C. C. Stillman.

EXHIBITIONS: Metropolitan Museum of Art, New York, 1921-1927; Fogg Art Museum, Cambridge, Mass., 1927; Chicago Art Institute, 1933; Wadsworth Atheneum, Hartford, 1937.

BIBLIOGRAPHY: G. VASARI: Le Vite de' Pittori (1568) Edn. G. Milanesi, Vol. II, 1881, p. 275; L. H. GEORGE: Galerie de S. E. le Cardinal Fesch, 1844, No. 682; F. MASSON: Catalogue des Tableaux, Colln. Princesse Mathilde, 1904, No. 53, *Illust.,* H. VOSS: Die Malerei der Spätrenaissance, Vol. I, 1920, pp. 174-177, *Illust.,* C. GAMBA: Pontormo, 1921, pp. 11-16, No. 31, *Illust.,* F. J. MATHER: *In* Art in America, Feb. 1922; p. 66, *Illust.,* F. J. MATHER: Hist. of Ital. Painting, 1923, pp. 252-253, *Illust.,* F. CLAPP: *In* Art Studies, Vol. I, 1923, pp. 65-66, *Illust. with the two drawings,* O. GIGLIOLI: *In* Dedalo, Vol. XVII, 1927, pp. 789-791; B. BERENSON: Ital. Pictures, 1932, p. 466, (Ital. Edn., 1936, p. 402, *Illust.*); L. VENTURI: Ital. Paintings in Amer., 1933, No. 458, *Illust.,* A. VENTURI: Storia dell'Arte, Vol. IX, 1932, pp. 172-173, *Illust.,* D. C. RICH: Exhibition of Paintings, etc., Art Inst. of Chicago, 1933, p. 21, No. 131, *Illust.,* A. SUTTON: *In* Amer. Mag. of Art, Sept. 1934, p. 459, *Illust.,* H. TIETZE: Meisterw. Europä. in Amer., 1935, No. 110, *Illust.,* A. E. AUSTIN, JNR.: Forty-three Portraits, Wadsworth Atheneum, Hartf., 1937, No. 11, *Illust.,* IDEM: *In* Art News, Jan. 30, 1937, p. 14, *Illust.,* B. BERENSON: Drawings of the Flor. Masters, Vol. I, 1938, p. 318.

POUSSIN, NICOLAS

FRENCH, 1594-1665

Born at Villiers in Normandy, and studied under Varin at Les Andelys. He visited Rome in 1624, and painted several pictures for Cardinal Barberini. He returned to France in 1640 and was appointed, through Cardinal Richelieu, painter in ordinary to Louis XIII; he, however, left again for Rome in 1642, and remained there until his death. Leading master of the classical trend in France during the seventeenth century.

288 The Funeral of Phocion.

Pl. 79 Painted in Rome in 1648. Phocion (402-317 B.C.) was a celebrated Athenian statesman, and commanded the Athenian fleet against the Spartans off Naxos in 376, and again in 339 against Philip of Macedon at Byzantium. He was a leader of the aristocratic party, and was put to death by the democrats on a false charge of treason. See Fénélon's *Dialogues des Morts* (1730) in which Poussin explains to Parrhasius, Greek painter of the IVc. B.C., the composition and story of the present picture.

Canvas: 47 x 71 inches.

LENT BY THE MUSÉE DU LOUVRE, PARIS.

COLLECTIONS: Le Sieur Cérisier, Paris, for whom it was painted; a collection in Guernsey; Société des Amis du Louvre.

ENGRAVED by E. Baudet, 1684.

BIBLIOGRAPHY: A. FELIBIEN: Entrétiens, Edn. de Trévoux, Vol. IV, 1725, pp. 59 and 148; F. DE FÉNELON: Dialogues des Morts, 1730 edn.; J. SMITH: Catalogue raisonné, Vol. VIII, 1837, No. 300; L. LALANNE, Édr.: Chantelou's Journal du Bernin (1665), Jn Gaz. des Beaux-Arts, Apr. 1878, p. 354; E. BONAFFE: Dict. des Amateurs, 1885, p. 5; E. MAGNE: Nicolas Poussin, 1914, p. 155; P. JAMOT: Jn Gaz. des Beaux-Arts, Dec. 1921, pp. 321-330, Jllust., IDEM: Jn Burl. Mag., Apr. 1922, pp. 158-163, Jllust.; R. H. WILENSKI: French Painting, 1931, pp. 73, 220, 316, Jllust.; E. K. WATERHOUSE: Jn Burl. Mag., March 1939, p. 103.

PREDIS, AMBROGIO DE'

MILANESE, ACTIVE 1472-1506

Morelli considers that he was born between 1450 and 1460, and supposes that he may have been a pupil of Cristoforo de Predis, a noted miniature painter. Formed under the influence of Zenale and Britinone; later one of the followers of Vincenzo Foppa prior to Leonardo's arrival in Milan about 1482, afterwards becoming an assistant and close follower of the latter. He was apparently the favorite portrait painter of Lodovico Sforza (il Moro), whom he accompanied to Innsbruck in 1499. In 1506 he designed some tapestries for the Emperor Maximilian, and after that year nothing more is known of him.

289 Portrait of Gian Galeazzo Sforza (Presumed).

Pl. 52 Painted about 1489. Gian Galeazzo Sforza, Count of Pavia, was born in 1468, and succeeded his father in 1476, his mother acting as regent. He married Isabel of Aragon in 1489. The power and government of Milan were usurped about 1480 by his uncle Lodovico. He died in 1494.

Panel: 21⅜ x 15¼ inches.

LENT ANONYMOUSLY.

COLLECTIONS: Count Porro di Santa Maria de Bicocca; Count Carlo Porro, Milan.

EXHIBITIONS: Circolo d'Arte, Milan, 1923; Royal Academy, London, 1930.

BIBLIOGRAPHY: H. COOK: Milanese Exhibition, Burlington F. A. Club, 1898, p. XLIX;

G. MORELLI: Italian Painters, Vol. I, 1900, p. 186; F. M. VALERI: La Corte di Lodovico il Moro, Vol. III, 1917, p. 13, *Illust.*, P. D'ANCONA: *In* Dedalo, Nov. 1923, p. 368, *Illust.*, ANON: Catalogo Anticha Pittura Lombarda, Milan, 1923; M. SALMI: *In* L'Arte, Vol. XXVI, 1923, p. 156, *Illust.*, S. SUIDA: Leonardo und sein Kreis, 1929, p. 171, *Illust.*, BALNIEL AND CLARK: Exhibition of Ital. Art, Royal Academy, London, 1930, p. 94, No. 271; B. BERENSON: Ital. Pictures, 1932, p. 472 (Ital. Edn., 1936, p. 405); W. SUIDA: *In* Thieme-Becker's Lexikon, 1933, Vol. XXVII, p. 369.

PREDIS, AMBROGIO DE' (Attributed)

MILANESE, 1472-1506

A Youth holding an Arrow.

Painted during the earlier period of the artist, about 1490-1495, under the direct influence of Leonardo da Vinci. Quite near in color and in type to a group of pictures given to Ambrogio such as the so-called 'Archinto' portrait dated 1494, in the National Gallery, London, the 'Girl with the Cherries' in the Metropolitan Museum, etc.

Canvas: (transferred): 13 x 10½ inches.

LENT BY MRS. STANLEY MORTIMER, NEW YORK.

RAEBURN, R.A., SIR HENRY

SCOTTISH, 1756-1823

Born at Stockbridge, near Edinburgh. In 1778 he went to London, where he made the acquaintance of Sir Joshua Reynolds. In 1785 he went to Italy, and after two years returned to Edinburgh. In 1812 he was elected President of the Royal Society of Artists, and in 1815 a Royal Academician. In 1822 he was knighted by George IV when on a visit to Scotland. The greatest painter in Scotland in the eighteenth century.

The Drummond Children.

Painted about 1808. George Drummond, his sister Margaret, and their foster-brother. George and Margaret were the children of George Harley Drummond, and his wife Margaret, of Stanmore and Drumtochty, of the house of Strathallan. George, the boy on the pony, was born in 1802, became a banker of Charing Cross, London, and married in 1831 Maryanne (d. 1842), sister of the 1st Viscount Portman. He died in 1851, leaving one son and four daughters. The Drummond family has given three queens to Scotland—Margaret, wife of David II (d. 1370); Anabella, wife of Robert III (d. 1402), and Margaret, wife of James IV (d. 1501). Queen Anabella is ancestress of all succeeding sovereigns of Scotland, Great Britain, and the United Kingdom.

Canvas: 94¼ x 60¼ inches.

LENT BY MR. EDWARD S. HARKNESS, NEW YORK.

RAEBURN, R.A., SIR HENRY

SCOTTISH, 1756-1823

292 *Master William Blair.*

Painted about 1810. William Blair, born in 1799 at Avontoun, Linlithgow, was the fourth and only surviving son of the Rt. Hon. Robert Blair (1741-1811), Lord-Pres. of the Court of Session in Scotland, and Solicitor-General under Pitt, by Isabella Craigie Halhett (d. 1858) of Lawhill, Fifeshire. He married, 1826, Jane Nourse of Cape Town (1808-1872) and was afterwards Chief-Justice in Corfu. He died in 1873. A replica of this portrait is in the Henry E. Huntington Art Gallery, San Marino, California.

Canvas: 30 x 25 inches.

LENT BY MR. AND MRS. CHARLES FINN WILLIAMS, CINCINNATI.

RAEBURN, R.A., SIR HENRY

SCOTTISH, 1756-1823

293 *The Hon. Mrs. Grant of Kilgraston.*

Painted about 1820. The Hon. Margaret Gray, born 1795, was the second daughter and third child of Francis, fourteenth Lord Gray (1765-1842) in the peerage of Scotland, and his wife Anne (d. 1858), daughter of Col. James Johnston. She married, in 1820, John Grant of Kilgraston and Pitcaithly, Perthshire, and died at the age of 27 years on April 24, 1822, leaving an only child, Margaret (1822-1878), who succeeded her aunt Madalina, Baroness Gray (d. 1869), and became the wife in 1840 of the Hon. David Henry Murray (d. 1862), third son of the third Earl of Mansfield.

Canvas: 30 x 25 inches.

LENT BY MR. AND MRS. CHARLES T. FISHER, DETROIT.

COLLECTIONS: John Grant of Kilgraston; The Hon. Morton Stuart Gray; Col. Walter Brown of Renfrew; Lord Duveen of Millbank.
EXHIBITIONS: Brighton Art Gallery, 1902; Agnew Galleries, London, 1905; French Gallery, Edinburgh, 1909; French Gallery, London, 1911; Detroit Institute of Arts, 1936.
BIBLIOGRAPHY: SIR WALTER ARMSTRONG: Sir Henry Raeburn, 1901, p. 103; J. GREIG: Sir Henry Raeburn, R.A., 1911, p. 47; D. C. THOMSON: Pictures by Raeburn at the French Gallery, London, 1911, No. 9, *Illust.*, W. R. VALENTINER: British Paintings, Detroit Inst., 1926, No. 26; E. SINGLE-TON: Old World Masters, 1929, p. 413, *Illust.*

RAPHAEL (RAFFAELLO SANZIO)
UMBRIAN, 1483-1520

Born at Urbino, first a pupil of Giovanni Santi, his father, afterwards of Perugino; was influenced by Timoteo Viti and Pintoricchio, and later by Leonardo and Michelangelo. In 1504 he went to Florence, and in 1508 he was called to Rome by Pope Julius II, and painted the "Stanze" in the Vatican. In 1514 he accepted the office of architect of St. Peter's. From his art, next to Michelangelo's, the style of the High Renaissance in Florentine and Roman painting developed, which intro-duced a greater simplicity and force into the representation of the human form, while the compositions became more monumental and spacious.

Giuliano de' Medici, Duke of Nemours.

26 Signed: R.S.M. . . . V (i.e. *Raffaello Santi*, 1514-or 1515). Giuliano II, born in 1479, was the third son of Lorenzo the Magnificent, and brother of Pope Leo X. When he was fifteen his parents were exiled from Florence, and he took refuge with the Duke of Urbino; in 1513, Leo X made him "Gonfalonier of the Papal forces," which necessitated his residence in Rome. In 1515, he was sent to France, and while there married Philiberte of Savoy, aunt of Francis I. The French King at the same time created him Duc de Nemours. He returned to Rome shortly after, and died in 1516.

Canvas: 32¾ x 26 inches.

LENT BY THE JULES S. BACHE COLLECTION, NEW YORK.

COLLECTIONS: Ottaviano de Medici; Baldovinetti Family; Professor Brini; Grand Duchess Marie of Russia; Prince Sciarra-Colonna; Oskar Huldschinsky; Lord Duveen of Millbank.
EXHIBITIONS: Kaiser Friedrich Museum, Berlin, 1909; "Daily Telegraph" Exhibition, Lon-don, 1928.
BIBLIOGRAPHY: G. VASARI: Lives of the Painters, Trans. by G. de Vere, Vol. IV, 1912, p. 232; G. G. BOTTARI: Raccolta di Lettere, Vol. V, 1766, p. 134; C. E. DE LIPHART: Un tableau de Raphael représentant Julien de Médicis, 1867; CROWE AND CAVALCASELLE: Raphael, Vol. II, 1885, pp. 320-323; O. FISCHEL: *In* Berlin Jahrbuch, 1907, p. 127, *Illust.*, W. VON BODE: Die Sammlung Oskar Huld-schinsky, 1909, pp. 6-8, 39, No. 41, *Illust.*, A. ROSENBERG: Raffael, 1909, p. 239, *Illust.*, G. F. YOUNG: The Medici, Vol. I, 1911, pp. 394-395, *Frontispiece;* B. BERENSON: Italian Pictures, 1932, p. 481, (Ital. Edn., 1936, p. 414, *Illust.*); L. VENTURI: Italian Paintings in America, Vol. III, 1933, No. 446, *Illust.*, O. FISCHEL: *In* Thieme-Becker's Lexikon, Vol. XXIX, 1935, p. 423; ANON: Cata-logue of the Bache Collection, New York, 1938, No. 13, *Illust.*

REMBRANDT HARMENSZ VAN RIJN
DUTCH, 1606-1669

Born at Leyden. He studied first at the Latin School, and later became a pupil of Jacob van Swanenburch at Leyden and of Pieter Lastman at Amsterdam. In 1630 he settled at Amsterdam, where he remained until his death. He married there, in 1634, Saskia van Uijlenburgh, who died in 1642. Rembrandt's fame quickly rose to its highest point. Notwithstanding the large income which must have accrued to him, Rembrandt incurred considerable debts, as he was very fond of collecting works of art of all periods, for which he sometimes paid extravagant prices. His difficulties continued to increase, and in 1656 he was publicly declared insolvent. After this time he lived with Hendrickje Stoffels and Titus, the son of Saskia, who died before the father. There exist about 700 paintings, 200 etchings, and nearly 2000 drawings by the artist, who was great in his art from the beginning, and is especially appreciated in our own times in the works of his late period from about 1650 to 1669.

295 The Rape of Europa.
Signed and dated, Rembrandt f. 1632.

Panel: 24 x 30½ inches.

LENT BY MR. AND MRS. PAUL KLOTZ, PONTRESINA, SWITZERLAND.

COLLECTIONS: Comtesse de Verrue, 1737; Duc de Morny, 1865; Princesse de Broglie, née Say; Thomas Agnew; Leopold Koppel.

EXHIBITION: Kaiser Friedrich Museum, Berlin (on loan).

BIBLIOGRAPHY: J. SMITH: Catalogue Raisonné, Vol. VII, 1836, p. 78, No. 188; P. LACROIX: In Annales des Artistes, 1862; ANON: Catalogue des Tableaux, Colln. Duc de Morny, 1865, p. 44, No. 70; E. DUTUIT: Rembrandt, 1885, p. 20; E. MICHEL: Rembrandt, Vol. I, 1895, p. 107; W. VON BODE: Complete Work of Rembrandt, Vol. I, 1897, No. 71, Illust., C. HOFSTEDE DE GROOT: Catalogue Raisonné, Vol. VI, 1916, p. 135, No. 201; S. MELDRUM: Rembrandt's Paintings, 1923, p. 187, No. 60, Illust., A. BREDIUS: Rembrandt, 1935, p. 19, No. 464, Illust.

REMBRANDT HARMENSZ VAN RIJN
DUTCH, 1606-1669

296 Portrait of Maarten Looten.
Inscribed on the letter in the sitter's hand: Marten Looten, XI. January, 1632, followed by four lines of writing.

Panel: 36⅝ x 30 inches.

LENT BY MR. J. PAUL GETTY, NEW YORK.

COLLECTIONS: Cardinal Fesch, Rome, 1845; William Conyngham, 1849; Sir George Lindsay Holford; Anton W. M. Mensing.

EXHIBITIONS: British Institution, London, 1851 and 1862; Royal Academy, London, 1887, 1899, and 1929; Rijksmuseum, Amsterdam, 1898; Museum Boymans, Rotterdam, 1938.

BIBLIOGRAPHY: L. H. GEORGE: Galerie de feu S. E. le Cardinal Fesch, 1844, pp. 208-210, No. 190; G. F. WAAGEN: Treasures of Art, Vol. II, 1854, p. 200; C. VOSMAER: Rembrandt, 1877, p. 114,

No. 495; E. DUTUIT: Rembrandt, 1885, p. 25, No. 220; A. VON WURZBACH: Rembrandt, 1886, p. 62, No. 198; E. MICHEL: Rembrandt, Vol. I, 1895, p. 117; W. VON BODE: Complete Work of Rembrandt, Vol. II, 1897, p. 24, No. 72, *Illust.*, C. HOFSTEDE DE GROOT: Rembrandt Exhibition, Amsterdam, 1898, Folio, *Illust.*, W. R. VALENTINER: Rembrandt (Kl. der Kunst), 1909, p. 77, *Illust.*, C. HOFSTEDE DE GROOT: Catalogue Raisonné, Vol. VI, 1916, p. 314, No. 659; D. S. MELDRUM: Rembrandt's Paintings, 1923, p. 188, No. 69, *Illust.*, A. BREDIUS: Rembrandt, 1935, p. 8, No. 166, *Illust.*

REMBRANDT HARMENSZ VAN RIJN
DUTCH, 1606-1669

7 Portrait of Petronella Buys.

Signed: *Rembrandt f. 1635*. Wife of Philips Lucasz (1600?-1641), Director-General of the Dutch East Indies; he left Batavia for Holland in 1633, and returned in 1635, the year of his marriage at Vlissingen, Holland. She was born about 1605, and died in 1670. This picture is a pendant to 'A Man's Portrait', No. 850, in the National Gallery, London, unofficially recorded as the portrait of Philips Lucasz. The name of the sitter is inscribed on the back of the panel.

Panel, oval: 30 x 23 inches.

LENT ANONYMOUSLY.

COLLECTIONS: Cornelis Sebille Roos, Amsterdam, 1820; H. Engelberts; C. E. Vaillant; J. Sargenton, 1830; Adrian Hope; Charles Sedelmeyer; Joseph Jefferson, New York; Knoedler Galleries, New York; A. Preyer; Francis Kleinberger, Paris; August de Ridder, Cronberg; M. Van Gelder, Brussels; D. Katz, Dieren.

EXHIBITIONS: Leyden, 1906; Amsterdam, 1938; Schaeffer Galleries, New York, 1939.

BIBLIOGRAPHY: J. SMITH: Catalogue Raisonné, Vol. VII, 1836, p. 160, No. 497; E. DUTUIT: Rembrandt, 1885, p. 62, No, 272; A. VON WURZBACH: Rembrandt, 1886, p. 62, No. 200; E. MICHEL: Rembrandt, Vol. II, 1895, p. 236; W. VON BODE: Complete Work of Rembrandt, Vol. II, 1897, No. 118, *Illust.*, C. SEDELMEYER: Catalogue of Three Hundred Paintings, 1898, No. 126, *Illust.*, C. HOFSTEDE DE GROOT: *In* Oud Holland, Vol. XXXI, 1913, p. 236; IDEM: Catalogue Raisonné, Vol. VI, 1916, p. 315, No. 661.

REMBRANDT HARMENSZ VAN RIJN
DUTCH, 1606-1669

8 Saskia van Uijlenburgh, Wife of Rembrandt.

Signed: *Rembrandt f. 1636*. The artist married in June 1634; Saskia died in 1642.

Canvas: 31 x 26 inches.

LENT BY MR. H. F. TEN CATE, ALMELO, HOLLAND.

COLLECTIONS: J. Carpenter Garnier; Sir J. Charles Robinson, C.B.; Charles Sedelmeyer; A. M. Byers.

EXHIBITIONS: Amsterdam, 1878; Sedelmeyer Gallery, Paris, 1899; Carnegie Institute, Chicago, 1925.

BIBLIOGRAPHY: C. SEDELMEYER: Paintings by Old Masters, 1899, No. 39, *Illust.*, W. VON BODE: Rembrandt, Vol. III, 1899, p. 58, No. 156, *Illust.*, W. R. VALENTINER: Rembrandt (*Kl. der Kunst*), 1909, No. 132, *Illust.*, A. W. MOES: Iconographia Batavia, No. 8168, p. 15; C. HOFSTEDE

146

DE GROOT: Catalogue Raisonné, Vol. VI, 1916, p. 296, No. 614; D. S. MELDRUM: Rembrandt's Paintings, 1923, p. 192, *Illust.*; H. SAINT-GAUDENS: Paintings by Old Masters from a Pittsburgh Collection, 1925, No. 59; A. BREDIUS: Rembrandt Gemälde, 1935, No. 106, *Illust.*

REMBRANDT HARMENSZ VAN RIJN
DUTCH, 1606-1669

299 An Elderly Man with a Ruff, known also as 'The Burgomaster'.

Signed: *Rembrandt f.* Painted about 1635.

Panel: 34⅜ x 28¾ inches.

LENT BY MR. AND MRS. MICHAEL VAN BEUREN, NEWPORT, R. I.

COLLECTIONS: John Barnard, 1761; Lord Scarsdale of Kedleston, 1836; Marquess Curzon of Kedleston; Viscount Scarsdale of Kedleston.

ENGRAVED by R. Houston, 1757, and C. Phillips.

EXHIBITIONS: Art Treasures, Manchester, 1857; Leeds, 1866; Royal Academy, London, 1899; Van Wisselingh Gallery, Amsterdam, 1932; Knoedler Galleries, New York, 1933.

BIBLIOGRAPHY: R. AND J. DODSLEY: London and its Environs, 1761, p. 286; J. SMITH: Catalogue Raisonné, Vol. VII, 1836, No. 352; G. SCHARF: Art Treasures of the United Kingdom, Manchester, 1857, p. 53, No. 684; ANON: Catalogue of the National Exhibition, Leeds, 1866, No. 802; W. VON BODE: Studien Geschichte, 1883, No. 167; E. DUTUIT: Rembrandt, 1885, p. 48, No. 311; E. MICHEL: Rembrandt, Vol. I, 1894, p. 305; ANON: Old Masters at the Royal Academy, 1899, No. 12; W. VON BODE: Complete Work of Rembrandt, Vol. IV, 1900, No. 276, *Illust.*; W. R. VALENTINER: Rembrandt (Kl. der Kunst), 1909, p. 557, No. 251, *Illust.*; C. HOFSTEDE DE GROOT: Catalogue Raisonné, Vol. VI, 1916, No. 740; D. S. MELDRUM: Rembrandt's Paintings, 1923, p. 190, *Illust.*; A. M. HIND: Rembrandt, 1932, p. 83, *Illust.*; ANON: Van Wisselingh Gallery Exhibition, Amsterdam, 1932, No. 7, *Illust.*; E. S. SIPLE: *In* Burl. Mag., April 1933, p. 190, *Illust.*

REMBRANDT HARMENSZ VAN RIJN
DUTCH, 1606-1669

300 The Visitation of St. Elizabeth.

Signed: *Rembrandt f. 1640.*

Panel: 22½ x 19 inches.

LENT BY THE DETROIT INSTITUTE OF ARTS.

COLLECTIONS: The King of Sardinia; Prince Eugene of Savoy; Charles Nieuwenhuys; Duke of Westminster; Alfred Charles de Rothschild.

ENGRAVED by J. Burnet; ETCHED by P. J. Arendzen.

EXHIBITIONS: British Institution, London, 1834; Royal Academy, London, 1870, 1895, 1899; Amsterdam, 1898; Detroit Institute of Arts, 1930.

BIBLIOGRAPHY: J. YOUNG: Pictures at Grosvenor House, 1820, p. 39, No. 122, *Illust.*; ANON: Catalogue of the Brit. Inst., London, 1834, No. 114; J. SMITH: Catalogue Raisonné, Vol. VII, 1836, pp. 22-23, No. 57; G. F. WAAGEN: Treasures of Art, Vol. II, 1854, p. 165; ANON: Catalogues of Old Masters, Roy. Acad., London, 1870, No. 36; 1895, No. 88; 1899, No. 52; C. VOSMAER: Rembrandt, 1877, pp. 212, 522; W. VON BODE: Studien, 1883, pp. 447, 589, No. 240; E. DUTUIT: Rembrandt, 1885, p. 49; E. MICHEL: Rembrandt, 1893, pp. 266, 588; C. HOFSTEDE DE GROOT: Masterpieces of Dutch Art in Eng. Collns., 1899, *Folio, Illust.*, w. von bode: The Complete Work of Rembrandt, Vol. IV, 1900, No. 241, *Illust.*, w. r. valentiner: Rembrandt (*Kl. der Kunst*), 1909, No. 224, *Illust.*, c. hofstede de groot: Catalogue Raisonné, Vol. VI, 1916, p. 63, No. 74; w. r. valentiner: Rembrandt Exhn., Detroit Inst., 1930, No. 30, *Illust.*, a. bredius: Rembrandt Gemälde, 1935, No. 562, *Illust.*

REMBRANDT HARMENSZ VAN RIJN
DUTCH, 1606-1669

The Standard Bearer.

Signed: *Rembrandt fe. 1654.*

Canvas: 55 x 45½ inches.

LENT BY THE JULES S. BACHE COLLECTION, NEW YORK.

COLLECTIONS: Sir Joshua Reynolds, P.R.A.; Earl of Warwick; George J. Gould; Lord Duveen of Millbank.

ENGRAVED in Mezzotint by W. Pether in the XVIII Century.

EXHIBITIONS: Manchester Exhibition, 1857; British Institution, 1860; Royal Academy, London, 1871; Hudson-Fulton Celebration, Metropolitan Museum, New York, 1909; Amsterdam, 1925; Detroit Institute of Arts, 1925; Royal Academy, London, 1929; Herron Art Institute, Indianapolis, 1937.

BIBLIOGRAPHY: j. smith: Catalogue Raisonné, Part VII, 1836, p. 103, No. 279; w. von bode: Studien zur Geschichte der Holländischen Malerei, 1883, pp. 539 and 592, No. 262; a. von wurzbach: Rembrandt Galerie, 1886, p. 68, No. 256, *Illust.*, e. michel: Rembrandt, Vol. II, 1895, pp. 81-82, *Illust.*, p. 179; w. von bode: The Complete Work of Rembrandt, Vol. V, 1901, pp. 26 and 150, No. 370; w. r. valentiner: Rembrandt, (Kl. der Kunst), 1909, p. 428, *Illust.*, idem: The Hudson-Fulton Celebration Catalogue, Metropolitan Museum, New York, Vol. I, 1909, p. 331, No. 98, *Illust.*, c. hofstede de groot: Catalogue Raisonné, Vol. VI, 1916, p. 163, No .259; w. g. constable and h. schneider: Exhibition of Dutch Art, Royal Academy, London, 1929, No. 106, *Illust.*, a. bredius: Rembrandt Gemälde, 1935, No. 275, *Illust.*, anon: Catalogue of the Bache Collection, New York, 1938, No. 36, *Illust.*

REMBRANDT HARMENSZ VAN RIJN
DUTCH, 1606-1669

Christ and the Woman of Samaria.

Signed: *Rembrandt f. 1655.*

Panel: 24½ x 19 inches.

LENT BY MRS. WILLIAM R. TIMKEN, NEW YORK.

COLLECTIONS: Hendrijk Reydon, Amsterdam; Rev. T. Sheepshanks, Harrogate; Capt. R. Langton Douglas; Marcus Kappel; Knoedler Galleries, London.

EXHIBITIONS: Leeds, 1889; Leyden, 1906; Detroit Institute of Arts, 1930.

BIBLIOGRAPHY: w. r. valentiner: Rembrandt (Kl. der Kunst), 1909, p. 379, *Illust.*, w. von bode: Gemälde-sammlung Marcus Kappel, Berlin, 1914, *Illust.*, c. hofstede de groot: Catalogue Raisonné, Vol. VI, 1916, p. 80, No. 101; d. s. meldrum: Rembrandt's Paintings, 1923, p. 201, *Illust.*, w. r. valentiner: Paintings by Rembrandt, Detroit Inst. of Arts, 1930, No. 54, *Illust.*, idem: In Art News, April 26, 1930, p. 3, *Illust.*, a. bredius: Rembrandt, 1935, No. 589, *Illust.*

REMBRANDT HARMENSZ VAN RIJN
DUTCH, 1606-1669

303 Titus, Son of Rembrandt.

Painted about 1655-1656.

Panel: 15⅝ x 13⅝ inches.

LENT BY MR. LAWRENCE P. FISHER, DETROIT.

COLLECTION: Dr. Marcel Lermoyez, Paris.

EXHIBITION: Detroit Institute of Arts, 1930.

BIBLIOGRAPHY: w. R. VALENTINER: Rembrandt, wiedergef. Gemälde, (Kl. der Kunst), 1923, No. 85, Illust., IDEM: In Art News, Apr. 26, 1930, Illust., IDEM: Paintings by Rembrandt, Detroit Inst. of Arts, 1930, No. 57, Illust., w. HEIL: In Antiquarian, Dec. 1930, p. 48, Illust., A. BREDIUS: Rembrandt Gemälde, 1935, No. 125, Illust.

REMBRANDT HARMENSZ VAN RIJN
DUTCH, 1606-1669

304 Portrait of a Gentleman, known as 'A Dutch Admiral'.

Signed: Rembrandt f. 1658.

Canvas: 42 x 34½ inches.

LENT RY MR. G. HUNTINGTON HARTFORD, NEW YORK.

COLLECTIONS: George Folliott of Chester; Mrs. E. I. E. Folingsby Walker; James Folliott Folingsby Walker; Howard Young.

EXHIBITION: British Institution, London, 1847; Asscher-Welker Galleries, London, 1930; Howard Young Galleries, New York, 1931.

BIBLIOGRAPHY: ANON: Catalogue of the Brit. Inst., London, 1847, No. 45; c. HOFSTEDE DE GROOT: Catalogue raisonné, Vol. VI, 1916, p. 381, No. 827a; T. BORENIUS: In Burl. Mag., Aug. 1930, p. 53, Illust., A. BREDIUS: Rembrandt Gemälde, 1935, No. 290, Illust.

REMBRANDT HARMENSZ VAN RIJN
DUTCH, 1606-1669

305 Titus, Son of Rembrandt.

Pl. 70 Signed, Rembrandt f. Painted about 1658.

Canvas: 30 x 25 inches.

LENT BY MRS. CHARLES S. PAYSON, NEW YORK.

COLLECTIONS: Robert Stayner Holford; Sir George Lindsay Holford, Dorchester House, London; Knoedler Galleries, New York.

EXHIBITIONS: British Institution, London, 1862 and 1867; Royal Academy, London, 1893 and 1899; Rijksmuseum, Amsterdam, 1898; Detroit Institute, 1930.

BIBLIOGRAPHY: ANON: Catalogues of the Brit. Inst., London, 1862, No. 15, and 1867, No. 75; ANON: Catalogues of the Royal Acad., London, 1893, No. 50, and 1899, No. 82; E. MICHEL: Rembrandt, Vol. II, 1895, p. 433; w. von BODE: Complete Work of Rembrandt, Vol. VI, 1902, No. 445, Illust., w. R. VALENTINER: Rembrandt (Kl. der Kunst), 1909, 1909, p. 562, No. 48, Illust.,

c. hofstede de groot: Catalogue Raisonné, Vol. VI, 1916, p. 333, No. 703; d. s. meldrum: Rembrandt, 1923, p. 199, No. 348, *Illust.*, r. benson: Catalogue of the Holford Collection, Dorchester House, Vol. II, 1927, p. 22, No. 129, *Illust.*, w. r. valentiner: Rembrandt Exhibition, Detroit Inst., 1930, No. 61, *Illust.*, a. bredius: Rembrandt, 1935, p. 13, No. 293, *Illust.*, h. tietze: Rembrandt Gemälde, 1935, p. 13, No. 293, *Illust.*

REMBRANDT HARMENSZ VAN RIJN
DUTCH, 1606-1669

6 *Titus, Son of Rembrandt.*

Signed: *Rembrandt f. 1659.*

Canvas: 15⅛ x 12¼ inches.

LENT BY THE JULES S. BACHE COLLECTION, NEW YORK.

COLLECTIONS: Consul Eduard F. Weber; Maurice Kann.

EXHIBITIONS: Stedelijk Museum, Amsterdam, 1898; Detroit Institute of Arts, 1925; Rijksmuseum, Amsterdam, 1935.

BIBLIOGRAPHY: w. von bode: Studien zür Geschichte der Holländischen Malerei, 1883, p. 571, No. 98; c. hofstede de groot: The Rembrandt Exhibition at Amsterdam, 1898, No. 103; w. von bode: The Complete Work of Rembrandt, Vol. VI, 1901, pp. 23 and 150, No. 459, *Illust.*, e. michel: Rembrandt, 1893, pp. 450 and 563, English edition, 1903, pp. 350 and 435; w. r. valentiner: Rembrandt und seine Umgebung, 1905; idem: Rembrandt (Kl. der Kunst), 1909, p. 419; c. hofstede de groot: Catalogue Raisonné, Vol. VI, 1916, p. 221, No. 411; d. s. meldrum: Rembrandt's Paintings, 1918, Plate CCCLXIV; f. schmidt-degener: Rembrandt Tentoonstellung, Rijksmuseum, Amsterdam, 1935, p. 57, No. 25; e. scheyer: *In* "Pantheon", Vol. XVI, 1935, p. 290, *Illust.*, a. bredius: Rembrandt Gemälde, 1935, No. 296, *Illust.*, anon: Catalogue of the Bache Collection, New York, 1938, No. 37, *Illust.*

REMBRANDT HARMENSZ VAN RIJN
DUTCH, 1606-1669

7 *Self Portrait.*

Signed: *Rembrandt f. 1659.*

Canvas: 33¼ x 26 inches.

LENT BY THE NATIONAL GALLERY (MELLON COLLECTION).
WASHINGTON, D. C.

COLLECTIONS: George Brudenell-Montagu, Duke of Montagu; Lady Elizabeth, Duchess of Buccleuch; Walter Francis, fifth Duke of Buccleuch; John Charles, seventh Duke of Buccleuch.

ENGRAVED in Mezzogravure by R. Earlom, and H. E. Dawe.

EXHIBITIONS: Royal Academy, London, 1872; Stedelijk Museum, Amsterdam, 1898; Rembrandt Exhibition, Royal Academy, London, 1899; National Gallery, London, 1916; Detroit Institute of Art, 1930; Knoedler Galleries, New York, 1930; Rijksmuseum, Amsterdam, 1935.

BIBLIOGRAPHY: j. smith: Catalogue Raisonné, 1835, Vol. VII, p. 88, No. 215; c. vosmaer: Rembrandt, 1877, pp. 358 and 560; w. von bode: Studien zur Geschichte der Hollandischen Malerei, 1883, pp. 542 and 585, No. 197; a. von wurzbach: Rembrandt Galerie, 1886, p. 58, No. 160; e. michel: Rembrandt, Vol. II, 1895, p. 235; c. hofstede de groot: The Rembrandt Exhibition at Amsterdam, Folio, 1898, No. 102, *Plate 33*, w. von bode: Complete Work of Rembrandt, 1901, Vol. VI, pp. 13-14, No. 431, *Jllust.*, w. r. valentiner: Rembrandt (Kl. der Kunst), 1909, p. 562, No. 403, *Jllust.*, a. von wurzbach: *Jn* Niederländisches Kunstler-Lexikon, 1910, Vol. II, p. 402; c. hofstede de groot: Catalogue Raisonné, Vol. VI, 1916, pp. 273-274, No. 554; d. s. meldrum: Rembrandt's Paintings, 1923, p. 199, No. 339, *Jllust.*, h. knackfuss: Rembrandt (Künstler-Monographien), 1924, p. 162, *Jllust. with Earlom's engraving*, w. r. valentiner: Rembrandt's Paintings in America, 1931, No. 141, *Jllust.*, f. schmidt-degener: Rembrandt Tentoonstelling, Rijksmuseum, Amsterdam, 1935, p. 57, No. 26, *Jllust.*, a. bredius: Rembrandt Gemälde, 1935, p. 4, No. 51, *Jllust.*

REMBRANDT HARMENSZ VAN RIJN
dutch, 1606-1669

308 *Christ with Folded Arms.*

Pl. 69 · Painted about 1659.

Canvas: 43 x 35½ inches.

LENT BY MRS. LOUIS F. HYDE, GLENS FALLS, NEW YORK.

COLLECTIONS: Cardinal Fesch; M. de Forcade; Charles Sedelmeyer; R. Bamberger; Count Alexis Orloff-Davidoff.

ETCHED by A. L. Gilbert; G. F. Schmidt; and J. Burnet.

EXHIBITIONS: Oesterreichisches Museum, Vienna, 1873; Palais du Corps Législatifs, Paris, 1874.

BIBLIOGRAPHY: w. von bode: Gesch. der Holland, Malerei, 1883, pp. 522, 603, No. 352; e. dutuit: Rembrandt, 1885, p. 54, No. 79; a. von wurzbach: Rembrandt Galerie, 1886, No. 426; e. michel: Rembrandt, 1893, pp. 443, 567; c. sedelmeyer: Paintings by Old Masters, 1898, p. 170, No. 150; w. von bode: The Complete Work of Rembrandt, Vol. VI, 1901, No. 415, *Jllust.*, w. r. valentiner: Rembrandt, (*Kl. der Kunst*), 1909, No. 392, *Jllust.*, c. hofstede de groot: Catalogue Raisonné, Vol. VI, 1916, p. 118, No. 162; d. s. meldrum: Rembrandt's Paintings, 1923, p. 202, No. 413, *Jllust.*, a. bredius: Rembrandt Gemälde, 1935, No. 275, *Jllust.*

REMBRANDT HARMENSZ VAN RIJN
dutch, 1606-1669

309 *A Pilgrim at Prayer*, known also as "The Apostle James".

Pl. 69 Signed: *Rembrandt f. 1661.*

Canvas: 35½ x 31 inches.

LENT BY MRS. VAN WIE WILLYS, NEW YORK.

COLLECTIONS: Mackenzie of Kintore; Sir J. Charles Robinson, C.B.; Consul Eduard F. Weber; Charles Sedelmeyer; Maurice Kann; Lord Duveen of Millbank; Henry Reinhardt; John N. Willys.

ETCHED by Albert Krüger.

EXHIBITIONS: Sedelmeyer Gallery, Paris, 1895; Detroit Institute of Arts, 1930.

BIBLIOGRAPHY: dr. woermann: *Jn* Graphischen Kunst, Vol. IV, 1891, p. 32, *Jllust.*, a. rosenberg: *Jn* Zeitschr. für Bild. Kunst, 1892, p. 168, *Jllust.*, e. michel: Rembrandt, 1895, p. 480, (Eng. Edn., Vol. II, p. 161), *Jllust.*, c. sedelmeyer: Paintings by Old Masters, 1896, No. 29, *Jllust.*, w. von bode: The Complete Work of Rembrandt, 1901, Vol. VI, p. 202, No. 485, *Jllust.*,

w. r. valentiner: Rembrandt (*Kl. der Kunst*), 1909, No. 457, *Illust.*, c. hofstede de groot: Catalogue Raisonné, Vol. VI, 1916, p. 121, No. 170; w. roberts: Catalogue Raisonné, J. N. Willys Colln., 1917, *Illust.*, w. r. valentiner: *In Art News*, Apr. 1926, p. 4, *Illust.*, idem: Rembrandt Exhibition, Detroit Inst., 1930, No. 67, *Illust.*

REMBRANDT HARMENSZ VAN RIJN
DUTCH, 1606-1669

0 *Old Lady with Black Head-dress.*

Signed: *Rembrandt f. 1561.*

Canvas: 30½ x 25¼ inches.

LENT BY MRS. ROGER W. STRAUS, NEW YORK.

COLLECTIONS: Sir Alexander Hume; Earl Brownlow; Charles Sedelmeyer; E. F. Milliken; Sir George Donaldson; Francis Kleinberger; Fritz von Gans; Daniel Guggenheim.

EXHIBITIONS: British Institution, London, 1818; Royal Academy, London, 1899, 1907; F. Müller Galleries, Amsterdam, 1907.

BIBLIOGRAPHY: anon: Catalogues of the British Institution, London, 1818, No. 121; anon: Catalogues of the Royal Academy, London, 1899, No. 78; 1907, No. 56; c. sedelmeyer: Catalogue of One Hundred Paintings, 1900, No. 29, *Illust.*, w. von bode: Complete Work of Rembrandt, Vol. VI, 1901, p. 192, No. 480, *Illust.*, anon: Catalogue of the F. Müller Exhibition, Amsterdam, 1907, No. 36; w. r. valentiner: Rembrandt (Kl. der Kunst), 1909, No. 496, *Illust.*, c. hofstede de groot: Catalogue Raisonné, Vol. VI, 1916, p. 252, No. 498; d. s. meldrum: Rembrandt's Paintings, 1923, p. 201, *Illust.*, a. bredius: Rembrandt, 1935, p. 16, No. 396, *Illust.*

REMBRANDT HARMENSZ VAN RIJN
DUTCH, 1606-1669

1 *Self-Portrait.*

Painted about 1662; signed on the right at top by a later hand.

Canvas: 22½ x 17¼ inches.

LENT BY MR. H. E. TEN CATE, ALMELO, HOLLAND.

COLLECTIONS: Marquis of Lothian, Newbattle Abbey, Dalkeith; D. Katz; Schaeffer Galleries, New York.

EXHIBITIONS: National Gallery, Edinburgh, Scotland; Rijksmuseum, Amsterdam, 1936; Schaeffer Galleries, New York, 1936; Los Angeles Museum, 1938; Springfield Museum, 1938; Rhode Island Museum, Providence, 1938.

BIBLIOGRAPHY: w. von bode: Complete Work of Rembrandt, Vol. VII, 1902, No. 502, *Illust.*, w. r. valentiner: Rembrandt (Kl. der Kunst), 1909, p. 476, *Illust.*, c. hofstede de groot: Catalogue Raisonné, Vol. VI, 1916, No. 561; d. s. meldrum: Rembrandt's Paintings, 1923, p. 202, No. 421, *Illust.*, a. bredius: Rembrandt, 1936, No. 637, *Illust.*, anon: Tentoonstelling van Oude Kunst, Rijksmuseum, Amsterdam, 1936, p. 32, No. 128, *Illust.*, w. stechow: Dutch Painting of the XVII c., Rhode Island Museum, 1938, No. 41, *Illust.*

REMBRANDT HARMENSZ VAN RIJN

DUTCH, 1606-1669

312 *Juno.* ('The Long-lost Picture').

Painted in 1664-65. This picture, the existence of which was known only through documents, was rediscovered in 1935 at the sale of the Wesendonck collection in Cologne. It was immediately recognized as the painting which Rembrandt finished in 1664-65 (*Urkunden über R. No. 278*), for Harmen Becker, a draper of Amsterdam, one of his creditors and a great collector, in whose inventory (Oct. 19, 1678) the painting is mentioned (*Oud Holland*, 1910, p. 196). Becker, to whom Rembrandt owed the sum of 537 guilders, held several of his paintings, drawings and etchings as security for the amount. On Aug. 29, 1665, the painter offered to refund the money and asked for the return of his works, but Becker, who had seen and coveted the unfinished *Juno*, refused to release them until that picture was finished. By Oct. 6, 1665, the debt had been paid, the pictures redeemed and Becker received his *Juno*.

Canvas: 50 x 42⅜ inches.

LENT ANONYMOUSLY.

COLLECTIONS: Harmen Becker (1665); J. Thomas Stanley, Turnbridge, Yorkshire; Otto von Wesendonck, Berlin; Provinzialmuseum, Bonn; D. Katz, Dieren, Holland.
EXHIBITIONS: Rijksmuseum, Amsterdam, 1935; Schaeffer Galleries, New York, 1936.
BIBLIOGRAPHY: ANON: Otto von Wesendonck Sammlung, 1888; A. BREDIUS: *In* Oud Holland, 1910, pp. 196 *et seq*, w. COHEN: Katalog, Provinzialmuseum in Bonn, 1914 and 1927; C. HOFSTEDE DE GROOT, *Edr.*: Urkunden über Rembrandt, No. 278; IDEM: Catalogue Raisonné, Vol. VI, 1916, p. 138, No. 207a; A. BREDIUS: *In* Pantheon, Sept. 1936, *Illust.*, w. VALENTINER AND A. BREDIUS: *In* Connoisseur, Jan. 1937, p. 3, *Illust. in color*, J. HELD: *In* Parnassus, April 1937, pp. 36-37, *Illust.*, ANON: *In* Art Digest, April 1, 1937, p. 12, *Illust.*, M. WEINBERGER: *In* Amer. Mag. of Art, May 1937, p. 312, *Illust.*

REMBRANDT HARMENSZ VAN RIJN

DUTCH, 1606-1669

313 *Old Man in a Black Beret.*

Signed: *Rembrandt f. 166(5)*.

Panel: 19 x 14 inches.

LENT BY MR. ALLAN P. KIRBY, NEW YORK.

COLLECTIONS: Marquess of Lothian, Newbattle Abbey; D. Katz; Schaeffer Galleries, New York.
BIBLIOGRAPHY: w. VON BODE: Complete Work of Rembrandt, Vol. VII, 1902, p. 92, No. 515, *Illust.*, w. R. VALENTINER: Rembrandt (Kl. der Kunst), 1909, No. 507a, *Illust.*, C. HOFSTEDE DE GROOT: Catalogue Raisonné, Vol. VI, 1916, p. 220, No. 408A; D. S. MELDRUM: Rembrandt's Paintings, 1923, p. 203, *Illust.*

REYNOLDS, P.R.A., SIR JOSHUA

Born at Plympton Earl in Devonshire. In 1740 he went to London and studied
under Thomas Hudson. In 1746 he established himself as a portrait painter, and
went to Rome in 1749. He returned to London in 1752, and became intimately
associated with Burke, Garrick, Goldsmith and Johnson, and established the "Literary Club" in 1764. In 1768 the Royal Academy was founded with Reynolds as
its first President; his annual addresses formed his well-known "Discourses". In
1790 he resigned the Presidency owing to a quarrel with the Council. His celebrated portrait of "Mrs. Siddons as the Tragic Muse" is now in the Huntington
Collection in Pasadena. He ranks as the head of the English School of portrait
painting of the eighteenth century.

4 *Children Playing Forfeits*, known also as "Children Playing with a Snail."

Painted about 1760. Three young daughters of George Montagu, 2nd Earl of Halifax (d. 1771), Anne (d. 1761), standing, with finger raised; Frances (d. 1764),
seated; Elizabeth, afterwards Lady Hinchinbroke (d. 1768), holding a snail; the
fourth child, kneeling, is evidently a country playmate, on whom the joke is being
imposed. A second picture, unfinished, belonged to Lord Manners (1903).

Canvas: 50 x 40 inches.

LENT BY MR. LAWRENCE P. FISHER, DETROIT.

COLLECTIONS: George Montague, second Earl of Halifax, Lord Lieut. of Ireland; Richard
Archdall, Fermanagh, Ireland; Dr. George Archdall Gratwicke; Rev. R. V. C. Kinleside; Howard
Young.
ENGRAVED by C. Turner, 1826, with the Archdall arms; R. Josey, 1877.
EXHIBITION: Detroit Institute of Arts (The Russell A. Alger House), 1938.
BIBLIOGRAPHY: H. GRAVES: Engravings from the Works of Sir Joshua Reynolds, P.R.A., Vol.
I, 1880, No. 61. *With Josey's engraving,* A. WHITMAN: Nineteenth Century Mezzotinters—Charles
Turner, 1907, p. 260, No. 818; W. HEIL: *In* Antiquarian, Dec. 1930, p. 49, *Illust.*

REYNOLDS, P.R.A., SIR JOSHUA

5 *Jane, Countess of Harrington, with her sons.*

93 Painted in 1786-87. Lady Harrington, daughter of Sir John Fleming, Bart., of
Brompton Park, was born in 1755, and married in 1779, Charles Stanhope, 3rd Earl
of Harrington (d. 1829), Governor of Windsor Castle. Her two sons, in this picture, are Charles, Viscount Petersham (b. 1780), and the Hon. Lincoln Edwin
Robert Stanhope (b. 1781). Her ladyship died in 1824.

Canvas: 44¾ x 56½ inches.

COLLECTIONS: Elizabeth, Countess of Harrington, Craig's Court, London (d. 1919); Dudley Stanhope, 9th Earl of Harrington; Knoedler Galleries, New York.

ENGRAVED by F. Bartolozzi, 1789; A. N. Sanders, 1878.

BIBLIOGRAPHY: G. F. WAAGEN: Treasures of Art in G. Britain, Vol. IV, 1857, p. 236; H. GRAVES: Engravings from the Works of Sir J. Reynolds, P.R.A., Vol. IV, 1863, No. 69, *Illust.*, C. R. LESLIE AND T. TAYLOR: Life and Times of Reynolds, Vol. II, 1865, pp. 431 and 500; A. GRAVES AND W. V. CRONIN: Works of Sir Joshua Reynolds, Vol. II, 1899, p. 439; SIR WALTER ARMSTRONG: Sir Joshua Reynolds, 1900, p. 211; J. SIME: Sir Joshua Reynolds, 1903, p. 172; ANON: Old Masters Exhn., Royal Acad., Lond., 1906, No. 87; H. MACFALL: The British Genius, 1911, p. 160.

RIGAUD, HYACINTHE

FRENCH, 1659-1743

Born at Perpignan in the Pyrénées. Studied at Montpellier under Antoine Ranc. He went to Paris in 1681, and on the advice of Lebrun gave up painting historical scenes and devoted himself to portraits. In 1700 he entered the Academy, and soon afterwards became leading painter at the court. His place in French portraiture is somewhat similar to that of Sir Godfrey Kneller in England, although he was far superior as an artist to Kneller. His painting typifies the pompous style of the Louis XIV and XV periods of French art.

316 *Portrait of President Hébert.*

Canvas: 54 x 41 inches.

LENT ANONYMOUSLY.

ROMNEY, GEORGE

ENGLISH, 1734-1802

Born at Beckside, Lancashire; he was apprenticed to a wood-carver, was a clever musician, and began very early to paint portraits. At the age of twenty-one he practised with Christopher Steele, at Kendal. In 1757 he married Mary Abbot. In 1762 he left for London. He visited Paris in 1764, and made a sojourn in Italy, returning to London in 1775, and painted a series of famous portraits, sharing the patronage of the aristocracy with Reynolds and Gainsborough. In 1782 he had a new sitter in Emma Hart, the future Lady Hamilton, who, for nine years, adapted herself to the imagination of the painter, resulting in many celebrated paintings of her in various characters. In 1789 he rejoined his wife, whom he had abandoned for thirty years, and spent the remainder of his life in retirement at Kendal, where he died.

317 *Elizabeth, Countess of Derby.*

Painted in 1776-1778. The original drawing for this portrait is in the Herbert Horne Collection, Florence. Elizabeth (the "Lady Betty Hamilton" of Boswell's

"Life of Johnson"), only daughter of James, Sixth Duke of Hamilton and his wife, Elizabeth Gunning, was born in 1753. In 1774 she married Lord Stanley, who became the twelfth Earl of Derby two years later. In 1794 she eloped with the Duke of Dorset, by whom she had a daughter, known as Lady Elizabeth Cole. After Lady Derby's death in 1797, her husband married Miss Farren, the celebrated actress.

Canvas: 50 x 40 inches.

LENT BY THE JULES S. BACHE COLLECTION, NEW YORK.

COLLECTIONS: Earl Granville, K.G.; Sir Charles Tennant, Bart.; Lord Glenconner; Knoedler Galleries.

ENGRAVED in Mezzotint by J. Dean, M. Commack, and G. H. Every.

EXHIBITIONS: Royal Academy, 1885, and 1892; Glasgow Exhibition, 1888; Grafton Galleries, 1894; Glasgow Exhibition, 1902.

BIBLIOGRAPHY: H. GAMLIN: George Romney and his Art, 1894, pp. 93-94, *Illust.*, ANON: Catalogue of the Pictures forming the Collection of Sir Charles Tennant, Bart., 1896, *Illust.*, H. H. WARD and W. ROBERTS: Romney, Catalogue raisonné, 1904, p. 44, *Illust.*, M. H. SPIELMANN: British Portrait Painting, Vol. II, 1910, p. 16, Plate LXXI; A. B. CHAMBERLAIN: Romney, 1910, p. 298, *Illust.*, E. SINGLETON: Old World Masters, 1929, pp. 398-402, *Illust.*, ANON: Catalogue of the Bache Collection, New York, 1938, No. 63, *Illust.*

ROMNEY, GEORGE

ENGLISH, 1734 - 1802

8 *Anne, Marchioness Townshend.*

Painted in 1780. Anne (born 1754), youngest daughter of Sir William Montgomery, Bart., of Magbie Hill, Peebles. Married in 1773, as his second wife, George, 4th Viscount Townshend (created 1st Marquis, 1786). He served at Dettingen, Fontenoy, Culloden, and Quebec, the latter being surrendered to him as Commander-in-chief on the death of Wolfe. Lady Townshend died in London in 1819. She is one of the 'Three Graces' surrounding the statue of Hymen, in Sir Joshua Reynolds' noted picture in the National Gallery, London.

Canvas: 30 x 25 inches.

LENT BY MR. AND MRS. FRED J. FISHER, DETROIT.

COLLECTIONS: George, Marquess of Townshend; Sir Charles Montolieu Lamb, Bart.; Robert Stayner Holford; Sir George Lindsay Holford; Howard Young.

ENGRAVED by T. G. Appleton, 1903.

EXHIBITIONS: Royal Academy, London, 1887; Grafton Gallery, London, 1894.

BIBLIOGRAPHY: ANON: Old Masters Exhibition Catalogue, Royal Academy, London, 1887, No. 20; ANON: "Fair Women" Exhibition, New Gallery, London, 1894, No. 120; H. GAMLIN: George Romney, 1894, p. 203; E. M. SYMONDS: 'George Paston'; George Romney, 1903, p. 198; H. WARD AND W. ROBERTS: Romney, Catalogue Raisonné, Vol. II, 1904, p. 159; LORD R. S. GOWER: George Romney, 1904, p. 128, No. 398; A. B. CHAMBERLAIN: Romney, 1910, p. 395; R. BENSON: The Holford Collection, Dorchester House, Vol. II, 1927, p. 40, No. 178, *Illust.*

ROMNEY, GEORGE

ENGLISH, 1734-1802

319 *Children of Captain Little.*

Canvas: 57½ x 42 inches.

LENT BY MR. AND MRS. EDWARD F. FISHER, DETROIT.

COLLECTIONS: Major W. H. Little; Arthur Sanderson; Otto H. Kahn; Lord Duveen of Millbank; Lord Michelham, K.C.V.O.

EXHIBITIONS: Guildhall, London, 1892; Grafton Galleries, London, 1895, and 1900-1; Detroit Institute of Arts, 1927.

BIBLIOGRAPHY: SIR A. G. TEMPLE: Collection of Pictures, Guildhall, London, 1892, No. 122a; F. G. PRANGE: Fair Children, Grafton Gallery, London, 1895, No. 141; ANON: In Art Journal, 1897, p. 37, Illust., H. WARD AND W. ROBERTS: Romney, Vol. I, p. 95, Vol. II, p. 92, 1904, Illust., W. C. LANE AND N. E. BROWNE, Edrs.: Portrait Index, Library of Congress, Wash., D. C., 1906, p. 879; ANON: Works of Art in the Collection of Lord Michelham, 1912, p. 6, Illust., W. HEIL: Old Masters, Detroit Inst. of Arts, 1927, No. 68, Illust., A. M. FRANKFURTER: In Art News, May 16, 1931, Illust., and Oct. 15, 1937.

RUBENS, SIR PETER PAUL

FLEMISH, 1577-1640

Born at Siegen, Westphalia. Pupil of Tobias Verhaecht, Adam van Noort, and Otto van Veen. From 1600 till 1608 he was in Italy in the service of Vincenzo Gonzago II, Duke of Mantua; in 1609 he married Isabella Brant (d. 1626) and became court painter to the Regents of the Netherlands at Antwerp. In 1621 he went to Paris, and was commissioned by Marie de'Medici to paint his celebrated 'events' in her life. In 1627 he went to Madrid where he became acquainted with Velazquez. In 1629-30 he went to London, and was knighted by Charles I. On his return to Antwerp he married his first wife's niece, Helen Fourment, who served as his model for many of his finest pictures. He was a prodigious worker, and produced ceaselessly with the help of a considerable number of assistants. He is ranked among the greatest masters of color, design, technique and drawing, and celebrated also in politics, culture, and learning.

320 *Francesco IV, Duke of Mantua.*

Pl. 60   Painted in Italy about 1607. Born at Mantua in 1586; a member of the princely family of Gonzaga who ruled Mantua for three centuries, and from 1432 were Marquises, from 1530 Dukes of Mantua. He was the son of Vincenzo I (1562-1612) and Eleanora de' Medici, eldest sister of Marie de' Medici. He married Margherita of Savoy in 1608 and succeeded his father in 1612, but only survived him by ten months.

Panel: 25 x 19½ inches.

LENT BY MRS. HENRY GOLDMAN, NEW YORK.

COLLECTIONS: Vicenzo II, 7th Duke of Mantua (1627); King Charles I of England; The

Palace of Whitehall, London; Edward Bass (1651); Leonard Gow.
EXHIBITION: Royal Academy, London, 1927.
BIBLIOGRAPHY: ANON: Inventorie of the Personall Estate of Ye late King (Charles I), 1649,
p. 155 (*Vic. and Albert Mus.*); ANON: Inventory of the Household Goods belonging to the late
King (Charles I), Harleian MSS., No. 4898, p. 490 (*British Mus.*); ANON: Catalogue of the Art
Collections of King Charles I, n.d., p. 2, No. 2 (*Vic. and Albert Mus.*); G. VERTUE: Catalogue
and desc. of King Charles I's Collections, 1757, p. 127, No. II (after Van der Doort's MSS);
M. W. BROCKWELL: *In* Burl. Mag., Dec. 1921, p. 285, *Illust.*; SIR M. CONWAY: Catalogue of the
Flemish-Belgian Exhn., Royal Academy, London, 1927, p. 106, No. 258.

RUBENS, SIR PETER PAUL

FLEMISH, 1577-1640

1 *Philippe Rubens, the Artist's Brother.*

From the early period of the master, probably between 1608, when he returned
from Italy, and 1611, when Philippe Rubens died. Perhaps identical with the portrait of Philippe which Rubens made for his brother's tomb in the Abbey Church of
St. Michel in Antwerp. This picture, which hung over the door of the sacristy, disappeared during the French Revolution.

Panel: 27 x 21¼ inches.

LENT BY THE DETROIT INSTITUTE OF ARTS.

COLLECTIONS: Peeters d'Aertselaer, Cleydael, 1817; H. J. Stier d'Aertselaer, Antwerp, 1822;
Baron Henry von Mecklenburg, 1854; Carl von Hollitscher, Berlin; Camillo Castiglioni, Vienna;
William E. Scripps, Detroit.
ENGRAVED by Corneille Gallé.
EXHIBITIONS: Kaiser Friedrich Museum, Berlin, 1909; Brussels, 1910; Detroit Institute, 1936.
BIBLIOGRAPHY: ANON: Tableaux des écoles flamande, hollandaise, etc., colln. H. J. Stier
d'Aertselaer, Anvers, 1822, No. 61; J. SMITH: Catalogue Raisonné, 1830, p. 227, No. 805; ANON:
Tableaux anciens, colln. Baron Henry de Mecklembourg, 1854, No. 67; M. ROOSES: Rubens, Vol.
IV, 1892, p. 247; W. VON BODE U. M. J. FRIEDLÄNDER: Die Gemalde-Sammlung Hollitscher, Berlin,
1912, No. 25, *Illust.*; ANON: Collections Camillo Castiglioni de Vienne, Vol. I, 1925, p. 24, No.
74, *Illust.*; C. H. BURROUGHS: *In* Detroit Inst. Bulletin, May 1926, p. 86, *Illust.*; W. HEIL and
C. H. BURROUGHS: Catalogue of Paintings in the Detroit Inst. of Arts, 1930, No. 193, *Illust.*;
W. R. VALENTINER: Exhibition of Paintings by Peter Paul Rubens, Detroit Inst., 1936, No. 19.

RUBENS, SIR PETER PAUL

FLEMISH, 1577-1640

2 *Two Fathers of the Church.*

Painted about 1609. A study for the central figures in the *Disputa* in St. Paul's
Church at Antwerp.

Panel: 26¼ x 20 inches.

LENT ANONYMOUSLY.

158

EXHIBITIONS: Van Diemen-Lilienfeld Galleries, New York, 1934; Detroit Institute of Arts, 1936.
BIBLIOGRAPHY: ANON: *In* Art Digest, Jan. 15, 1934, p. 16, *Illust.*; ANON: Catalogue of Six Centuries and Six Countries Exhn., Van Diemen-Lilienfeld Gall., N. Y., 1934; W. R. VALENTINER: Exhibition of Paintings by Peter Paul Rubens, Detroit Inst., 1936, p. 11, No. 8, *Illust.*

RUBENS, SIR PETER PAUL

FLEMISH, 1577 - 1640

323 *Study of an Old Man.*

Painted about 1611-14. Presumed to be a sketch for one of the group in 'The Descent from the Cross' in Antwerp Cathedral.

Paper on Canvas: 20 x 17 inches.

LENT BY MR. AND MRS. CLARENCE Y. PALITZ, NEW YORK.

COLLECTION: Van Diemen-Lilienfeld Galleries, New York.

RUBENS, SIR PETER PAUL

FLEMISH, 1577 - 1640

324 *Meleager and Atalanta,*

Pl. 61 known also as 'The Calydonian Hunt'.

Painted about 1613-14. In Greek legend, a savage boar was sent by the Goddess Artemis to ravage the country of Oeneus, King of Calydon in Aetolia, as a form of punishment for his having forgotten her in a sacrifice. During the chase, brought about by the Argonauts, Meleager, the son of the King, slew the monster, and presented its head and skin to Atalanta, daughter of the King of Arcadia, as a prize of victory, since she inflicted the first wound.

Panel: 53 x 42 inches.

LENT BY MRS. HENRY GOLDMAN, NEW YORK.

COLLECTIONS: Duke of Marlborough, Blenheim Palace; The Hon. George-Cavendish-Bentinck; Rodolphe Kann, Paris; Lord Duveen of Millbank; Henry Goldman.
ENGRAVED by Cornelis Bloemart.
EXHIBITION: British Institution, London, 1861.
BIBLIOGRAPHY: J. SMITH: Catalogue Raisonné, Vol. II, 1830, p. 247, No. 841; ANON: Catalogue of the British Institution, London, 1861, No. 67; G. SCHARF: Catalogue of Pictures at Blenheim Palace, 1862, p. 24; M. ROOSES: L'Oeuvre de P. P. Rubens, Vol. III, 1890, p. 121, No. 643; Vol. V, p. 339; W. VON BODE: Catalogue of the Rodolphe Kann Colln., 1907, No. 23, *Illust.*; W. R. VALENTINER: Catalogue of the Henry Goldman Colln., 1922, No. 11, *Illust.*, IDEM: *In* Art News, May 14, 1927, p. 14, *Illust.*

RUBENS, SIR PETER PAUL

FLEMISH, 1577-1640

Hygieia, Goddess of Health.

Painted about 1615. In Greek mythology, daughter of Aesculapius, God of Medicine, with whom she is often worshipped. In works of art she is usually represented by his side, with a serpent, to which she is giving water from a vessel. A replica, as 'Cleopatra', (Kl. der Kunst, 1921, p. 71) is in the collection of Schloss Raudnitz, Prince Lobkowitz.

Panel: 41¼ x 29¼.

LENT BY MR. HENRY REICHHOLD, BIRMINGHAM, MICHIGAN.

COLLECTIONS: Comte Charles de Proli, Antwerp, 1785; P. de Smeth van Alphen, Amsterdam, 1810; H. Francken, Lockeren, 1830; Charles J. Nieuwenhuys, Brussels, 1840; Prosper Crabbe, Brussels, 1890; Galerie Charpentier, Paris, 1936.

BIBLIOGRAPHY: M. ROOSES: L'Oeuvre de Rubens, Vol. III, 1890, p. 110; C. SEDELMEYER: Catalogue de Tableaux, Collection Prosper Crabbe, 1890, p. 58, No. 47, Illust., ANON: In Revue de l'Art, July 1936, p. 48, Illust.

RUBENS, SIR PETER PAUL

FLEMISH, 1577-1640

The Return from Egypt.

Painted about 1615. A highly finished drawing of this picture by a follower, and perfected by Rubens, for an engraving is in the Louvre, Paris.

Canvas: 89½ x 59 inches.

LENT BY THE WADSWORTH ATHENEUM, HARTFORD, CONN.

COLLECTIONS: The Château Royal de Tervueren, Brussels; The Duke of Marlborough, Blenheim Palace, 1708-1886; Charles Butler, Hatfield.

ENGRAVED by L. Vorsterman, 1680.

BIBLIOGRAPHY: J. SMITH: Catalogue Raisonné, Vol. II, 1830, p. 243, No. 830; W. HAZLETT: Criticisms of Art and sketches of the Galleries of Eng., 1843, pp. 129 et seq; G. F. WAAGEN: Art Treasures in Great Britain, Vol. III, 1854, p. 124; G. SCHARF: Catalogue of Pictures at Blenheim Palace, 1862, p. 57; V. SCHNEEVOOGHT: Estampes Gravées d'aprés Rubens, 1873, p. 26, No. 124; ANON: Pictures at Oxford and Blenheim, N.D., p. 135; M. GACHARD: Les Tableaux de Rubens . . . enléeves de Bruxelles par le Duc de Marlborough. In Bull. Rubens, Vol. II, 1883, pp. 279-282; W. BODE: Versteigerung der Gal. Blenheim. In Rep. für Kunstw., Vol. X, 1887, pp. 58-62.

RUBENS, SIR PETER PAUL

FLEMISH, 1577-1640

Bust of Caspar, King of Tarsus, known as 'The Greek Magus'.

Painted about 1615. A study for one of the Kings in 'The Adoration of the Magi', in the Malines Cathedral, Belgium, which was executed between 1617-19. The study for the whole painting is in the Metropolitan Museum, New York.

Canvas: 26 x 20 inches.

LENT BY THE CHESTER DALE COLLECTION, NEW YORK.

COLLECTIONS: Comte de Beaufort; J. W. Wilson; Mme. Gauchez, Paris; H. Boesch, Vienna; Charles H. Senff, New York; Mrs. Louise Senff-Cameron.

EXHIBITION: Detroit Institute of Arts, 1936.

ETCHED by Charles Walthner.

BIBLIOGRAPHY: w. r. valentiner: p. mantz: Catalogue de Tableaux, John W. Wilson Collection, Paris, 1881, p. 86, No. 97, *with etching by Walthner*; w. r. valentiner: Catalogue of Paintings by P. P. Rubens, Detroit Inst., 1936, No. 13; idem: *In* Art News, Feb. 15, 1936, p. 6.

RUBENS, SIR PETER PAUL

FLEMISH, 1577-1640

328 Christ Descending to Earth.

Painted about 1615-20.

Panel: 22 x 16 inches.

LENT BY MR. ALBERT KELLER, NEW YORK.

COLLECTIONS: H. Löhr, Leipzig; M. von Boxberg, Dresden; Dr. Martin Schubert, Munich.

EXHIBITIONS: Alte Pinakothek, Munich, 1895; Detroit Institute of Arts, 1936; Musée Royaux, Brussels, 1937.

BIBLIOGRAPHY: m. rooses: L'Oeuvre de P. P. Rubens, Vol. V, 1890, p. 328, No. 351a; c. hofstede de groot: Sammlung Schubart, Munchen, 1894, No. 7, *Illust.*, t. von frimmel: *In* Zeitsch. für Bild.-Kunst, 1894, pp. 217-218; h. pallmann: Aus dem Kunstbesitz Dr. Martin Schubart, 1899, p. 18, No. 58; m. rooses: Rubens, 1904, p. 144; a. rosenberg: P. P. Rubens (Kl. der Kunst), 1906, No. 57, *Illust.*, e. dillon: Rubens, 1909, p. 220, No. 91, *Illust.*, w. r. valentiner: Catalogue of Rubens Exhn., Detroit Inst., 1936, No. 39, *Illust.*, l. van puyvelde: L'Exposition Esquisses de Rubens, Musées Royaux, Brussels, 1937.

RUBENS, SIR PETER PAUL

FLEMISH, 1577-1640

329 The Vision of the Emperor Constantine.

Painted 1621-1622. According to Eusebius (*Vita Const.*, I, XXVI-XXXI), Constantine (275-337 A.D.), in choosing Christianity as the religion of the Roman state, was influenced by a heavenly manifestation, in which he believed he saw the emblem of Christ.

Panel: 17⅝ x 22 inches.

LENT BY THE JOHN G. JOHNSON COLLECTION, PHILADELPHIA.

COLLECTION: Duc d'Orleans, 1798.

ENGRAVED by Nicholas Tardieu, and Laurent Léonard.

EXHIBITION: Worcester Art Museum, 1939; Pennsylvania Museum, Philadelphia, 1939.

BIBLIOGRAPHY: j. smith: Catalogue Raisonné, Vol. II, 1830, p. 202, No. 734; m. rooses:

L'Oeuvre de P. P. Rubens, Vol. III, 1904, p. 211, No. 719; R. A. M. STEVENSON: P. P. Rubens, 1898, pp. 58 and 61; A. ROSENBERG: P. P. Rubens (Kl. der Kunst), 1906, p. 231, Jllust., H. REA: P. P. Rubens, 1908, pp. 33 and 94; E. DILLON: Rubens, 1909, p. 223, No. 232, Jllust., W. R. VALEN-TINER: Catalogue of Flemish Paintings, J. G. Johnson Colln., 1913, p. 162, No. 659, Jllust., R. OLDENBOURG: P. P. Rubens (Kl. der Kunst), 1921, p. 231, Jllust., H. MARCEAU and others: Cata-logue, Flemish Exhibition, Worcester-Philadelphia Museums, 1939, p. 64, No. 121, Jllust.

RUBENS, SIR PETER PAUL

FLEMISH, 1577-1640

Briseis Restored to Achilles.

Painted about 1620-23. One of a series of eight studies for a set of tapestries painted by Rubens for Charles I of England (d. 1649), and woven in 1662, after the King's death, by Geraert van der Strecken at Brussels. (These tapestries were sold, Jan. 28, 1852, at the sale of King Louis-Philippe's effects). Six of these studies, from the Lord Barrymore Collection, are now in the Rotterdam Museum. A school repetition, on canvas, was until recently in the Jacob H. Schiff collection, New York, the provenance of which has been confused with that of the present picture. In Homer's Jliad, Briseis was the favorite slave of Achilles, and the cause of his quarrel with Agamemnon; the latter took Briseis from Achilles by way of compen-sation for the surrender of Chryseis, who had fallen to Agamemnon as a prize of war; Achilles flying into a rage, does not repent of it until after the fall of Troy, when he became reconciled to Agamemnon and Briseis is returned to him.

Panel: 17 x 26¼ inches.

LENT BY MR. AND MRS. EDGAR B. WHITCOMB, DETROIT.

COLLECTIONS: Daniel Fourment (d. 1643), Rubens' father-in-law; Dr. Richard Mead (1673-1754), Rector of Stepney, London; R. Fulke Greville (d. 1806); The Barberini Palace, Rome, 1829; the Hon. George John, afterwards 5th Baron Vernon (1803-1866); Francis Lawrence, 9th Baron Vernon (1933); Colnaghi Galleries, London.

ENGRAVED by F. Ertinger in 1679, and B. Baron in 1724.

EXHIBITION: Detroit Institute of Arts, 1927, and 1936.

BIBLIOGRAPHY: JOHN SMITH: Catalogue Raisonné, Vol. II, 1830, pp. 250 and 252, No. 854; J. P. COLLOT: Sept esquisses de Rubens représ. la vie d'Achille, 1850; P. GERARD: P. P. Rubens, n.d., p. 413, (contains D. Fourment's Inventory, 1643); ANON: Jn Art Journal, 1855, p. 166; A. WAUTERS: Tapisseries Bruxelloises, 1878, pp. 236-238; J. GUIFFREY: Hist. de la Tapisserie, 1886, pp. 323, 486-488, No. 17; M. ROOSES: L'Oeuvre de Rubens, Vol. III, 1890, pp. 42-43; P. LAFOND: Jn Les Arts Anciens de Flandres, Vol. IV, 1902, p. 129; G. L. HUNTER: Jn International Studio, Dec. 1913; W. R. VALENTINER: The Art of the Low Countries, 1914, p. 188; R. OLDENBOURG: P. P. Rubens (Kl. der Kunst), 1921, p. 227, Jllust. Schiff version; H. GÖBEL: Tapestries of the Lowlands, 1924, p. 68; W. HEIL: Catalogue of Old and Modern Masters, Detroit Inst., 1927, p. 33, No. 54; W. R. VALENTINER: Catalogue of the Rubens Exhn., Detroit Inst., 1936, No. 45, Jllust.

RUBENS, SIR PETER PAUL

FLEMISH, 1577-1640

331 Study of a Negro.

Painted about 1624. One of the studies from life by Rubens for one of his 'Adorations of the Magi.'

Panel: 18 x 14 inches.

LENT BY MRS. LOUIS F. HYDE, GLENS FALLS, NEW YORK.

COLLECTION: Count Schwanenberg, Czechoslovakia.

BIBLIOGRAPHY: ANON: Catalogue of the Count Schwanenberg Collection, n.d., No. 19.

RUBENS, SIR PETER PAUL

FLEMISH, 1577-1640

332 Self Portrait.

Painted about 1625. Two other well-known versions of this portrait are in existence, differing in minor details, one in Windsor and one in the Offizi, Florence. The Windsor version, mentioned in a letter by Rubens in 1625, was painted by the artist at the request of the Prince of Wales, later Charles I.

Canvas: 32½ x 24½ inches.

LENT BY MR. ANDRÉ DE COPPET, NEW YORK.

COLLECTION: Madame Tampé, Paris.

EXHIBITION: Detroit Institute of Art, 1936; Dallas Museum, Texas, 1936.

BIBLIOGRAPHY: W. HEIL: In The Antiquarian, Dec. 1930, Illust., W. R. VALENTINER: Catalogue of the Rubens Exhn., Detroit Inst. of Arts, 1936, No. 28, Illust., E. P. RICHARDSON: In Detroit Inst. Bulletin, Feb. 1936, Illust., ANON: Catalogue of Paintings, Dallas Museum, Texas, 1936, p. 24, Illust.

RUBENS, SIR PETER PAUL

FLEMISH, 1577-1640

333 Clara Serena, the Artist's Daughter.

Painted about 1625. Born 1611, died 1623; one of the few portraits of the artist's daughter by his first wife Isabella Brandt.

Panel: 14 x 10¼ inches.

LENT BY MR. FREDERICK R. BAY, NEW YORK.

COLLECTION: Madame Camille Groult, Bagatelle, Paris; Sir Robert Abdy; Mrs. Cooper Hewitt (Lucy Work Hewitt), New York.

EXHIBITION: Detroit Institute of Arts, 1936.

BIBLIOGRAPHY: W. R. VALENTINER: Catalogue of the Rubens Exhibition, Detroit Inst., 1936, No. 29, Illust., M. VAUGHAN: In Parnassus, May 1939, p. 11, Illust.

RUBENS, SIR PETER PAUL

FLEMISH, 1577 - 1640

14 *Triumphal Entry of Henry IV into Paris after the Battle of Ivry.*

Painted between 1628-31. Preliminary sketch for the painting in the Uffizi, Florence (No. 729), which was painted for Marie de' Medici, Wife of Henry IV; probably inspired by Mantegna's noted 'Triumph of Caesar' at Hampton Court. The Battle of Ivry, between Henry IV and the Duke of Mayenne, General of the League, took place in March, 1590.

Panel: 19⅝ x 33½ inches.

LENT BY MRS. JOHN W. SIMPSON, NEW YORK.

COLLECTIONS: John Bligh, 4th Earl of Darnley; Ivo Francis, 9th Earl of Darnley, Cobham Hall, Kent.

EXHIBITIONS: Royal Academy, London, 1895; Detroit Institute of Arts, 1936.

BIBLIOGRAPHY: G. F. WAAGEN: Treasures of Art in Gt. Britain, Vol. III, 1854, pp. 23-24; E. MICHEL: Une Lettre inédite de Rubens, Paris, 1894 (re picture in the Bonnat Colln.); ANON: Catalogue of Old Masters, Royal Acad., Lond., 1895, p. 18, No. 65; M. ROOSES: L'Oeuvre de P. P. Rubens, Vol. II, 1904, pp. 523-529, *Uffizi picture Illust.*; E. DILLON: Rubens, 1909, pp. 158 and 232, *Uffizi picture Illust.*; W. R. VALENTINER: The Art of the Low Countries, 1914, p. 192; IDEM: Catalogue of the Rubens Exhn., Detroit Inst., 1936, No. 48, *Illust.*

RUBENS, SIR PETER PAUL

FLEMISH, 1577 - 1640

15 *The Crowning of Venus by Mars.*

Painted about 1630. Similar in style to the two compositions representing Venus, Mars, and Amor in Dulwich College and in Berlin (*Kl. der Kunst,* 1921, *p.* 330).

Canvas: 24 x 18½ inches.

LENT BY MR. JOHN BASS, NEW YORK.

EXHIBITION: Detroit Institute of Arts, 1936.

BIBLIOGRAPHY: W. R. VALENTINER: Catalogue of the Rubens Exhn., Detroit Inst., 1936, No. 51, *Illust.*

RUBENS, SIR PETER PAUL

FLEMISH, 1577 - 1640

Peace and Abundance.

Painted about 1634-35. A sketch for one of the Whitehall Ceiling series painted for Charles I. The complete sketch representing "The Benefits of the Government of James I", of which the present work is a detail, is in the Vienna Academy (*Kl der Kunst,* 1921, p. 335).

164

Panel: 25 x 18¼ inches.

LENT BY MR. AND MRS. PAUL KLOTZ, PONTRESINA, SWITZERLAND.
COLLECTIONS: King Charles I. of England (d. 1649); M. Davoust (sale 1772); J. B. Horion, Brussels (sale 1781); Sir Joshua Reynolds, President of the Royal Academy (sale 1795); Matthew Mitchell, Enfield (sale 1819); Colonel H. Baillie (1830); Leopold Koppel, Berlin; Kleinberger Galleries, New York.
EXHIBITION: Kleinberger Galleries, New York, 1911.
BIBLIOGRAPHY: J. SMITH: Catalogue Raisonné, Vol. II, 1830, p. 199, No. 717, and p. 235; M. ROOSES: L'Oeuvre de P. P. Rubens, Vol. II, 1890, p. 284, No. 766; E. DILLON: Rubens, 1909, pp. 156, 157 (re Whitehall ceiling); ANON: Paintings by Old Masters, Kleinberger Galleries, N. Y., 1911, No. 93, *Illust.*, R. OLDENBOURG: P. P. Rubens, (Kl. der Kunst), 1921, p. 336, *Illust.*

RUBENS, SIR PETER PAUL

FLEMISH, 1577 - 1640

337 *Allegory of the Reunion of England and Scotland.*

Painted about 1634-35. Sketch for one of the Whitehall ceiling series painted for Charles I alluding to the good government of James I. The child in the picture is intended for Charles I, with Britannia holding the Crown of England above his head. The complete sketch is in the Hermitage, Leningrad (*Kl. der Kunst*, 1921, p. 334).

Panel: 32½ x 27½ inches.

LENT BY THE MINNEAPOLIS INSTITUTE OF ARTS.
COLLECTIONS: Charles I, King of England (d. 1649); M. Davoust (sale 1772); J. B. Horion, Brussels (sale 1781); Sir Joshua Reynolds, President of the Royal Academy (sale 1795); Anatoli, Prince Demidoff (d. 1870); Prince Paul Demidoff, Palazzo San Donato, Florence (sale 1880); Charles Porgés, Paris; Albert Lehmann, Paris.
ENGRAVED by F. A. Milius.
EXHIBITIONS: Brussels, 1910; Ghent, 1915; Detroit Institute of Arts, 1936.
BIBLIOGRAPHY: G. VERTUE: Catalogue of King Charles the First's Colln. (after Vanderdoort's MSS), 1757, p. 161, No. 5; J. SMITH: Catalogue Raisonné, Vol. II, 1830, p. 199, No. 717, and p. 235; C. PILLET: Palais de San Donato Catalogue, Demidoff Colln., 1880, p. 231, No. 1098, *With Milius' engraving*; M. ROOSES: L'Oeuvre de P. P. Rubens, Vol. III, 1890, p. 286, No. 769; R. OLDENBOURG: P. P. Rubens, (Kl. der Kunst), 1921, p. 333, *Illust.*, W. R. VALENTINER: Catalogue of Rubens Exhibition, Detroit Inst., 1936, No. 52, *Illust.*

RUBENS, SIR PETER PAUL

FLEMISH, 1577 - 1640

338 *Daedalus and Icarus.*

Painted about 1636-1638. In Greek mythology, Daedalus constructed the labyrinth at Gnosus for the Minotaur, but he and his son Icarus were confined in it, because he had given Ariadna its clue. They succeeded in escaping by wings of wax made by Daedalus; Icarus, however, flew too near the sun, his wings melted and he fell into the sea.

Panel: 12¼ x 15 inches.

COLLECTIONS: Duc de l'Infantado; Duc de Pastrana, Madrid; Dowager Duchess of Pastrana, 1890.

BIBLIOGRAPHY: w. r. valentiner: Catalogue of Flemish Paintings, J. G. Johnson Collection, 1913, No. 665, *Illust.*

RUISDAEL, JACOB VAN

DUTCH, C. 1629-1682

Born at Haarlem. Son of a frame-maker, Jacob van Ruisdael. Did not devote himself at once to painting but practised surgery for a few years. Probably a pupil of Cornelius Vroom and of his uncle Salomon van Ruysdael. Worked at Haarlem and Amsterdam from 1657 to 1681. He became a citizen of Amsterdam in 1659. He was one of the greatest landscape painters of all time.

A View of Haarlem.

Signed in full at the lower left. One of the rare distant views of the artist, executed during his mature period, about 1660.

Canvas: 17 x 15 inches.

LENT BY THE RIJKSMUSEUM, AMSTERDAM, HOLLAND.

COLLECTIONS: Baron Nagel van Ampsen, The Hague, 1842; A. W. C. Baron Nagel van Ampsen, 1851; L. Dupper, Dordrecht, who bequeathed it to the museum in 1870.

BIBLIOGRAPHY: j. smith: Catalogue Raisonné, Supplement, 1842, p. 698, No. 52; w. p. brous: Wegwijzer door s'Rijksmuseum, Amsterdam, 1910, No. 2071; c. hofstede de groot: Catalogue Raisonné, Vol. IV; c. brière-misme: La Peinture Hollandaise, 1927, p. 42, *Illust.*, j. rosenberg: Jacob van Ruisdael, 1928, p. 74, No. 38.

RUISDAEL, JACOB VAN

DUTCH, C. 1630-1682

View of the Dunes.

Signed J. R. Painted in the early 'fifties. A very remarkable example of the artist's earlier period.

Panel: 13½ x 19 inches.

COLLECTIONS: John Smith, purchased in Paris, 1835; Charles Brind, 1849; Mrs. Lyne Stephens, Norfolk, 1895; Agnew Galleries, London.

EXHIBITION: British Institution, London, 1840.

BIBLIOGRAPHY: john smith: Catalogue Raisonné, Supplement, 1842, p. 699, No. 53; c. hofstede de groot: Catalogue Raisonné, Vol. IV, 1911, pp. 281, Nos. 897 and 914; w. r. valentiner: Catalogue of Dutch Paintings in the J. G. Johnson Colln., 1913, No. 563, *Illust.*, j. rosenberg: Jacob van Ruisdael, 1928, p. 107, No. 561, *Illust.*

RUISDAEL, JACOB VAN

DUTCH, C. 1630-1682

341 *Landscape with Windmill.*

Pl. 76 Signed with monogram, and dated 1657. One of the finest compositions of the artist in small compass.

> Panel: 12¾ x 14 inches.

LENT BY MR. AND MRS. EDGAR B. WHITCOMB, DETROIT.

COLLECTIONS: General R. de Verdier, 1816; Dr. M. Saportas, Amsterdam, 1829; W. Chaplin, London; Maurice Kann, Paris; Francis Kleinberger; Ludwig Mandl, Wiesbaden, 1923.

EXHIBITIONS: Detroit Institute of Arts, 1926, 1927.

BIBLIOGRAPHY: J. SMITH: Catalogue Raisonné, Vol. VI, 1835, p. 49, No. 155; C. HOFSTEDE DE GROOT: Catalogue Raisonné, Vol. IV, 1912, p. 62, No. 181; W. R. VALENTINER: Catalogue of Old Masters, Detroit Inst., 1926, No. 42, *Illust.*, IDEM: Catalogue of Old and Modern Masters, Detroit Inst., 1927, No. 49; J. ROSENBERG: Jacob van Ruisdael, 1928, p. 79, No. 110, *Illust.*

RUISDAEL, JACOB VAN

DUTCH, C. 1630-1682

342 *A Road by a Pool.*

Signed with monogram. One of the characteristic forest scenes of the artist, belonging to his mature period, c. 1660.

> Canvas: 19½ x 26 inches.

LENT BY MR. ADOLF MAYER, NEW YORK.

COLLECTIONS: The Empress Catherine II of Russia; The Hermitage, Leningrad.

EXHIBITIONS: The Hague, 1936-37; Museum Boymans, Rotterdam, 1938; Providence, Rhode Island, 1939.

BIBLIOGRAPHY: J. SMITH: Catalogue Raisonné, Vol. VI, 1835, p. 97, No. 310; F. REBER U. A. BAYERSDORFER: Klass. Bilderschatz, Vol. IX, 1899, No. 47; A. SOMOF: Ermitage Impérial, Catalogue des Tableaux, 1901, p. 379, No. 1141; C. HOFSTEDE DE GROOT: Catalogue Raisonné, Vol. IV, 1911, p. 160, No. 511; J. ROSENBERG: Jacob van Ruisdael, 1928, p. 91, No. 316; N. GERSON: *In* Burl. Mag., August 1934, p. 80, *Illust.*, D. HANNEMA: Meesterwerken uit vier eeuwen, 1400-1800, Museum Boymans, Rotterdam, 1938, p. 32, No. 128, *Illust.*, W. STECHOW: Dutch Painting in the XVII c., Rhode Island Museum, 1939, No. 43, *Illust.*

RUYSDAEL, SALOMON VAN

DUTCH, 1602-1670

Born at Haarlem, uncle of Jacob van Ruisdael. He appears to have studied under J. van Goyen, and probably influenced by E. van der Velde and P. Molyn. A member of the Haarlem Guild in 1623, and dean in 1648. He is said to have been the inventor of some artificial marble. He and Jan van Goyen were the chief of the Haarlem landscape painters prior to Jacob van Ruisdael.

343 *River Scene.*

Signed with monogram and dated 1645.

Canvas: 39 x 52⅜ inches.

LENT ANONYMOUSLY.

COLLECTIONS: Schamp d'Aveschoot, Leuven, 1840; Mme. Durray; Lord Aldenham, London; D. Katz, Dieren.

EXHIBITIONS: Amsterdam, 1938; Schaeffer Galleries, New York, 1939.

BIBLIOGRAPHY: W. STECHOW: Salomon van Ruysdael, 1938, p. 129, No. 517.

RUYSDAEL, SALOMON VAN

DUTCH, 1602-1670

4 *Winter Scene.*

Signed with monogram and dated—S V R. 1653.

Panel: 22 x 33 inches.

LENT ANONYMOUSLY.

COLLECTIONS: Major E. B. Forster, Dorchester, Eng.; Frank T. Sabin, London; D. Katz, Dieren.

EXHIBITIONS: Winter Landscapes, Amsterdam, 1932, No. 80; Rijksmuseum, Amsterdam, 1936; Dutch and Flemish Paintings, Amsterdam, 1938, No. 92; Museum of Art, Rhode Island School of Design, Providence, 1938.

BIBLIOGRAPHY: ANON: Catalogus, Tentoonstelling van oude Kunst Rijksmuseum, 1936, No. 140; W. STECHOW: Salomon van Ruysdael, 1938, pp. 68-69, No. 6, *Illust.*, IDEM: Dutch Painting in the Seventeenth Century, Rhode Island Museum, Providence, 1938, No. 48, *Illust.*

SANO DI PIETRO

SIENESE, 1406-1481

Asano di Pietro di Mencio, born and died in Siena, was a pupil of Sassetta, and greatly influenced by Giovanni di Paolo; he was a prolific artist, and his altarpieces still adorn many churches and convents of his native city. His works, although inclined to be sentimental they have great decorative qualities, and possess a sweetness of color which makes them very popular.

6 *Madonna and Child, with SS. Jerome and Francis, and two Angels.*

Panel: 10¼ x 15¾ inches.

LENT BY MR. ROBERT LEHMAN, NEW YORK.

BIBLIOGRAPHY: R. VAN MARLE: Ital. Schools, Vol. IX, 1927, p. 530; E. GAILLARD: Sano di Pietro, 1923, p. 204.

SANO DI PIETRO

SIENESE, 1406-1481

Madonna and Saints.

Panel: 29 x 20 inches.

LENT BY SENATOR AND MRS. SIMON GUGGENHEIM, NEW YORK.
COLLECTIONS: Sansedoni Family, Siena; Marquis de Grolée-Virvelle, Florence; Luigi Grassi, Florence.

SASSETTA (STEFANO DI GIOVANNI)
SIENESE, 1392-1450

Stefano di Giovanni, known as Sassetta, was a pupil of Paolo di Giovanni Fei, and perhaps of Bartolo di Fredi; influenced by the Lorenzetti, and probably by Masolino, Paul de Limbourg and similar Franco-Flemish artists and miniaturists. He was commissioned to design a font for the Duomo, Siena, in 1427. In 1447 he began the frescoes of the Porta Romana, Siena, which were afterwards finished by Sano di Pietro.

347 *St. Anthony distributes his Money to the Poor.*
Pl. 7 (Companion to No. 347A).

Painted about 1420-1430. According to Waterhouse, this picture, and its companion, formed part of a polyptych dedicated to St. Anthony which is now distributed among the respective collections of the Kaiser Friedrich Museum, Berlin, Yale University, Samuel H. Kress, and Philip Lehman.

Panel: 17¾ x 13½ inches.

LENT BY THE ESTATE OF DAN FELLOWS PLATT, ENGLEWOOD, N. J.
COLLECTION: Dr. Nevin, Rector of the American Church, Rome.
EXHIBITION: Kleinberger Galleries, New York, 1917.
BIBLIOGRAPHY: F. M. PERKINS: In Rassegna d'Arte, Vol. VII, 1907, p. 45, Illust., B. BERENSON: Central Ital. Painters, 1909, p. 245; O. SIREN AND M. W. BROCKWELL: Loan Exhibition, Kleinberger Gall., 1917, p. 141, Illust., R. VAN MARLE: Ital. Schools, Vol. IX, 1927, p. 328; E. K. WATERHOUSE: In Burl. Mag., Sept. 1931, p. 108, Illust., B. BERENSON: Ital. Pictures, 1932, p. 512 (Ital. Edn., 1936, p. 440); L. VENTURI: Ital. Paintings in Amer., 1933, No. 138, Illust.

SASSETTA (STEFANO DI GIOVANNI)
SIENESE, 1392-1450

347a *St. Anthony leaves the Monastery for Alexandria.*
(Companion to No. 347).

Panel: 17¾ x 13½ inches.

LENT BY THE ESTATE OF DAN FELLOWS PLATT, ENGLEWOOD, N. J.
Refer to previous entry for particulars.

SASSETTA (STEFANO DI GIOVANNI)
SIENESE, 1392-1450

18 ## St. George and St. Nicholas.

When in the Butler Collection these panels formed the wings of a portable triptych, the central panel of which represented the Madonna and Child, by a Follower of Simone; the panel is now in the Philip Lehman Collection.

Panels: Each 9¾ x 3½ inches.

LENT BY MR. ROBERT LEHMAN, NEW YORK.

COLLECTIONS: Charles Butler; Captain H. L. Butler; Captain R. Langton Douglas, London; Philip Lehman, New York.

BIBLIOGRAPHY: CROWE AND CAVALCASELLE: Painting in Italy, Vol. III, 1908, p. 70; R. LEHMAN: The Philip Lehman Collection, New York, 1928, No. 40, *Illust.*, B. BERENSON: Ital. Pictures, 1932, p. 513 (Ital. edn. 1936, p. 441); L. VENTURI: Ital. Paintings in America, 1933, No. 153, *Illust.*

SASSETTA (STEFANO DI GIOVANNI)
SIENESE, 1392-1450

19 ## The Journey of the Three Kings.

Painted about 1430. The main panel of the polyptych, 'The Birth of the Virgin', etc., of which this painting formed part of the *predella*, is now in the Collegiata of Ascanio.

Panel: 9 x 12 inches.

LENT BY MR. MAITLAND F. GRIGGS, NEW YORK.

COLLECTIONS: Samuel Rogers, London, 1856; Rev. Walter Davenport Bromley, 1863; Monckton Milnes, afterwards Lord Houghton; Marchioness of Crewe, 1912; Capt. R. Langton Douglas.

EXHIBITIONS: Knoedler Galleries, London, 1929; Royal Academy, London, 1930; Wadsworth Atheneum, 1931; Chicago Institute of Art, 1933; Detroit Institute of Arts, 1933; Century Club, New York, 1935; Cleveland Museum of Art, 1936.

BIBLIOGRAPHY: R. FRY: *In* Burl. Mag., Vol. XXII, 1912, p. 131, *Illust.*, R. VAN MARLE: Ital. Schools, Vol. IX, 1927, pp. 340-341, *Illust.*, H. COMSTOCK: *In* International Studio, Oct. 1927, p. 41, *Illust.*, E. CECCHI: *In* Trecentisti senesi, 1928, pp. 117-118, *Illust.*, T. BORENIUS: *In* Apollo, Vol. XI, 1930, p. 155, *Illust.*, W. R. VALENTINER: Unknown Masterpieces, 1930, No. 4, *Illust.*, BALNIEL AND CLARK: Exhn. of Ital. Art, Royal Acad., London, 1930, p. 31, No. 88; B. BERENSON: Ital. Pictures, 1932, p. 513 (Ital. edn., 1936, p. 441, *Illust.*); L. VENTURI: Ital. Paintings in America, 1933, No. 143, *Illust.*, W. R. VALENTINER: Ital. Paintings of the XIV-XV c., Detroit Inst., 1933, No. 49a; IDEM: *In* Pantheon, Aug. 1936, p. 240; D. C. RICH: Exhibition of Paintings, Chicago Art Inst., 1933, pp. 15-16, No. 94, *Illust.*, H. TIETZE: Meisterw. Europä. in Amerika, 1935, No. 36, *Illust.*, H. S. FRANCIS: Exhibition of Paintings, Cleveland Museum of Art, 1936, pp. 62-73, *Illust.*, A. M. FRANKFURTER: *In* Art News, May 1, 1937, *Illust. in Color.*

SASSETTA (STEFANO DI GIOVANNI)

SIENESE, 1392-1450

350 *The Adoration of the Shepherds, with SS. John and Bartholomew.*

A Triptych, painted about 1430.

Panels: 21¼ x 16 inches.

LENT BY MR. AND MRS. HAROLD I. PRATT, NEW YORK.

COLLECTIONS: Max Chabrières-Arlés, Lyons; Lord Duveen of Millbank; Francis Kleinberger.

EXHIBITIONS: Kleinberger Galleries, New York, 1917; Fogg Art Museum, Cambridge.

BIBLIOGRAPHY: O. SIRÉN: *In* Art in America, June 1917, pp. 206-207, *Illust.;* IDEM and M. W. BROCKWELL: Exhibition of Ital. Primitives, Kleinberger Gall., 1917, pp. 137-138, No. 51, *Illust.;* R. VAN MARLE: Ital. Schools, Vol. XI, 1927, p. 361; B. BERENSON: Ital. Pictures, 1932, p. 247 (Ital. edn., 1936, p. 212), as *Giovanni di Paolo.*

SASSETTA (STEFANO DI GIOVANNI)

SIENESE, 1392-1450

351 *The Virgin Annunciate.*

Painted between 1430-1432. This panel formed, originally, the right pinnacle crowning the so-called 'Madonna of the Snow' Altarpiece of the Duomo, Siena, the large centre panels and the predella of which are now at Chiusdino; the left pinnacle, the *Angel Annunciate,* is at Massa Marittima.

Panel: 21¾ x 13½ inches.

LENT ANONYMOUSLY.

COLLECTIONS: Capt. Langton R. Douglas; Dan Fellows Platt.

BIBLIOGRAPHY: F. M. PERKINS: *In* Rassegna d'Arte, Vol. XI, 1911, p. 4, *Illust.;* IDEM: *In* Rassegna d'Arte, Vol. XII, 1912, p. 196; G. DE NICOLA: *In* Burl. Mag., Aug. 1913, p. 278, *Illust.;* R. VAN MARLE: Italian Schools, Vol. IX, 1927, pp. 334-5, *Illust.;* B. BERENSON: Italian Pictures, 1932, p. 512, (*Ital. edn.,* 1936, p. 440); L. VENTURI: Italian Pictures in America, 1933, No. 144, *Illust.*

SEGHERS, HERCULES

DUTCH, 1589-1638

Born probably at Haarlem. At Amsterdam he became a pupil of Gillis van Coninxloo. In 1612 he became a member of the Guild in Haarlem at the same time as E. van de Velde and Willem Buytewech. Most of his life he was active in Amsterdam, except for some years at Utrecht and The Hague. He was misunderstood by artists as well as by his family, and died in poverty. He made about sixty etchings, many of which were printed on linen, said by some to be from his shirts and bed-linen. Only few paintings are known by him. Seghers may be called the prede-

cessor of Van Gogh, not only in his artistic efforts but also in his tragic life. His
was a similarly intense, searching nature. Isolated from the movement of art in his
time and from the world about him. In works by Fraenger and Pfister (1921) he is
characterized as an "expressionist" and compared with the modern German expres-
sionists, whose art at that time was at its height. Segher's great historical importance lies in the fact that he brings to completion sixteenth century landscape art
and connects it with the future subjective style of Rembrandt.

52 *The Valley of the Maas.*

Painted about 1630. The color scheme is based upon the three planes of sixteenth
century landscape painting, brown, grey and blue, in receding order, yet it is combined with realistic observation refined to a degree unknown to any of the earlier
artists. In this work we are reminded of the panoramic views of the 'world-land-
scape' conception which prevailed from Patinir to Breughel.

Canvas: 15⅜ x 25 inches.

LENT BY THE DETROIT INSTITUTE OF ARTS.

BIBLIOGRAPHY: W. R. VALENTINER: *In* Detroit Inst. of Arts, Bulletin, Nov. 1938, pp. 4-8,
Illust., IDEM: *In* Art News, Nov. 5, 1938, p. 14, *Illust.*, Art Digest, Nov. 15, 1938, p. 12, *Illust.*,
M. BREUNING: *In* Amer. Mag. of Art, May 1939, p. 281.

SEGHERS, HERCULES

DUTCH, 1589-1638

53 *A Romantic Landscape.*

Closely related in style and composition to Seghers' etching, "The city with the
four towers". Painted about 1620-30.

Panel: 18 x 35 inches.

LENT BY MR. H. E. TEN CATE, ALMELO, HOLLAND.

COLLECTIONS: A private collection in Germany; D. Katz, Dieren.
EXHIBITIONS: Kleykamp Galleries, The Hague, 1934; Rhode Island Museum, School of De-
sign, Providence, 1938; Schaeffer Galleries, New York, 1939.
BIBLIOGRAPHY: J. SPRINER: Die Radierung des H. Seghers, Vol. LIX, 1912, p. 26, *Illust.* the
'Four Towers' etching, E. TRAUTSCHOLDT: *In* Thieme-Becker's Lexikon, Vol. XXX, 1936, p. 44;
W. STECHOW: Dutch Painting in the XVII c., Rhode Island Mus. Providence, No. 49, *Illust.*,
A. P. A. VORENKAMP: *In* Art News, Dec. 1938, p. 11, *Illust.*, A. M. FRANKFURTER: *In* Art News,
Feb. 1939, p. 8, *Illust.*

SIGNORELLI, LUCA

UMBRO-FLORENTINE, 1450?-1523

Born at Cortona; was the pupil of Piero della Francesca and much influenced by
Antonio Pollaiuolo, Perugino, and Francesco di Giorgio. He worked especially in
frescoes, and was painting in Arezzo in 1472 and in Città di Castello in 1474; he

visited Rome about 1482, and there painted, in the Sistine Chapel, scenes from the history of Moses. In 1484 he was back again in Cortona, where, in 1488, he was elected a magistrate; his chief works, the frescoes in the Cathedral of Orvieto, were painted after his sixtieth year. Signorelli holds a place among the greatest mural painters of the Renaissance, and may be called a predecessor of Michelangelo.

354 The Madonna and Child.

Painted about 1490-1495.

Panel: 20¼ x 18½ inches.

LENT BY THE JULES S. BACHE COLLECTION, NEW YORK.

COLLECTIONS: Casa Tommasi, Cortona; Robert H. and Evelyn Benson; Lord Duveen of Millbank.

EXHIBITIONS: Burlington Fine Arts Club, London, 1893, and 1910; New Gallery, London, 1893-1894; Manchester Art Gallery, 1927; Royal Academy, London, 1930.

BIBLIOGRAPHY: R. VISCHER: Luca Signorelli, 1879, p. 260; M. CRUTTWELL: Luca Signorelli, 1899, p. 13; L. CUST: In Les Arts, Oct. 1907, p. 30, Illust., B. BERENSON: Central Italian Painters, 1909, p. 249; Burl. F. A. Club: Catalogues of the Signorelli Exhibition, 1910, p. X; and the Umbrian Exhibition, 1910, p. 26; T. BORENIUS: Catalogue of the Benson Collection, 1912, pp. 85-86, Illust., A. VENTURI: Storia dell'Arte Italiana, Vol. VII, Part 2, 1913, p. 406, Note 1; CROWE AND CAVALCASELLE: History of Painting in Italy, Ed. by T. Borenius, Vol. V, 1914, p. 116, Note 5, Illust., T. BORENIUS: In Apollo, Aug. 1727, p. 65, Illust., L. DUSSLER: Signorelli, 1927, p. 56, Illust., W. HEIL: In "The Art News," April 27, 1929, p. 31, Illust., W. R. VALENTINER: Unknown Masterpieces, 1930, No. 14, Illust., B. BERENSON: Italian Pictures of the Renaissance, 1932, p. 532, (Ital. Edn., 1936, p. 458); L. VENTURI: Italian Paintings in America, Vol. II, 1933, No. 278, Illust., H. TIETZE: Meisterwerke Europäischer Malerei in Amerika, 1935, No. 59, Illust., ANON: Catalogue of the Bache Collection, New York, 1938, No. 14, Illust.

SIGNORELLI, LUCA

UMBRO-FLORENTINE, C. 1450-1523

355 Eunostos of Tanagra (Presumed).

Pl. 21   Painted about 1500. One of a series of eulogistic panels devoted to 'Heroes and Heroines' by various masters, probably painted for a member of the Piccolomini family. Six other panels of this series are known; Claudia, by Neroccio (Kress Colln.); Sulpicia, by Pacchiarotto (Walters Colln.); Scipio Africanus, by Francesco di Giorgio (Bargello); Alexander the Great, by Signorelli (Cook Colln.); Tiberius Gracchus, by Signorelli (Budapest); St. Barbara, by Signorelli (Poldi-Pezzoli, Milan). B. Berenson believes the backgrounds of the three last mentioned pictures and the present one to be by the hand of the so-called 'Griselda Master'. Eunostos, a hero of Tanagra, Boeotia, Greece, son of Elicus, was so named because he was brought up by the nymph Eunoste. His cousin, Ochne, fell in love with him, but he repulsed her. In revenge her brothers slew him and she, in remorse, threw herself over a cliff.

Panel: 35 x 21 inches.

LENT ANONYMOUSLY.

COLLECTIONS: Lord Ashburnham; Lord Northampton; Edouard Kann; Morland Agnew.
EXHIBITIONS: Chicago Art Institute, 1934; Cleveland Museum of Art, 1936.
BIBLIOGRAPHY: G. DE NICOLA: Jn Burl. Mag., Nov. 1917, p. 224; B. BERENSON: Jn Dedalo, Apr. 1931, p. 753, Jllust., IDEM: Jn International Studio, Apr. 1931, p. 20, Jllust., L. VENTURI: Ital. Paintings in Amer., 1933, No. 280, Jllust., D. C. RICH: Exhibition of Paintings, Chicago Inst., 1934, No. 37, Jllust., H. COMSTOCK: Jn International Studio, Oct. 1934, pp. 258-260, Jllust., H. S. FRANCIS: Catalogue of Paintings, Cleveland Museum of Art, 1936, pp. 63-64, No. 147.

SIGNORELLI, LUCA

UMBRO-FLORENTINE, 1450?-1523

56 St. Mary Magdalen.

Panel: 24½ x 17½ inches.

LENT BY THE JOHN G. JOHNSON COLLECTION, PHILADELPHIA.
COLLECTION: Marchese Mancini, Citta di Castello.
BIBLIOGRAPHY: F. MASON-PERKINS: Jn Rassegna d'Arte, 1905, p. 121; B. BERENSON: Central Italian Painters, 1909, p. 250; IDEM: Italian Paintings in the John G. Johnson Collection, Philadelphia, 1913, No. 135, Jllust., CROWE AND CAVALCASELLE: Painting in Italy, Vol. V, 1914, p. 112; B. BERENSON: Italian Pictures, 1932, p. 533; R. VAN MARLE: Italian Schools of Painting, Vol. XIV, 1933, p. 466.

SOLARIO, ANDREA

MILANESE, ACTIVE 1490-1515

Born at Milan. Possibly instructed by his brother, Cristofero, a sculptor and architect of eminence; he was formed under Alvise Vivarini and strongly influenced by Gentile Bellini, Antonello, and Leonardo da Vinci. With his brother he went to Venice in 1490, and returned to Milan about 1495. In 1507 he went to France and worked at the Chateau de Gaillon (destroyed during the Revolution) near Louviers, for Cardinal George of Amboise; he returned to Milan in 1509. His later paintings show in their enamel-like technique the influence of Flemish art.

57 The Madonna and Child, known as 'The Pitti Madonna'.

Painted about 1500. "Later than the Brera 'Madonna', dated 1495, and earlier than the 'Madonna of the Green Cushion' in the Louvre, this is perhaps the first composition of the nursing Madonna imagined by the artist. The Venetian and Antonellian tradition is very much alive in him." (L. Venturi).

Canvas, transferred: 20 x 14 inches.

LENT BY MR. AND MRS. HAROLD I. PRATT, NEW YORK.

COLLECTIONS: The Pitti Family, Florence; E. Finzi, Cremona; Comm. Cristoforo Benigno Crespi, Milan; F. Kleinberger.

EXHIBITION: Kleinberger Galleries, New York, 1917.

BIBLIOGRAPHY: A. VENTURI: Galleria Crespi, 1900, p. 230, *Illust.*, B. BERENSON: Study and Criticism, Vol. I, 1903, p. 107; IDEM: North Ital. Painters, 1907, p. 294; CROWE AND CAVALCASELLE: Painting in North Italy, Vol. II, 1912, p. 385; L. DE SCHLEGEL: *Jn* Rassegna d'Arte, Vol. XIII, 1913, p. 91, *Illust.*, M. NICOLLE: Galerie Crespi, 1914, pp. XV, 71, No. 57, *Illust.*, K. BADT: Andrea Solario, 1914, p. 202; A. VENTURI: Storia dell'Arte Ital., Vol. VII, 4, 1915, p. 958; O. SIREN and M. W. BROCKWELL: Exhn. of Ital. Paintings, Kleinberger Gall., N. Y., 1917, p. 214, *Illust.*, B. BERENSON: Ital. Pictures, 1932, p. 542 (Ital. Edn., 1936, p. 466); L. VENTURI: Ital. Paintings in America, 1933, No. 473, *Illust.*

STEEN, JAN

DUTCH, C. 1626-1679

Born at Leyden and died there at the age of fifty-three. He studied at The Hague under Jan Van Goyen whose daughter he married in 1649. He entered the corporation of painters at Leiden in 1648, went to The Hague in 1649 and remained there until 1654, when he went to Delft and leased a brewery for six years. During 1661-1669 he resided at Haarlem, and afterwards returned to Leyden, where he opened a tavern but still worked diligently at his easel. Next to Rembrandt the most imaginative artist of the Dutch school; a great narrator and humorist, and a master in characterizing the life of the middle classes in Holland. His great predecessor is Pieter Breugel, while in literature the comedies of Shakespeare form the parallel to Steen's versatile art.

358 *The Doctor's Visit.*

Pl. 74   Signed: J. Steen.

Panel: 17¾ x 14⅜ inches.

LENT BY THE JOHN G. JOHNSON COLLECTION, PHILADELPHIA.

COLLECTIONS: J. H. and C. Van Heemskerck; Baron Nagel; Quintin Crawford; Lord Kinnaird; Albert Levy; J. Louis Miéville; John G. Johnson.

EXHIBITION: Royal Academy, London, 1878.

BIBLIOGRAPHY: J. SMITH: Catalogue Raisonné, Vol. IV, 1833, p. 24, No. 76; T. VAN WESTRHEENE: Jan Steen, 1856, No. 362; C. HOFSTEDE DE GROOT: Catalogue Raisonné, Vol. I, 1907, p. 58, No. 172; W. R. VALENTINER: Flemish and Dutch Paintings in the John G. Johnson Collection, Phila., 1913, p. 101, No. 510, *Illust.*

STEEN, JAN

DUTCH, C. 1626-1679

359 *The Artist and his Family.*

Signed: J. Steen.

Canvas: 26 x 34 inches.

COLLECTIONS: Gerard van Oostrum; Duc d'Alberg; G. W. Taylor; Jacob Roelofs; John N. Hughes; H. A. J. Munro; Charles Butler; Maurice Kann; W. K. Bixby; Joseph L. Buttenwieser.
EXHIBITIONS: Royal Academy, London, 1881; Lawrie Gallery, London, 1903; Schaeffer Gallery, Berlin, 1929; Kleinberger Galleries, New York, 1931; Cleveland Museum, 1936.
BIBLIOGRAPHY: J. SMITH: Catalogue Raisonné; Supl., 1842, p. 509, No. 94; G. F. WAAGEN: Treasures of Art, Vol. II, 1854, p. 137; T. VAN WESTRHEENE: Jan Steen, 1856, p. 116, No. 75; C. HOFSTEDE DE GROOT: Catalogue Raisonné, Vol. I, 1907, p. 236, No. 869; G. K. NÄGLER: Kunstler-Lexikon, Vol. XIX, 1912, p. 318; H. S. FRANCIS: Catalogue of the Great Lakes Exposition, Cleveland Museum, 1936, p. 926, No. 242; W. R. VALENTINER: In Art News, Oct. 31, 1931, Illust.

STEEN, JAN

DUTCH, C. 1626-1679

60 Peasants before an Inn.

An early work. The landscape shows the influence of Van Goyen; the grey silvery tone is connected with the painters of the Frans Hals school. "Painted with the addition of that natural humour and variety of character, peculiar alone to Jan Steen" (Smith).

Panel: 24½ x 26½ inches.

LENT BY MR. H. E. TEN CATE, ALMELO, HOLLAND.
COLLECTIONS: Gerard Copius, The Hague, 1786; Paigron Dijonval, Paris, 1821; Thomas Emmerson; Jeremiah Harman, 1844; Thomas French, London, 1855; Charles Nieuwenhuys; Sir Hugh Campbell; Lord Masham; Lady Cunliffe-Lister; D. Katz, Dieren.
EXHIBITIONS: "Arti et Amictiae", Amsterdam, 1938; Museum Boymans, Rotterdam, 1938.
BIBLIOGRAPHY: J. SMITH: Catalogue Raisonné, Vol. IV, 1833, p. 43-44, No. 133; T. VON WESTRHEENE: Jan Steen, 1856, No. 84; C. HOFSTEDE DE GROOT: Catalogue Raisonné, Vol. I, 1907, pp. 168-169, No. 645; ANON: Tentoonstelling schilderijen van oude incesters, Amsterdam, 1938, No. 81; D. HANNEMA: Meesterwerken uit vier eeuwen, 1400-1800, Museum Boymans, Rotterdam, 1938, p. 35, No. 140.

STEEN, JAN

DUTCH, C. 1626-1679

61 The Fair at Oegstgeest.

Signed: J. Steen. An early work of the artist showing his rich imagination in the variety of different types.

Canvas: 28 x 39 inches.

LENT ANONYMOUSLY.
COLLECTIONS: De Schieter van Lophen, Brussels; D. Katz, Dieren.
EXHIBITIONS: Rijksmuseum, Amsterdam, 1936; Rhode Island Museum, Providence, R. I., 1938.
BIBLIOGRAPHY: ANON: Tentoonstelling Oude Kunst, Rijksmuseum, Amsterdam, 1936, p. 38, No. 152, Illust., W. STECHOW: Dutch Painting in the XVII century, Rhode Island Mus., Providence, 1938, No. 57, Illust.

STEEN, JAN

DUTCH, C. 1626-1679

362 *The Twelfth-Night Feast*, known also as *Le Roi Boit*

Pl. 73 ('The King Drinks')

Signed and dated, J. *Steen, 1662*. One of the most important compositions of the artist, painted during his best period in the early sixties.

Canvas: 51 x 63½ inches.

LENT BY MRS. J. C. HARTOGS, ARNHEM, HOLLAND.

COLLECTIONS: M. Crawford, London, 1806?; Henry Hirsch; H. Van Praagh; Kleykamp Galleries, The Hague.

EXHIBITIONS: Kleykamp Galleries, The Hague, 1934; Museum Boymans, Rotterdam, 1934 and 1938.

BIBLIOGRAPHY: ANON: Catalogue of Pictures, Henry Hirsch Collection, London, 1934, p. 6, No. 144, *Illust.*, D. HANNEMA: Meesterwerken uit vier eeuwen, 1400-1800, Museum Boymans, Rotterdam, 1938, p. 36, No. 146, *Illust.*

STRIGEL, BERNHARD

GERMAN, C. 1460-1528

Born at Memmingen, Bavaria. About 1480 he went to Ulm, where he studied for some time in the workshop of Zeitblom, later becoming his assistant; he returned to Memmingen before 1516 and remained there until his death. He was employed at different times by the Emperor Maximilian I.

363 *Portrait of a Man.*

Probably the Burgomaster of Memmingen. (Companion to No. 364.)

Dated 1527. (*Translation of inscription on frame:* "Just in the year reported I too had myself painted 1527, and it was done on the 16th day of October, my age being 26 as I stated").

Panel: 17 x 13½ inches.

LENT BY THE RALPH HARMAN BOOTH COLLECTION, DETROIT.

COLLECTIONS: Manoli Mandelbaum; Julius Böhler.

EXHIBITIONS: Städel-Institut, Frankfurt, 1926; Detroit Institute of Arts, 1923, 1926, and 1927; Chicago Art Institute, 1933.

BIBLIOGRAPHY: W. R. VALENTINER: *In* Detroit Inst. Bul., March 1923, p. 52, *Illust.*, K. T. PARKER U. W. HUGELSHOFER: *In* Belvedere, Vol. VIII, 1925, pp. 32-33; G. SWARZENSKI, Edr.: Zweite Veröffentl. des Städels ches Kunstinst. 1926, p. 70, No. 201, note; A. L. MAYER: *In* Pantheon, Vol. III, 1929, p. 1, *Illust.*, D. C. RICH: Catalogue of Paintings and Sculpture, Art. Inst. of Chicago, 1933, p. 5, No. 32a; C. L. KUHN: German Paintings in Amer. Collections, 1936, p. 63, No. 258, *Illust.*

STRIGEL, BERNHARD

GERMAN, C. 1460-1528

4
45
Portrait of a Woman.

Probably the wife of the Burgomaster of Memmingen. (Companion to No. 363.) Dated 1527.

Panel: 17 x 13½ inches.

LENT BY THE RALPH HARMAN BOOTH COLLECTION, DETROIT.

COLLECTIONS: Manoli Mandelbaum; Julius Böhler.

EXHIBITION: Städel-Institut, Frankfort, 1926; Detroit Institute of Arts, 1923, 1926, and 1927.

BIBLIOGRAPHY: w. r. valentiner: Jn Detroit Inst. Bul., March 1923, p. 52, Jllust., k. t. parker u. w. hugelshofer: Jn Belvedere, Vol. VIII, 1925, pp. 32-33, Jllust., g. swarzenski, Edr.: Zweite Veröffentl. des Städels'ches Kunstinst., 1926, p. 70, No. 201, note; a. l. mayer: Jn Pantheon, Vol. III, 1929, p. 1, Jllust., c. l. kuhn: German Paintings in Amer. Collections, 1936, p. 63, No. 259, Jllust.

SUSTERMANS, JUSTUS

FLEMISH, 1597-1681

Born at Antwerp. Pupil of William de Vos in 1610, and of F. Pourbus II in Paris. Went to Italy and was painter to Cosimo II de' Medici at Florence in 1620. In 1624 he was sent to Vienna and was ennobled with his five brothers. In 1645 he went to Rome, Geneva, Medina, Parma, Milan, and in 1653 to Innsbruck. He was influenced greatly by Rubens and the Italian baroque painters.

5
Portrait of a Cavalier.

Painted about 1630. In the Holford Catalogue the portrait is given as that of Cardinal Gian Carlo de' Medici.

Canvas: 81 x 47 inches.

LENT BY MR. JACOB EPSTEIN, BALTIMORE, MD.

COLLECTIONS: Robert Stayner Holford; Sir George Lindsay Holford, Dorchester House, London; Knoedler Galleries, New York.

EXHIBITIONS: Royal Academy, London, 1908 and 1927; Chicago Art Institute, 1934.

BIBLIOGRAPHY: anon: Catalogue of Old Masters, Royal Academy, London, 1908, No. 128; anon: Arundel Club Publication, 1908, No. 9, Jllust., p. bautier: Juste Suttermans, 1912, pp. 32, 123, Jllus., idem: Jn Cicerone, Vol. VI, 1914, p. 613, Jllust., r. benson: The Holford Collection, Vol. II, 1927, p. 18, No. 122, Jllust., t. borenius: Catalogue of Dutch and Flemish Paintings, Royal Academy, London, 1927, p. 66, No. 148; p. lambotte: Flemish and Belgian Art, 1300-1900, 1927, p. 118, Jllust., idem: Flemish Painting before the XVIII c., 1927, Jllust., m. chamot: Jn Country Life, London, Vol. LXIII, 1928, pp. 635-636, Jllust., w. gibson: Jn Apollo, Vol. VII, 1928, p. 203, Jllust. in color, d. c. rich: Exhibition of Paintings, Chicago Art Inst., 1934, p. 19, No. 110, Jllust.

TENIERS THE YOUNGER, DAVID

FLEMISH, 1610-1690

Born at Antwerp. Was taught painting by his father, the elder Teniers, and was later strongly influenced by Adriaen Brouwer. In 1632-33 he became a member of the Antwerp Guild. He soon became the most popular genre painter in Flanders, and his works were in universal request. The Archduke Leopold William, Governor of the Spanish Netherlands, appointed him his court painter and one of his chamberlains. He became wealthy and bought a country-seat at Perck, a village near Antwerp, which became the constant resort of Spanish and Flemish nobility. He died in Brussels.

366 *The Prodigal Son.*

Signed in full at the left. Belongs to the best period of the artist, about 1640. The high price it fetched at the San Donato sale in 1880 (81,000 francs = $20,000) corresponds to the somewhat exaggerated appreciation of Teniers during the XVIII and XIX c. Rembrandt's 'Girl in a Doorway', now in the Chicago Art Institute, fetched at the same sale 123,000 francs. According to the present estimation of Rembrandt it would be worth at least ten times as much as any painting by Teniers.

Copper: 22½ x 30½ inches.

LENT BY MRS. I. D. LEVY, NEW YORK.

COLLECTIONS: The Escurial Palace, Madrid; Maréchal Sebastiani, 1851; Chevalier Sebastian Erard, Chateau Muette, 1833; Robert White; John Webb, 1853; Davis MacIntosh, 1857; Joseph Eugène Schneider; Charles E. Newton, 1870; Prince Paul Demidoff, San Donato, 1880; Sir Anthony Rothschild; Hon. Mrs. Yorke, London, 1927.
ENGRAVED by Jules Jacquemart, in Gazette des Beaux-Arts, 1877, p. 419.
EXHIBITION: Derby Art Gallery, 1870.
BIBLIOGRAPHY: J. SMITH: Catalogue Raisonné, Vol. III, 1831, p. 307, No. 172; Supplement, 1842, p. 427, No. 68; ANON: Catalogue of the Erard Collection, 1833, No. 142; C. PILLET: Catalogue, Palais de San Donato, Florence, 1880, pp. 244-245, No. 1119.

TERBORCH, GERARD

DUTCH, 1617-1681

Gerard Terborch, or Terburg, was born at Zwolle. His father was a wealthy man, four of whose children were noted in the arts. Gerard, the eldest son, was chiefly influenced by the school of Frans Hals, but by repeated travelling to England, Germany, and Italy, he was enabled to study the works of Titian, Valesquez, and other great masters. In 1646 he went to Munster, and painted the "Ratification of the Treaty of Peace", now in the National Gallery. In 1654 he married at Deventer, of which town he became Burgomaster. There he passed the remainder of his life. He is the greatest genre painter of Holland in representing scenes from the daily life of the upper classes. He also painted excellent portraits of small size.

7 Curiosity.

74 Painted during the best period of the artist, about 1660-65.

Canvas: 29 x 32 inches.

LENT BY THE JULES S. BACHE COLLECTION, NEW YORK.

COLLECTIONS: Gaillard de Gagny, 1762; Lalive de Jully, 1770; Randon de Boisset, 1777; M. Robit, 1801; Duchesse de Berry, 1837; Baron von Mecklenburg, 1854; Prince Demidoff, 1868; Baron Achille Seillière; Baroness Mathilde de Rothschild; Baron Goldschmidt de Rothschild; Lord Duveen of Millbank.

EXHIBITIONS: London, 1834, with the Collection of the Duchesse de Berry, for private sale; Royal Academy, London, 1929.

BIBLIOGRAPHY: P. RÉMY: Catalogue des tableaux du cabinet de Gaillard de Gagny, 1762; IDEM: Catalogue des tableaux du cabinet de Lalive de Jully, 1770; IDEM: Catalogue des tableaux du cabinet de Randon de Boisset, 1777, p. 26, No. 52; PAILLET ET DELAROCHE: Riche Collection de Tableaux, Collection Robit, 1801; W. BUCHANAN: Collection of the Citizen Robit. In Memoirs of Painting, Vol. II, 1824, p. 67, No. 45; J. SMITH: Catalogue Raisonné, Vol. IV, 1835, No. 6; C. HOFSTEDE DE GROOT: Catalogue Raisonné, Vol. V, 1913, No. 169; A. ALEXANDER: In La Renaissance, March 1929, p. 122, Illust., W. G. CONSTABLE and H. SCHNEIDER: Exhibition of Dutch Art, Royal Academy, London, 1929, No. 231, Illust., W. HEIL: In The Art News, April 27, 1929, p. 16, Illust., P. HENDY: Catalogue of the Gardner Museum, Boston, 1931, p. 252; CATALOGUE of the Bache Collection, New York, 1938, No. 39, Illust.

TERBORCH, GERARD
DUTCH, 1617-1681

The Music Lesson.

Painted about 1650. Signed, with the Monogram. Another version is in the Isabella Stewart Gardner Museum, Boston; and a third belonged to C. Sedelmeyer, Paris, in 1898.

Canvas: 25 x 19¼ inches.

LENT BY THE ART INSTITUTE OF CHICAGO.

COLLECTIONS: Gabriel François Joseph, Chevalier de Verhulst, Brussels, 1779; Prince Galitzine, 1825; John Fairlie, 1830; Prince Paul Demidoff (?) San Donato, 1880; Charles T. Yerkes, Chicago, 1891.

ETCHED by Daniel Mordant (1853-1914).

EXHIBITIONS: Detroit Institute of Arts, 1929; Art Institute of Chicago, 1933-1934.

BIBLIOGRAPHY: J. SMITH: Catalogue Raisonné, Vol. IV, 1833, p. 124, No. 20; F. HELLENS: Gérard Terborch, 1911, p. 127; C. HOFSTEDE DE GROOT: Catalogue Raisonné, Vol. V, 1913, pp. 47-48, No. 130; ANON: In Antiquarian, Sept. 1927, p. 27, Illust., W. R. VALENTINER: Exhibition of Dutch Painting, Detroit Inst., 1929, No. 74, Illust., P. HENDY: Catalogue of the Isabella Stewart Gardner Museum, Boston, 1931, p. 355; D. C. RICH: Exhibition of Paintings, Art Inst. of Chicago, 1933, p. 13, No. 79, Illust., 1934, p. 20, No. 113.

TERBORCH, GERARD

DUTCH, 1617-1681

369 *A Gentleman Greeting a Lady.*

One of the finest works by the master, painted in the 'sixties of the XVII century.

Canvas: 32 x 30 inches.

LENT BY THE NATIONAL GALLERY OF ART
(MELLON COLLECTION), WASHINGTON.

COLLECTIONS: Charles-Auguste-Louis-Joseph, Duc de Morny, Paris; Marquis de Salamanca, Madrid; Baron Adolf de Rothschild, Paris; Baron Maurice de Rothschild.

ENGRAVED on Wood by E. Sotain.

BIBLIOGRAPHY: L. LEGRANGE: *In* Gaz. des B.-Arts, April 1863, pp. 296-298, *Illust.*; ANON: Catalogue des Tableaux, Colln. de Duc de Morny, 1865, pp. 52-53, No. 82; E. LE ROY: Catalogue des Tableaux, Galerie de Marquis de Salamanca, 1867, p. 95, No. 126; C. HOFSTEDE DE GROOT: Catalogue Raisonné, Vol. V, 1913, p. 72, No. 196 (confused with the dissimilar Stafford picture).

TIEPOLO, GIOVANNI BATTISTA

VENETIAN, 1696-1770

Tiepolo, the last of the great Venetian painters, studied under Gregorio Lazzarini, and influenced by Paolo Veronese. In 1715 he married Guardi's sister. He worked in Venice until 1740, when he went to Genoa, Milan, and Würtzburg, returning to Venice in 1753. In 1755 he became first director of the Venice Academy, resigned in 1762, and went to Madrid, where he died.

370 *The Madonna and Child: with an Adoring Figure.*

Pl. 36   Painted about 1715-16. The picture belongs to the earliest phase of the painter's work, which is very rare in Europe and hitherto not represented by any important picture in America; it reveals him as a baroque artist before his study of Paolo Veronese had changed his palette and produced the rococo artist with whom we are familiar. A. Morassi (*Burl. Mag.*) believes this picture was originally of larger proportions, and served as a great altarpiece. In the Cassel Gallery is a small *modello,* with other figures added, which must have served as a preliminary study for the Detroit picture.

Canvas: 74 x 57 inches.

LENT BY THE DETROIT INSTITUTE OF ARTS.

COLLECTION: A private owner in Bologna. (Given to the Detroit Museum by Mr. and Mrs. Edsel Ford in 1938.)

BIBLIOGRAPHY: A. MORASSI: *In* Burl. Mag., Oct. 1935, pp. 143-149, *Illust.*, ANON: *In* Art News, Nov. 19, 1938, p. 18; E. P. RICHARDSON: *In* Detroit Inst. Bulletin, Dec. 1938, pp. 1-6, *Illust.*, ANON: *In* Art Quarterly, Detroit Inst. of Arts, Autumn, 1938, p. 327, *Illust.*, ANON: *In* Art Digest, Dec. 15, 1938, p. 13, *Illust.*

TIEPOLO, GIOVANNI BATTISTA

VENETIAN, 1696-1769

1 *The Procession to Calvary ('Via Dolorosa').*

Painted between 1745-1750.

Canvas: 34¾ x 31¼ inches.

LENT ANONYMOUSLY.

COLLECTIONS: Mme. Antoine Brentano, *née* de Birchenstock; Charles Sedelmeyer; Consul Eduard Weber; Samuel H. Kress; Knoedler Galleries.

ETCHED by Charles Courtry, 1872.

EXHIBITIONS: Il Settecento Italiano, Venice, 1929; Toronto Art Gallery, 1931; Springfield Museum, 1933; Chicago Art Institute, 1938.

BIBLIOGRAPHY: ANON: Catalogue de la Galerie de Mme. A. Brentano, 1870, p. 86, No. 173; C. SEDELMEYER: Gemälde moderne und alter Meister, 1872, No. 159, *Illust.*, J. VON PFLUGK-HARTUNG: *In* Rep. für Kunstw., Vol. VIII, 1885, p. 83; F. HARCK: *In* Arch. Storico, Vol. IV, 1891, p. 89; J. NÖHRING: Sammlung Weber, 1898, No. 45, *Illust.*, C. SEDELMEYER: Paintings by Old Masters, 1898, p. 282, No. 256, *Illust.*, B. BERENSON: Venetian Painters, 1903, p. 133; K. WOERMANN: Der Galerie Weber, 1907, No. 159, *Illust.*, P. MOLMENTI: G. B. Tiepolo, 1909, p. 273; E. SACK: G. and D. Tiepolo, 1910, p. 189, No. 330, *Illust.*, A. SEEMANN: G. B. Tiepolo, n.d., No. 3, *Illust. in color*, L. ROSENBERG: *In* Gaz. d. Beaux-Arts, Jan. 1930, p. 40, *Illust.*

TIEPOLO, GIOVANNI BATTISTA

VENETIAN, 1696-1769

2 *The Crucifixion (Golgotha).*

Painted between 1755-1760.

Canvas: 34¾ x 31¼ inches.

LENT ANONYMOUSLY.

COLLECTIONS: Mme. Antoine Brentano, *née* de Birckenstock; Charles Sedelmeyer; Consul Eduard F. Weber; Samuel H. Kress; Knoedler Galleries.

ETCHED by Charles Courtry, 1872.

EXHIBITIONS: Wadsworth Atheneum, Hartford, Conn., 1928; Il Settecento Italiano, Venice, 1929; Toronto Art Gallery, 1931; Springfield Museum, 1933; Durlacher Gallery, New York, 1934; Knoedler Galleries, London, 1935, and New York, 1936; Chicago Art Institute, 1938.

BIBLIOGRAPHY: ANON: Catalogue de la Galerie de Mme. A. Brentano, 1870, p. 87, No. 174; C. SEDELMEYER: Gemälde moderner und alter Meister, 1872, No. 160, *Illust.*, J. VON PFLUGK-HARTUNG: *In* Rep. für Kunstw., Vol. VIII, 1885, p. 83; F. HARCK: *In* Arch. Storico, Vol. IV, 1891, p. 89; J. NÖHRING: Sammlung Weber, 1898, No. 45, *Illust.*, C. SEDELMEYER: Paintings by Old Masters, 1898, p. 282, No. 257, *Illust.*, B. BERENSON: Venetian Painters, 1903, p. 133; K. WOERMANN: Der Galerie Weber, 1907, No. 160, *Illust.*, P. MOLMENTI: G. B. Tiepolo, 1909, p. 273; E. SACK: G. and D. Tiepolo, 1910, p. 189, No. 329, *Illust.*, L. ROSENBERG: *In* Gaz. d. Beaux-Arts, Jan. 1930, p. 40.

TIEPOLO, GIOVANNI BATTISTA
VENETIAN, 1696-1770

373 The Last Supper.

Painted about 1760. A preliminary study for an altarpiece.

Canvas: 32¾ x 23¼ inches.

LENT BY THE WADSWORTH ATHENEUM, HARTFORD, CONN.

EXHIBITION: Springfield Museum of Fine Arts, 1933.

BIBLIOGRAPHY: A. E. AUSTIN: In Wadsworth Museum Bulletin, July 1931, p. 1, Illust., E. S. SIPLE: In Burl. Mag., Feb. 1932, p. 111, Illust., T. H. PARKER: Catalogue of the Opening Exhibition, Springfield Museum, 1933, No. 85.

TIEPOLO, GIOVANNI BATTISTA
VENETIAN, 1696-1770

374 The Flight into Egypt.

This imaginative composition is an early work by the artist of the same period as the large 'Madonna and Child' at Detroit (this Exhibition No. 370).

Canvas: 24¾ x 19¾ inches.

LENT ANONYMOUSLY.

COLLECTIONS: Bernardo Speranza, Bergamo.
ENGRAVED by Fabio Berardi, Venice.
EXHIBITION: Palazzo Pitti, Florence, 1922.
BIBLIOGRAPHY: C. CAVERSAZZI: In Emporium, Feb. 1924, p. 135, Illust. with Berardi's engraving, A. MORASSI: In Burl. Mag., pp. 91-92, Illust. also with Berardi's engraving, M. NUGENT: Alla Mostra d. Pittura Italiana, Palazzo Pitti, 1925, p. 102; P. MOLMENTI: Tiepolo, la sua Vita e le sue Opere, n.d., p. 58; H. DE CHENNEVIERES: Le Tiepolo, 1898, p. 18; E. SACK: G. B. Tiepolo u. Dom. Tiepolo, 1910, p. 228; ANON: Catalogo, Mostra d. Pittura Italiana, 1600-1700, Palazzo Pitti, 1922, No. 995.

TIEPOLO, GIOVANNI DOMENICO
VENETIAN, 1727-1804

Born in Venice. Son of Giovanni Battista Tiepolo, and nephew of Francesco Guardi. He was a pupil of and assistant to his father. In 1743 he went to Dresden, at the court of Charles Philip, Duke of Franconia, and returned to Venice in 1745. In 1750 he was in Würzburg. In 1761 he accompanied his father, and his brother Lorenzo to Spain, and after the death of his father in Madrid (1769) he returned to Venice. In 1771 became President of the Venice Academy, and reproduced many of his father's works as etchings on copper. In 1783 he went to Genoa and worked in the Doge's palace. In 1788 he dropped out of active life and retired to Murano.

5 *Landscape, with Mars and Venus.*

6 *Landscape, with Fishing Scene.*

Canvas: 25 x 35 inches each.

LENT BY MR. JAMES SPEYER, NEW YORK.

COLLECTION: Bought in Venice in 1912.

TINTORETTO (JACOPO ROBUSTI)

VENETIAN, 1518-1594

Born in Venice. Pupil of Titian; influenced by Michelangelo. Devoted a great part of his life in Venice to the decoration of palaces and public buildings. He was one of the greatest draughtsmen of the sixteenth century, and ranks with Titian as a portrait painter. Berenson says of him that he "painted portraits not only with much of the air of good breeding of Titian's likenesses, but with even greater splendour, and with an astonishing rapidity of execution."

7 *Christn on the Sea of Galilee.*

13 Painted about 1550.

Canvas: 45¾ x 66¼ inches.

LENT BY MR. ARTHUR SACHS, NEW YORK.

COLLECTIONS: Count J. Galotti; Durlacher Galleries, New York.
EXHIBITIONS: Fogg Art Museum, 1927; Metropolitan Museum of Art, New York, 1932-33; Art Institute of Chicago, 1933; Knoedler Galleries, New York, 1938; California Palace of the Legion of Honor, San Francisco, 1938; Durlacher Galleries, New York, 1939.
BIBLIOGRAPHY: D. C. RICH: Exhn. of Paintings, Art Inst. of Chicago, 1933, No. 135, *Illust.*, ANON: *In* Connoisseur, May 1933, p. 344, *Illust.*, ANON: Catalogue of Venetian Exhn., Knoedler Galleries, N. Y., 1938, p. 25, No. 16, *Illust.*, W. HEIL: Venetian Painting, XV-XVI c., Cal. Pal. of the Legion of Honor, San Francisco, 1938, No. 66, *Illust.*, A. M. FRANKFURTER: *In* Art News Suppt., March 26, 1938, p. 31, *Illust.*, J. W. LANE: *In* Apollo, April 1938, p. 210, *Illust.*, M. VAUGHAN: *In* Parnassus, April 1938, p. 12, *Illust.*, ANON: Catalogue of the Tintoretto Exhn., Durlacher Galleries, N. Y., 1939, No. 5; T. BORENIUS: *In* Burl. Mag., Mar. 1939, p. 138.

TINTORETTO (JACOPO ROBUSTI)

VENETIAN, 1518-1594

Lucretia and Tarquinius.

Painted about 1560. In Roman legendary history, Lucretia was the wife of Tarquinius Collatinus. Her criminal attack by Sextus Tarquinius led to the overthrow of his father, Tarquinius Superbus (534-510 B.C.) and the establishment of the republic.

Canvas: 68¾ x 60 inches.

184

COLLECTION: Cardinal Bernis.
EXHIBITION: Knoedler Galleries, New York, 1939.
BIBLIOGRAPHY: ANON: Classics of the Nude Exhn., Knoedler Galleries, N. Y., 1939, p. 15, No. 10, *Illust.*

TINTORETTO (JACOPO ROBUSTI)
VENETIAN, 1518-1594

379 *Hercules and Antaeus.*

Painted about 1568-70. In Greek mythology, Antaeus, a Libyan giant and wrestler, son of Poseidon, was invincible while his feet remained on his mother Earth. Strangers in his country were compelled to wrestle with him, but with inevitable defeat, and Antaeus built a mansion for his father with his victims' skulls. Hercules discovered the secret of his strength and, lifting him off the ground, held him aloft until he had killed him.

Canvas: 60 x 40 inches.

LENT BY THE WADSWORTH ATHENEUM, HARTFORD, CONN.
COLLECTIONS: Viscountess Wolseley, Scanes Hill, Sussex.
EXHIBITIONS: Toronto Art Gallery, 1935; State University of Iowa, 1936; Durlacher Galleries, New York, 1939.
BIBLIOGRAPHY: A. E. AUSTIN: *In* Wadsworth Atheneum Bull., Jan. 1928, p. 2, *Illust.,* ANON: *In* Revue de l'Art Bulletin, 1928, p. 114; B. BERENSON: Ital. Pictures, 1932, p. 560 (Ital. edn., 1936, p. 481); L. VENTURI: Ital. Paintings in Amer., 1933, No. 550, *Illust.,* A. M. FRANKFURTER: *In* Art News Annual, March 1938, p. 172, *Illust.,* ANON: Catalogue of Tintoretto Exhn., Durlacher Galleries, N. Y., 1939, No. 2.

TINTORETTO (JACOPO ROBUSTI)
VENETIAN, 1518-1594

380 *Tancred Baptising Clorinda.*

Pl. 34 Painted about 1582. In Tasso's 'Jerusalem Delivered' (1581) Clorinda is an Amazonian leader, and of acknowledged prowess in the infidel army. She is beloved by Tancred, one of the chief heroes of the first Crusade (1096-99), but she cares only for the glories of war. Tancred kills her unwittingly during a night attack, but gives her a Christian baptism before she expires.

Canvas: 66½ x 45 inches.

LENT BY MRS. FRANK Y. LOGAN, CHICAGO.
EXHIBITIONS: Art Institute of Chicago, 1925; California Palace of the Legion of Honor, San Francisco, 1938; Durlacher Galleries, 1939.
BIBLIOGRAPHY: D. VON HADELN: *In* Art in America, June 1924, p. 156, *Illust.,* R. M. F.: *In*

Art Inst. of Chicago Bulletin, May 1925, p. 59, *Illust.*; B. BERENSON: Ital. Pictures, 1932, p. 558 (Ital. edn., 1936, p. 480); L. VENTURI: Ital. Paintings in America, 1933, No. 552, *Illust.*, W. HEIL: Catalogue of Venetian Paintings, Calif. Palace of Legion of Honor, 1938, No. 65, *Illust.*, ANON: Catalogue of Tintoretto Exhn., Durlacher Galleries, 1939, No. 10; M. BREUNING: *In* Amer. Mag. of Art, Feb. 1939, p. 99, *Illust.*; T. BORENIUS: *In* Burl. Mag., Mar. 1939, p. 138.

TITIAN (TIZIANO VECELLIO)

VENETIAN SCHOOL, 1477?-1576

Titian, or Tiziano Vecellio, son of Gregorio Vecelli and elder brother of Francesco, was born at Pieve di Cadore, Friuli, about 1477 (or, according to other sources, ten years later); he first studied at his native place, and as a boy was put in the care of Giovanni Bellini; he was later influenced by Raphael and Michelangelo. From 1507-1508 he worked with Giorgione in the decoration of the Fondaco dei Tedeschi at Venice. In 1511 he executed three frescoes in the Scuola del Santo at Padua. In 1516 he painted the "Assumption of the Virgin" for Santa Maria de Frari; and in 1528 "St. Peter Martyr" for San Giovanni e Paolo. After 1530 he executed several commissions for Federigo Gonzaga, the Pope Paul III, and the Emperor Charles V. After the abdication of Charles V, Titian found as great a patron in Philip II of Spain. He died at Venice on August 17, 1576, during a plague. He was the greatest Venetian painter of the sixteenth century.

1 *Giorgio Cornaro with a Falcon* (Presumed).

30 Painted about 1535. Signed *Ticianus f.* The subject is said to be a member of a Venetian noble family and brother of Caterina Cornaro (1454-1510), who married James II of Cyprus in 1472, and was noted for her court for poets and scholars at Asolo, near Bassano. Giorgio was a statesman and General of the Venetian Republic, born in 1455 and died in 1527. According to L. Venturi the picture was once entitled "A portrait of Federigo Gonzaga". It is possible, therefore, that it represents a member of the Gonzaga-Este family. It recalls the cavalier in the so-called 'Alfonso d'Este and his Mistress', in the Kress Collection.

Canvas: 43 x 38 inches.

LENT ANONYMOUSLY.

COLLECTIONS: The Carignan Branch of the Royal House of Piedmont; Louis-François de Bourbon, Prince de Conti (1717-1776); Earl of Carlisle, Castle Howard, Yorks.; Edward F. Milliken, New York; Dr. Eduard Simon, Berlin; Lord Duveen of Millbank; Alfred W. Erickson, New York.

ENGRAVED by William Skelton, 1811.

EXHIBITIONS: British Institution, London, 1818 and 1844; New Gallery, London, 1894-95; Kaiser-Friedrich Museums-Verein, Berlin, 1909; Detroit Institute of Arts, 1928; Wadsworth Atheneum, 1937.

BIBLIOGRAPHY: ANON: Catalogues des Tableaux, Prince de Carignan, Paris, 1743, p. 42; ANON: Collection Louis François de Bourbon, Paris, 1777, p. 32, No. 92; ANON: Catalogues, British Inst., London, 1818, p. 15, No. 73, and 1844, p. 9, No. 44; G. F. WAAGEN: Treasures of

Art in Gt. Britain, Vol. II, 1854, p. 278; CROWE AND CAVALCASELLE: Life and Times of Titian, Vol. II, 1881, pp. 19-20; ANON: Venetian Art at the New Gallery, 1894-95, p. 44, *Illust.*, G. GRONAU: Titian, 1904, p. 307; O. FISCHEL: Titian (Kl. der Kunst), 1907, p. 233, No. 62, *Illust.*, 5th edn., n.d., p. 310, No. 74, *Illust.*, ANON: Ausstellung von Bildnissen, Kaiser Friedrich Museums-Verein, 1909, p. 23, No. 148, *Illust.*, C. RICKETTS: Titian, 1910, No. 77, *Illust.*, V. BASCH: Titian, 1918, p. 157; E. WALDMANN: Tizian, 1922, p. 224; F. E. W. FREUND: *In* International Studio, May 1928, p. 36, *Illust.*, E. SINGLETON: Old World Masters, 1929, p. 147, *Illust.*, B. BERENSON: Ital. Pictures, 1932, p. 573 (Ital. Edn. 1936, p. 493, *Illust.*); L. VENTURI: Ital. Paintings in Amer., 1933, No. 513, *Illust.*, H. TIETZE: Meisterw. Europä. Malerei in Amer., 1935, No. 86, *Illust.*, IDEM: Titian, 1937, p. 336, No. 77, *Illust.*, W. SUIDA: Tizian, 1933, p. 168, No. 128, *Illust.*

TITIAN (TIZIANO VECELLIO)

VENETIAN, 1477?-1576

382 *A Portrait of a Venetian Nobleman.*

Pl. 30   Painted about 1550.

Canvas: 47½ x 36½ inches.

LENT BY THE JULES S. BACHE COLLECTION, NEW YORK.

COLLECTIONS: Prince Alberto Giovanelli; Lord Duveen of Millbank.

EXHIBITION: Detroit Institute of Arts, Sixth Loan Exhibition of Old Masters, 1928.

BIBLIOGRAPHY: LAFENESTRE ET RICHTENBERGER: La Peinture en Europe: Venise, N.d., p. 317; B. BERENSON: Venetian Painters of the Renaissance, 1897, p. 139; U. OJETTI: *In* "Dedalo", July 1925, pp. 133-136, *Illust.*, F. E. WASHBURN-FREUND: *In* International Studio, May 1928, p. 39, *Illust.*, IDEM: *In* Der Cicerone, Vol. XX, 1928, p. 254, *Illust.*, W. HEIL: Catalogue of the Loan Exhibition of Paintings by Titian, Detroit Inst. of Arts, 1928, No. 17, *Illust.*, IDEM: *In* The Art News, April 27, 1929, p. 15, *Illust.*, H. E. WORTHAM: *In* Apollo, Vol. XI, 1930, p. 350, *Illust.*, A. L. MAYER: *In* Pantheon, Vol. VI, 1930, p. 537, *Illust.*, B. BERENSON: Italian Pictures of the Renaissance, 1932, p. 573, (Ital. Edn., 1936, p. 493); L. VENTURI: Italian Paintings in America, Vol. III, 1933, No. 522, *Illust.*, W. SUIDA: Tizian, 1933, p. 167, pl. CLXXXIV; ANON: Catalogue of Paintings in the Bache Collection, New York, 1938, No. 15, *Illust.*

TITIAN (TIZIANO VECELLIO)

VENETIAN SCHOOL, 1477?-1576

383 *Giulia di Gonzaga-Colonna, Duchess of Traetto* (presumed).

Painted about 1550. Giulia di Gonzaga-Colonna was noted for her grace and beauty. She was married to Vespasiano Colonna, Duke of Trajetti, who was forty years her senior; becoming a widow in 1528 she was much sought after by some of the most prominent men of her time, among them being Cardinal Hippolyte de' Medici, and Soliman II, Sultan of Turkey, who, in 1539, ordered Admiral Barberoussa to kidnap her during his occupation of Fondi, near Naples, but she had already taken flight. She died in 1566.

Canvas: 38½ x 29⅛ inches.

TITIAN (TIZIANO VECELLIO)

VENETIAN SCHOOL, 1477?-1576

4 *Venus and Adonis.*

Painted about 1658-1560. Adonis, the son of Myhrra, was brought up by the
Dryades, and possessed such beauty that Venus, in her fascination, left Olympus
to follow him in his hunting pursuits; he was killed by a boar, and from the spot
on which his blood fell sprang the anemone. So great was the grief of Venus that
the gods allowed him to return to life and to spend half of the year in the lower
and the other half in the upper world. This allegory has reference to the death of
nature in winter and its revival in spring.

Canvas: 42 x 52½ inches.

TITIAN (TIZIANO VECELLIO)

VENETIAN, 1477?-1576

5 *Adoration of the Magi.*

Painted about 1560. A replica of this picture is in the Prado, Madrid. In the
Brocklebank Catalogue the present picture is referred to as coming from the
Orleans and West collections.

Canvas: 55½ x 88 inches.

188

LENT BY MR. ARTHUR SACHS, NEW YORK.
COLLECTIONS: The Orleans Gallery; Walsh Porter, 1810; Benjamin West, President of the Royal Academy; Samuel Rogers, Noted English Poet (1856); Hugh A. J. Munro, Novar Collection, 1878; Butler Johnstone; William Graham, 1886; Ralph Brocklebank, 1922; Durlacher Galleries, New York.
EXHIBITIONS: Fogg Art Museum, Cambridge; Metropolitan Museum of Art, New York, 1930; Chicago Art Institute, 1933; Cleveland Museum of Art, 1936.
BIBLIOGRAPHY: ANON: Catalogue of Pictures, Walsh Porter Collection (Christie's), April 14, 1810, No. 38; G. F. WAAGEN: Treasures of Art in Gt. Britain, Vol. II, 1854, p. 267; CROWE AND CAVALCASELLE: Life and Times of Titian, Vol. II, 1881, p. 308; G. REDFORD: Art Sales, Vol. I, 1888, p. 104; R. R. CARTER: Pictures at Haughton Hall, Brocklebank Collection, 1904, pp. 4-5, No. 2; B. BURROUGHS: Metro. Mus. Bull., Dec. 1930, p. 268, Illust.; A. L. MAYER: In Pantheon, Feb. 1930, pp. 60-61, Illust., L. VENTURI: Ital. Paintings in Amer., 1933, No. 526, Illust., D. C. RICH: Exhibition of Paintings, Art Inst. of Chicago, 1933, p. 22, No. 138, Illust.; H. S. FRANCIS: Exhn. of Paintings, Cleveland Museum, 1936, p. 76, No. 180, Illust., H. TIETZE: Titian, 1937, p. 336, No. 257, Illust.

TITIAN (TIZIANO VECELLIO)
VENETIAN SCHOOL, 1477?-1576
386 *A Man with a Flute.*
Signed: *Titianus f.* Painted about 1560.

Canvas: 38½ x 27 inches.

LENT BY THE DETROIT INSTITUTE OF ARTS.
COLLECTIONS: Baron von Stumm; Van Diemen; R. Langton Douglas.
EXHIBITIONS: Agnew Galleries, New York, 1926; Detroit Institute of Arts, 1927 and 1928; Dallas Museum of Fine Arts, 1936; California Palace of the Legion of Honor, San Francisco.
BIBLIOGRAPHY: DETLEV BARON V. HADELN: In Burl. Mag., Nov. 1926, p. 234, Illust., F. J. MATHER, JNR.: In The Arts, Vol. X, 1926, p. 312, Illust., W. HEIL: In Detroit Mus. Bul., Nov. 1927, pp. 14-15, Illust., L. VENTURI: Italian Paintings in America, 1933, No. 529, Illust., W. SUIDA: Titian, 1933, pp. 111, 177, 182, Illust., H. TIETZE: Titian, 1936, p. 286, Illust., W. HEIL: Catalogue of Paintings, Cal. Palace of the Legion of Honor, San Francisco, 1938, No. 72, Illust.

TITIAN (TIZIANO VECELLIO)
VENETIAN, 1477?-1576
387 *Self-Portrait.*
Painted about 1565. The inscription on the drawing board is not contemporary, and the date and age of the subject is evidently erroneous. L. Venturi identifies this portrait as the one in the Renieri collection, Vienna, in 1663. Another version, on a circular panel, was at one time in the collection of the Earl of Malmesbury.

Canvas: 45 x 37 inches.

LENT BY MR. WILLIAM R. TIMKEN, NEW YORK.

COLLECTIONS: Niccolo Renieri (Nicholas Regnier), Venice (1590-1667); Catherine II. of Russia, who gave it to Count Raczinsky; Raczinsky Colln.; Lord Melbourne; Van Diemen Galleries, New York.

ENGRAVED by Giovanni Britto without the 'Medici Venus' for which Pietro Aretino wrote a sonnet in 1550.

BIBLIOGRAPHY: P. ARETINO: Libro delle Lettere, Vol. V, 1550, p. 288; F. SANSOVINO: Venetia citta nobilissima, Venice, 1663, p. 377; G. CAMPORI: Raccolta di Cataloghi, 1870, pp. 442-443; CROWE AND CAVALCASELLE: Life and Times of Titian, Vol. II, 1881, p. 65; G. REDFORD: Art Sales, Vol. I, 1888, p. 250, Vol. II, p. 253, (Malmesbury portrait); G. GRONAU: In Berlin Jahrbuch, 1907, p. 47, With Britto's engraving; P. KONODY: In Thieme-Becker's Lexikon, Vol. V, 1911, p. 31; G. M. RICHTER: In Burl. Mag., April 1931, p. 167; L. VENTURI: Ital. Paintings in America, Vol. III, 1933, No. 528, Illust.

TITIAN (TIZIANO VECELLIO)

VENETIAN SCHOOL, 1477?-1576

8
31
Judith with the Head of Holofernes.

Painted about 1565-70.

Canvas: 44¼ x 37 inches.

LENT BY THE DETROIT INSTITUTE OF ARTS.

COLLECTIONS: Marchese Andrea Gerini, Florence, 1759; Col. W. Cornwallis West; A. L. Nicholson.

EXHIBITION: Burlington Fine Arts Club, London, 1914.

BIBLIOGRAPHY: ANON: Raccolta di Stampe rappresentanti i quadri piu scelti de' Signori Marchesi Gerini, Firenze, 1759, Illustrated with engraving, R. H. BENSON: The Venetian School, Burl. F. A. Club, London, 1915, p. 57, No. 47, Illust., T. BORENIUS: In Burl. Mag., Aug. 1922, p. 88, Illust., A. VENTURI: Storia dell'Arte Ital., Vol. IX, 3, 1928, p. 367, Illust., O. FISCHEL: Tizian, (Kl. der Kunst), 5th edn., p. 325, No. 271, Illust., G. BIERMANN: In Cicerone, Vol. XXI, 1929, pp. 317-320, Illust., W. SUIDA: Tizian, 1933, pp. 133, 172, No. 233a, Illust., W. R. VALENTINER: In Detroit Inst. Bul., May 1935, pp. 102-104, Illust., G. M. RICHTER: In Burl. Mag., Nov. 1938, p. 191.

TURA, COSIMO

FERRARESE, C. 1430-1495

Born at Ferrara. Studied in the school of Squarcione at Padua, afterwards strongly influenced by Donatello, Castagno, and other Florentines; possibly also by Tavernier and other miniaturists of the Burgundian court. From 1451 he was in the permanent service of the Dukes of Ferrara but painted for other noble patrons elsewhere. About 1470 he painted frescoes for Duke Borso in the Schifanoia Palace, and in 1480 he worked in the Ferrara Cathedral. He was the first Ferrarese painter to reach a position of eminence, and his art is noted for its extraordinary intensity and sharpness of design.

9
The Madonna and Child.

Closely related to the artist's small Madonna in the Palazzo Colonna, Rome; the ornamental details recall the Enthroned Allegorical Figure in the National Gallery (Layard Collection), London.

Panel: 21 x 15 inches.

LENT BY MR. AND MRS. HAROLD I. PRATT, NEW YORK.

COLLECTIONS: Lord Duveen of Millbank; Francis Kleinberger.

EXHIBITIONS: Kleinberger Galleries, New York, 1917; Century Club, New York, 1935.

BIBLIOGRAPHY: o. sirén and m. w. brockwell: Italian Masters Exhibition, Kleinberger Galleries, N. Y., 1917, p. 197, Illust.; a. venturi: Studi dal Vero, 1927, p. 156, Illust., idem: La Pittura del Quattrocentro nell'Emilia, 1931, p. 38; idem: North Italian Painters of the Quattrocento Emilia, n.d., pp. 40, 97, Illust., b. berenson: Ital. Pictures, 1932, p. 581 (Ital. Edn., 1936, p. 500); l. venturi: Ital. Paintings in America, 1933, No. 344, Illust., anon: Catalogue of Ital. Renaissance Paintings, Century Club, N. Y., 1935, No. 16; a. m. frankfurter: In Art News, March 9, 1935, p. 11.

UCCELLO, PAOLO

FLORENTINE, 1397-1475.

Born in Florence; brought up as a goldsmith, assisting Ghiberti, influenced by Donatello and Domenico Veneziano. He painted frescoes in the Cathedral at Florence in 1437, and in S. Maria Novella in 1447. He was mostly active in Florence, but travelled to Venice during the earlier part of his life, and towards the end of his life worked in Urbino. He was one of the pioneers in perspective foreshortenings, and in his decorative sense, and his monumental expression of movement and character, is one of the leading Florentine masters in the earlier part of the fifteenth century.

390 Profile Portrait of a Girl.

Pl. 13

Probably a portrait of Elisabetta da Montefeltro, wife of Roberto Malatesta, and daughter of Federigo of Urbino and Battista Sforza. The painting is a masterpiece of Florentine portraiture of about 1460-65. The rarity of portraits of this period and the greater difficulty in recognizing an artist's hand in a portrait than in other paintings have caused the art critics to hesitate between an attribution to Domenico Veneziano (B. Berenson), Paolo Uccello (L. Venturi, P. Hendy) and the Master of the Castello Nativity (R. Offner). The picture is most likely by the same hand which executed the profile of a girl in the Gardner Collection in Boston and the portrait of the Duchess of Urbino in the Philip Lehman Collection, New York. All three seem to have been executed in Urbino, the two girl portraits representing probably two daughters of the Duchess. As Uccello (and the Master of the Castello Nativity) worked at Urbino at that time, an attribution to one of the two masters is more likely than the one to Domenico Veneziano. Also the style is nearer to Paolo Uccello.

Panel: 15½ x 10½ inches.

LENT BY THE JULES S. BACHE COLLECTION, NEW YORK.

COLLECTIONS: Robert S. Holford; Sir George Lindsay Holford; Lord Duveen of Millbank.

EXHIBITIONS: Burlington Fine Arts Club, 1910 and 1921-22.

BIBLIOGRAPHY: ANON: Exhn. Catalogues, Burl. Fine A. Club, 1910, p. 18, No. 5, *Illust.*, and 1921-22, p. 17, No. 12; R. FRY: *In* Burl. Mag., Feb. 1910, p. 274; O. FISCHEL: *In* Amtliche Berichte, Berlin Mus. Vol. XLI, Col. 116-117, *Illust.*, R. H. BENSON: Cat. of Holford Colln., 1924, pp. 42-43, No. 14, *Illust.*, W. HEIL: *In* Art News, Apr. 27, 1929, p. 32, *Illust.*, A. L. MAYER: *In* Pantheon, Vol. VI, 1930, p. 537, *Illust.*, L. VENTURI: *In* L'Arte, 1930, p. 64, *Illust.*, B. BERENSON: Ital. Pictures, 1932, p. 172; R. OFFNER: *In* Burl. Mag., Oct. 1933, p. 178; L. VENTURI: Ital. Paintings in Amer., 1933, No. 195, *Illust.*, G. PUDELKO: *In* Art Bulletin, Vol. XVI, 1934, p. 249; M. SALMI: Uccello, Castagno, and Dom. Veneziano, 1936, p. 107, *Illust.*, J. LIPMAN: *In* Art Bulletin, 1936, p. 74, *Illust.*, ANON: Cat. of the Bache Colln., 1938, No. 6, *Illust.*, W. R. VALENTINER: *In* Art Quarterly, Autumn, 1938, pp. 275-288, *Illust.*

UCCELLO, PAOLO

FLORENTINE, 1397-1475

1 *Portrait of Michéle Olivieri.*

13 Inscribed: Michael Olivieri Mathei filius. ('Michéle Olivieri son of Matteo').

Panel: 19 x 13¼ inches.

LENT BY MR. AND MRS. JOHN D. ROCKEFELLER, JR., NEW YORK.

COLLECTION: Lord Duveen of Millbank.

BIBLIOGRAPHY: L. VENTURI: *In* L'Arte, Jan. 1930, pp. 63 *et seq*, *Illust.*, IDEM: Italian Paintings in America, 1933, No. 197, *Illust.*, P. HENDY: Catalogue of the Gardner Museum, Boston, 1931, p. 388; B. BERENSON: Italian Pictures, 1932, p. 172, (Ital. edn., 1936, p. 148); W. BOECK: *In* Zeitschrift f. Künstgeschichte, 1933, p. 272; G. PUDELKO: *In* Art Bulletin, Vol. XVI, 1934, p. 249, *Illust.*, M. SALMI: Uccello, Castagno, Dom. Veneziano, 1936, p. 123, No. 161, *Illust.*, J. LIPMAN: *In* Art Bulletin, Mar. 1936, p. 81, *Illust.*, M. VAUGHAN: *In* Parnassus, May 1939, p. 13, *Illust.*

UGOLINO DA SIENA

SIENESE, ACTIVE C. 1300-c.1339

Regarded as the closest spiritual relative of Duccio, and an intimate friend of Stefano Fiorentino, nephew and pupil of Giotto.

2 *The Last Supper.*

Originally, the first of seven panels of the Master's great Altarpiece at Santa Croce, Florence, painted after 1294 when Arnolfo laid the foundation of the church; four of the panels are now in the National Gallery, London, and two are in Berlin.

Panel: 13½ x 20¾ inches.

LENT BY MR. ROBERT LEHMAN, NEW YORK.

COLLECTIONS: At Santa Croce until the end of the XVIc.; afterwards in a local convent until the beginning of the XIXc.; William Young Ottley; Rev. John Fuller Russell; Lindo Myers.

EXHIBITIONS: Manchester, 1857; Royal Academy, London, 1878.
BIBLIOGRAPHY: G. VASARI: Le Vite (1568), Edn. G. Milanesi, Vol. I, 1878, pp. 454-455;
PADRE DELLA VALLE: Lettere Sanesi, 1782; G. F. WAAGEN: Art Treasures in Gt. Britain, Vol. II, 1854,
pp. 461-462; G. SCHARF: Art Treasures of Manchester, 1857, p. 14, No. 25; ANON: Old Masters,
Royal Acad., London, 1878, No. 177; CROWE AND CAVALCASELLE: Hist. of Painting in Italy, Vol.
III, 1908, pp. 24-25; P. G. KONODY: Jn Apollo, Sept. 1925, pp. 187-188; R. R. TATLOCK: Jn Apollo,
Feb. 1935, p. 65, Illust. in color, B. BERENSON: Pitture Italiane, 1936, p. 501.

UGOLINO-LORENZETTI

SIENESE, FOURTEENTH CENTURY

A tentative name for an artistic personality emerging from Ugolino da Siena
(d. 1339) and passing over to the Lorenzetti (Pietro, c. 1305-48, and Ambrogio,
c. 1319-48).

393 *Madonna of Humility.*

Painted during the artist's late period, and a fairly early example of the use of the
motive of the Madonna seated on the ground, which was later much favored by
various painters of Siena.

Panel: 11⅞ x 7¾ inches.

LENT BY MR. ROBERT LEHMAN, NEW YORK.

COLLECTIONS: Dr. Padelletti, Montalcino, Siena; Philip Lehman.

BIBLIOGRAPHY: F. M. PERKINS: Jn Art in Amer., Vol. VIII, 1920, p. 287, Illust., R. VAN
MARLE: Ital. Schools, Vol. II, 1924, pp. 121, 125; R. LEHMAN: The Philip Lehman Collection,
1928, No. 30, Illust., P. HENDY: Jn Burl. Mag., Vol. LV, 1930, p. 232; M. MEISS: Jn Art Bulletin,
Sept. 1931, p. 379; B. BERENSON: Ital. Pictures, 1932, p. 295, (Ital. Edn., 1936, p. 501).

VANNI, ANDREA

SIENESE, C. 1332-1414

Born in Siena. Perhaps a pupil of Lippo Memmi; worked with Bartolo di Fredi;
influenced strongly by Barna, Simone Martini and the Lorenzetti. He was also
noted as a diplomat, and was sent on missions to Rome, Naples and Avignon.
Paintings by him are rare, probably because of his activity in other fields.

394 *The Madonna and Child.*

Pl. 6   Panel: 28½ x 20½ inches.

LENT BY THE EDWIN D. LEVINSON COLLECTION, NEW YORK.

COLLECTION: Wildenstein Galleries, New York.

BIBLIOGRAPHY: W. R. VALENTINER: Italian Paintings of the XIV to XVI Century, Detroit
Inst., 1933, No. 47, Illust., IDEM: Jn Pantheon, August 1933, pp. 238-239, Illust.

VELAZQUEZ, DIEGO DE SILVA Y

SPANISH, 1599-1660

Born at Seville. He was the son of Juan Rodriguez de Silva and Geronima Velasquez, and studied under Herrara and Pacheco. In 1623 Philip IV commissioned him to paint his portrait, and appointed him *pintor de camera*. In 1627, he was made usher of the chamber. In 1629 he went for two years to Italy. He was in Italy again in 1648-50, this time with a commission from the king to purchase works of art. In 1652 he was appointed *Aposentador Mayor*, a high dignity. His works remained for the most part royal property, only to be seen on palace walls, and the transfer of the royal pictures to the Museo del Prado at Madrid was virtually a revelation of Velazquez. He was a master in portrait, genre, landscape, animal pictures and every branch of painting except the marine.

A Self-Portrait.

Painted about 1633-34.

Canvas: 27 x 21¾ inches.

LENT BY THE JULES S. BACHE COLLECTION, NEW YORK.

COLLECTIONS: David Bernhard Hausmann; King George of Hanover; Duke of Brunswick-Luneburg; Duke of Cumberland; Lord Duveen of Millbank.

EXHIBITIONS: Provincial Museum of Hanover, 1894-1926; Metropolitan Museum of Art, New York, 1928; Brooklyn Museum, 1935.

BIBLIOGRAPHY: ANON: Catalogue of the Hausmann Collection, Hanover, 1831, No. 257; ANON: Catalogue of the Museum of Hanover, 1905; A. L. MAYER: *In* Zeitschr. für bild. Kunst, Nov. 1917, *Illust.*; IDEM: *In* Art in America, Vol. XIV, 1926, pp. 101-102, *Illust.*; B. BURROUGHS: Catalogue of Spanish Paintings from El Greco to Goya, Met. Mus. of Art, New York, 1928, No. 63, *Illust.*; R. CORTISSOZ: *In* International Studio, June 1928, p. 39, *Illust.*; A. L. MAYER: Velazquez, a catalogue Raisonné, 1936, No. 170, Plate 71; ANON: Catalogue of the Bache Collection, New York, 1938, No. 43, *Illust.*

VELAZQUEZ, DIEGO DE SILVA Y

SPANISH, 1599-1660

The Infanta Maria Theresa.

Painted about 1653-54. Daughter of Philip IV and Isabella of Spain, born 1638. She married, in 1660, her cousin Louis XIV of France; her dowry, fixed at five thousand crowns, was never paid, resulting in the War for the possession of Flanders in 1667-68, as her heritage. She bore Louis XIV several children; when she died in 1683, he declared that her death was his first pain.

Canvas: 17½ x 15¾ inches.

LENT BY THE JULES S. BACHE COLLECTION, NEW YORK.

COLLECTIONS: Philippe Ledieu; Colonel H. Payne Bingham, New York; Lord Duveen of Millbank.

EXHIBITIONS: Palais du Corps Legislatifs, Paris, 1874; Ecole des Beaux-Arts, Paris, 1897; Metropolitan Museum of Art, New York, 1922-27.

BIBLIOGRAPHY: ANON: Notice Sommaire des Objets d'Art, Société Alsaciens et Lorraine, Lorrains, 1874, p. 86, No. 504; C. B. CURTIS: Velasquez and Murillo, a descriptive Catalogue, 1883, p. 249; ANON: Catalogue des Portraits de Femmes et d'Enfants, l'Ecole des B.-Arts, Paris,

194

1897, p. 56, No. 205; w. w. s. cook: *In* The Art Bulletin, Vol. VII, 1924-25, p. 61, *Illust.*, B. BUR-ROUGHS: Catalogue of Paintings, Met. Mus., N. Y., 1926, p. 364, No. V, 54-51, Gal. 29; A. L. MAYER: Velazquez, a Catalogue Raisonné, 1936, p. 123, No. 521, *Illust.*, ANON: Catalogue of the Bache Collection, 1938, No. 44, *Illust.*

VELAZQUEZ, DIEGO DE SILVA Y

SPANISH, 1599-1660

397 *Portrait of a Girl*, known also as 'The Sibyl'.

Pl. 88   A late work of the master. "Closely connected in style with the *Hilanderas*, 'The Tapestry Weavers' (Prado, 1173). One of the models for that picture seems to have been used here for a new version of the Sibyl motive" (*Mayer*).

Canvas: 25¼ x 22¾ inches.

LENT BY MRS. VAN WIE WILLYS, NEW YORK.

COLLECTIONS: Private collection, Milan; Julius Böhler; Reinhardt Galleries, New York; Edward D. Libbey, Toledo; John N. Willys, Toledo.

EXHIBITION: Metropolitan Museum of Art, New York, 1928.

BIBLIOGRAPHY: A. L. MAYER: *In* Zeitschrift für B.-Kunst, Vol. XXIV, p. 40, *Illust.*, M. T. JACKSON: *In* Art in America, Vol. IV, 1916, p. 119, *Illust.*, B. BURROUGHS: Catalogue of Spanish Paintings, Metropolitan Mus., N. Y., 1928, pp. XVIII, 10, No. 62, *Illust.*, A. L. MAYER: Velasquez, 1936, pp. 30, 135, No. 570, *Illust.*

VERMEER DER DELFT, JAN

DUTCH, 1632-1675

Born in Delft where he spent his whole life, where he died at the age of forty-three. He studied under Rembrandt's pupil, Carel Fabritius. When only twenty he married Catherina Bolnes, and by her had eight children. In 1653 he entered the Guild of St. Luke at Delft, was often on its committee, and once its president. Most of Vermeer's paintings represent scenes of recreation, sometimes with only a single figure. He painted, besides a few landscapes, portraits and religious paintings. Not more than about forty paintings are known by him. In contrast to Rembrandt and his school his colors are cool and his technique is smooth and enamel-like. His compositions bathed in clear day-light, and his color harmonies of blue and yellow, appeal especially to the modern taste. He is the leading master of the third generation of Dutch painting in the seventeenth century.

398 *The Milkmaid*.

Pl. 71   Signed: J. V. Meer (J and M intertwined). This picture is one of the masterpieces of the artist; belongs to his earlier period, painted about 1655-57.

Canvas: 18 x 16¼ inches.

LENT BY THE RIJKS-MUSEUM, AMSTERDAM.

COLLECTIONS: Jacob van Hoek; Pieter Leendert de Neufville; Jan Jacob de Bruyn; Hendrik

Muilman; P. H. Six van Vromade; Jan Six, from whom it was bought in 1907 for the Rijks-Museum.

EXHIBITIONS: Six Collections, Stedelijk Museum, Amsterdam, 1900; Tuileries, Paris, 1921; Royal Academy, London, 1929; Boymans Museum, Rotterdam, 1935.

BIBLIOGRAPHY: w. BURGER: Jn Gaz. des B.-A., Oct.-Dec., 1866, pp. 297 et seq; H. HAVARD: Jn Gaz. des B.-A., May 1883, p. 389, Jllust.; J. SIX: Catalogus der Schilderijen van P. H. Six van Vromade, Stedelijk Museum, Amsterdam, 1900; C. HOFSTEDE DE GROOT: Vermeer and Fabritius, Folio, 1906, Plate X; IDEM: Catalogue raisonné, Vol. I, 1907, p. 589, No. 17; G. VANZYPE: Vermeer de Delft, 1908, p. 60, (1821 Edn., p. 8), Jllust.; E. PLIETZSCH: Vermeer van Delft, 1911, p. 113, Jllust.; P. L. HALE: Jan Vermeer of Delft, 1913, p. 177, Jllust. (1937 Edn., p. 175, Jll. in Color); L. BENEDITE: Exposition Hollandais aux Tuileries, Paris, 1921, No. 105; E. V. LUCAS and SIR C. HOLMES: Vermeer, 1922, p. 16, Jllust.; w. HAUSENSTEIN: Vermeer van Delft, 1924, No. 13, Jllust.; S. LANE: Jan Vermeer portfolio, 1925, No. 6, Jllust. in color; SIR G. CLAUSEN: Vermeer (Charlton Lecture), 1925, pp. 63-81; H. SCHNEIDER and w. G. CONSTABLE: Exhn. of Dutch Art, Royal Acad., London, 1930, No. 302, Jllust.; w. R. VALENTINER: Jn Pantheon, Oct. 1932, pp. 305 et seq, A. ALEXANDRE: Jn L'Art et les Artistes, Feb. 1933, pp. 149-158, Jllust., D. HANNEMA: Vermeer Exhibition, Rotterdam, 1935, No. 81, Jllust.

VERMEER, JAN

DUTCH, 1632-1675

9   *A Lady Writing*.

72   A superb work by the artist painted during his mature period, about 1660-65.

Canvas: 18½ x 14½ inches.

LENT BY THE J. PIERPONT MORGAN COLLECTION, NEW YORK.

COLLECTIONS: Vermeer Sale (?), Feb. 16, 1696; Dr. Luchtmans (?), Rotterdam, 1816; Jan Kamermans (?), Rotterdam, 1825; H. Reydon, Amsterdam, 1827; Comte F. de Robiano, Brussels, 1837.

EXHIBITIONS: Metropolitan Museum of Art, New York, 1909; Museum Boymans, Rotterdam, 1935.

BIBLIOGRAPHY: G. HOET: Catalogue of Naamlyst van Schilderyen, Vol. I, 1772, p. 36, No. 35 (Vermeer Sale of 1696); w. BURGER: Jn Gaz. des B.-Arts, Dec. 1866, No. 40; H. HAVARD: Johannes Vermeer, 1888, No. 43; C. HOFSTEDE DE GROOT: Vermeer and Carel Fabritius, Folio, 1906, No. 43, Jllust., IDEM: Catalogue Raisonné, Vol. I, 1907, p. 598, No. 36; w. R. VALENTINER: Hudson-Fulton Exhn. of Old Dutch Masters, Met. Mus., N. Y., 1909, p. 457, No. 136, Jllust.; K. COX: Jn Burl. Mag., 1910, Jan., p. 246; Feb., 302, Jllust.; E. PLEITZSCH: Vermeer van Delft, 1911, p. 118, No. 36; P. L. HALE: Jan Vermeer, 1913, p. 240, Jllust.; G. VANZYPE: Jan Vermeer of Delft, 1921, No. 28, Jllust.; E. V. LUCAS: Vermeer of Delft, 1922, p. 35; w. HAUSENSTEIN: Vermeer van Delft, 1924, p. 27, Jllust.; w. R. VALENTINER: Jn Pantheon, Oct. 1933, pp. 305 et seq, D. HANNEMA: Catalogue of Vermeer Exhn., Museum Boymans, Rotterdam, 1935, No. 137, Jllust.

VERMEYEN, JAN CORNELIS

FLEMISH, 1500-1559

Born at Malines. Appointed court painter to Margaret of Austria in 1529, and in 1534 went to Spain and accompanied Charles V on the latter's expedition to Tunis, where the artist made drawings of several events of the campaign. These drawings served subsequently as the basis of cartoons for tapestries made in Brussels for the Emperor. In addition to military scenes Vermeyen also painted religious subjects, landscapes, and portraits.

400 *Portrait of a Man.*

Panel: 38 x 27 inches.

LENT ANONYMOUSLY.

COLLECTIONS: von Harnier, Burgomaster of Frankfort, XVIII c.; Staedel Museum, Frankfort, 1896; Kaiser Friedrich Museum, Berlin, 1927.

EXHIBITIONS: Dresden, 1871; Breslau, 1924; Worcester-Philadelphia, 1939.

BIBLIOGRAPHY: M. J. FRIEDLÄNDER: Altniederlandische Malerei, Vol. XII, 193, p. 162, No. 398, *Illust.*, H. MARCEAU, and others: The Worcester-Philadelphia Exhibition of Flemish Painting, 1939, p. 55, No. 97, *Illust.*

VIGÉE-LEBRUN, ELISABETH

FRENCH, 1755-1842

Born in Paris; daughter of Louis Vigée, a painter. Studied under Briard and Doyen. In 1776 she married J. B. P. Le Brun, art dealer, thereby involving herself in difficulties regarding her election into the Academy; in 1779 Marie-Antoinette removed the obstacle by patronizing her studio, which became filled with clients of court rank. She went to Italy at the outbreak of the Revolution and after a succession of triumphs through Europe she arrived in London in 1802, under the patronage of the royal family. In 1805 she returned to France, where she spent the rest of her life.

401 *Mme. Grant, afterwards Princesse de Talleyrand.*

Signed and dated, *L. E. Le Brun,* 1783. Madame Grant, *née* Worley, was born in India; her father was an officer at Pondicherry; she married at the age of fifteen a Mr. Grant, a Swiss resident at Calcutta, but never lived with him. She obtained a divorce, and went to Paris at the time of the Consulate. She married, in 1803, Charles-Maurice de Périgord-Talleyrand (1754-1838), Prince of Benevento, Bishop of Autun, French Minister and Ambassador. The wedding took place on account of pressure put upon the Prince by Napoleon Bonaparte after the former had been released by the Pope from the ban of excommunication (1791) and restored to secular life. In 1815 the Princess and her husband separated and she retired to her house in the Faubourg St. Germain, Paris, and died in 1835. In 1793, after the overthrow of the monarchy, Talleyrand escaped to the United States, and returned to France in 1795; on his rise again to power he strove, in 1803, to prevent the sale of Louisiana.

Canvas: oval: 35⅜ x 28⅜ inches.

LENT BY EDWARD S. HARKNESS, NEW YORK.

COLLECTIONS: Jacques Doucet, Paris; Knoedler Galleries, New York.
EXHIBITIONS: Salon du Louvre, Paris, 1783; Metropolitan Museum of Art, New York, 1935.
BIBLIOGRAPHY: ANON: Livret de Salon, Académie Royale, Paris, 1783, p. 34, No. 117; E. L. VIGÉE-LE BRUN: Souvenirs, Vol. I, 1835, p. 249 (Eng. Edn., Trans. by G. Shelley, n.d., p. 169); M. TOURNEAUX: Jn Gaz. des B.-Arts, June 1897, p. 456; LADY DILKE: French Painters of the XVIII c., 1899, p. 158, Jllust.; P. DE NOLHAC: Mme. Vigée Le Brun, 1908, p. 36, Jllust. in color; H. MAC-FALL: The French Genius, 1911, p. 257; M. NICOLLE: Catalogue des Tableaux, Collection Jacques Doucet, 1912, Vol. II, p. 83, No. 190, Jllust.; W. H. HELM: Vigée-Le Brun, 1914, p. 222.

VIVARINI, ALVISE

VENETIAN, ACTIVE 1440-1476

Pupil of his father, Antonio Vivarini, q.v., and his uncle Bartolommeo; influenced strongly by Antonello de Messina and Giovanni Bellini.

Portrait of a Man.

Panel: 12¾ x 17½ inches.

LENT BY MRS. WATSON B. DICKERMAN, NEW YORK.
EXHIBITION: Knoedler Galleries, New York, 1935.
BIBLIOGRAPHY: ANON: Catalogue of XV. Century Portraits, Knoedler Galleries, N. Y., 1935, No. 9, Jllust.; M. MORSELL: Jn Art News, April 20, 1935, p. 6, Jllust.

VIVARINI, ANTONIO

VENETIAN, ACTIVE 1440-1476

Follower of Jacobello del Fiore, Gentile da Fabriano, and perhaps of Masolino. From 1440 to 1450 he was a partner of Giovanni d'Alemanna, who matured under kindred and trans-Alpine influences and shared in work of these years. From 1450 for some time, he was similarly associated with his younger brother Bartolommeo, who was earlier his pupil. He was the father of Alvise Vivarini, q.v.

Madonna and Child.

A work of the artist's maturity, very much akin to the polyptych in the Bologna Gallery.

Panel: 33 x 16½ inches.

LENT BY MR. PERCY S. STRAUS, NEW YORK.
COLLECTIONS: Palazzo Rimbaldi, Bologna; Earl of Northesk, Ethie Castle, Arbroath, Scotland.
BIBLIOGRAPHY: F. M. PERKINS: Jn Art in America, Vol. XVI, 1927, p. 12, Jllust.; L. VENTURI: Ital. Paintings in Amer., 1933, No. 336, Jllust.; B. BERENSON: Ital. Pictures, 1932, p. 599 (Ital. Edn., 1936, p. 515).

VOS, CORNELIS DE

FLEMISH, 1584?-1651

Born at Hulst, and resided at Antwerp after 1596 where he apprenticed himself to David Remeeus. Between the years 1604 and 1608 he travelled and upon his return to Antwerp in 1608 was admitted to the St. Luke Guild. He was influenced by Rubens and Van Dyck. His fame rests upon his portraits, especially family groups.

404 *Portrait of Abraham Grapheus the Elder.*

Signed and dated: C. DE VOS. F. ANNO. 1620. The person represented was the *courrier* and general *factotum* of the Guild of St. Luke, Antwerp; the metal objects which figure in the picture were presents made to the Guild or prizes awarded in competitions by the members. In 1794 these objects were surrendered to the tax authorities in payment of dues, and afterwards thrown into the crucible and melted up. This picture was commandeered by the French revolutionaries in 1794, and taken to Paris; it was returned to Antwerp in 1815 by order of Louis XVIII. The painting is one of the masterpieces of the artist.

Canvas: 47¼ x 40⅛ inches.

LENT BY THE MUSÉE ROYAL DES BEAUX-ARTS, ANTWERP, BELGIUM.

BIBLIOGRAPHY: w. BURGER: Musée d'Anvers, 1862, p. 75; ANON: Catalogue des peintures, Musée d'Anvers, 1894, p. 136, No. 104; LAFENESTRE ET RICHTENBERGER: La Belgique, 1896, p. 246, No. 104, *Jllust.*, P. DE MONT: La Peinture Ancienne au Musée Royal des Beaux-Arts d'Anvers, 1914, p. 54, *Jllust.*

WARD, R.A., JAMES

ENGLISH, 1769-1859

Born in London. First apprenticed to the engraver, J. R. Smith, then to his own brother, William, famous for his mezzotints. After some engraving he took to painting, in the style and subjects of his brother-in-law, George Morland. Ward so early displayed artistic gifts that Morland was jealous of him, and would not allow him to see him at work. In 1794 he became painter and engraver to the Prince of Wales, later George IV. The commission from the Royal Agricultural Society "to paint a *high-bred* cow", in 1796, turned him to animal painting on which his fame rests. He lived and worked to a very old age, and died at Cheshunt, Hertfordshire.

405 *Coursing in Sussex.*

Signed and dated, J. W. 1809. The gentleman on horseback is a portrait of a Mr. Briggs, believed to be the father of one of Ward's pupils.

Canvas: 41 x 59 inches.

LENT BY THE ESTATE OF HENRY W. SAGE, NEW YORK.

COLLECTIONS: Henry Briggs, 1894; Agnew Galleries, London; Knoedler Galleries, New York.
ENGRAVED in 1907.
EXHIBITIONS: Royal Academy, London, 1809; Agnew's Galleries, London, 1906.
BIBLIOGRAPHY: ANON: Catalogue of the Royal Academy, London, 1809, No. 37; ANON: Agnew's Exhibition Catalogue, London, 1906, No. 24; C. R. GRUNDY: James Ward, R.A., 1909, p. 50, No. 674.

WATTEAU, JEAN ANTOINE
FRENCH SCHOOL, 1684-1721

Born at Valenciennes and first studied under Sérin. He afterwards went to Paris, and came in touch with Claude Gillot, with whom he worked until he went to live with Audran at the Luxembourg. In 1709 he was admitted to the Academy. He had a restless and discontented disposition, frequently aggravated by sickness. In 1719 he went to London to consult a specialist, but the journey weakened his strength, and he was obliged to stay for two years. He returned to Paris, where he died. Watteau is the earliest and greatest representative of the elegant French eighteenth century art which developed around the court in Paris. He was a master of spirited drawing, of charming color-schemes and beautifully balanced compositions.

The French Comedians.

The actors in this picture are the most famous of the time of Watteau. M. Couet, Librarian of the Comédie Française, believes that the two figures standing en face are Mdlle. Duclos and M. Beaubourg respectively; the actor mounting the stairs being Paul Poisson, in the familiar part of Crispin. Watteau evidently wished to express in this picture the different manifestations of Tragedy and Comedy in France during his time. On the left, Tragedy, with its three typical characters: L'Amant, l'Amante and la Confidente, and on the right, Comedy, represented by Matamore and Crispin.

Canvas: 22½ x 28¾ inches.

LENT BY THE JULES S. BACHE COLLECTION, NEW YORK.

COLLECTIONS: Jean de Jullienne; Frederick the Great; The Prussian Royal Family; William II, Emperor of Germany; Lord Duveen of Millbank.
ENGRAVED by Joanne Liotard, 1731.
EXHIBITIONS: Royal Academy, Berlin, 1883, and again in 1910, Exhibition of French Art; Three Reigns, London, 1933; Paris, 1934; Copenhagen, 1935; Paris, 1937.
BIBLIOGRAPHY: EDMOND DE GONCOURT: Catalogue raisonné de l'oeuvre d'Antoine Watteau, 1875, p. 64; R. DOHME: Jn Berlin Jahrbuch, Vol. IV, 1883, pp. 240-242; P. SEIDEL: Friedrich der Grosse, und die Französische Malerei seiner Zeit, N.D., p. 43, Jllust., IDEM: Französische Kunstwerke in Besitze Seiner Majestät des Deutschen Kaisers, 1900, pp. 147-148, No. 157, Jllust., J. L. VAUDOYER: Jn Les Arts, July 1910, Jllust., E. H. ZIMMERMANN: Watteau (Kl. der Kunst), 1912, p. 101, Jllust., E. DACIER ET A. VUAFLART: Jean de Jullienne et les graveurs de Watteau au XVIIIe siecle, Vol. III, 1922, p. 95, No. 205, Jllust. after Liotard; M. AGHION: Le Théâtre à Paris au

200

XVIIIe siecle, 1927, p. 109, *Illust.* after Liotard; L. DIMIER: Les Peintres Français du XVIIIe siècle, Vol. I, 1928, p. 34, No. 53; M. OSBORN: Die Kunst des Rokoko, 1929, p. 610, *Illust.*, p. 156; ANON: Catalogue of Paintings in the Bache Collection, New York, 1938, No. 55, *Illust.*

WATTEAU, JEAN ANTOINE

FRENCH, 1684-1721

407 *The Judgment of Paris.*

In Greek legend, Paris was the second son of Priam, King of Troy, and Hecuba, and noted for his gallantry and accomplishments. During the marriage of Peleus and Thetis, Eris threw a golden apple among the guests, inscribed 'To the fairest'. A dispute arose between Hera, Aphrodite, and Athene over the apple, and Zeus ordered the goddesses to submit to the judgment of Paris. To influence his decision Hera offered him power, Aphrodite the most beautiful of women, and Athene martial glory. He awarded the prize to Aphrodite, who in return helped him to abduct Helen of Sparta.

Panel: 18½ x 12⅛ inches.

LENT BY THE MUSÉE DU LOUVRE, PARIS.

COLLECTION: Louis La Caze, 1869.
BIBLIOGRAPHY: F. REISET: Catalogue La Caze, Musée imperial du Louvre, 1870, No. 265; V. JOSZ: Antoine Watteau, r.d., p. 177, *Illust.*; E. STALEY: Watteau and his school, 1902, p. 129; J. J. FOSTER: French Art from Watteau to Prud'hon, 1905, p. 94; P. G. KONODY and M. W. BROCKWELL: The Louvre, 1910, p. 263; E. HILDEBRANDT: Watteau (Kl. der Kunst), 1912, p. 107, *Illust.*, A. ORHAND: Les Musées expliqués, Le Louvre, 1912, pp. 35-36, No. 988; P. VITRY: Le Musée du Louvre, 1913, pp. 174-175, No. 988; G. BRIERE: Catalogue des Peintures, Ecole Francaise, Musée National du Louvre, 1924, p. 268, No. 988; C. MAUCLAIR: Antoine Watteau, n.d., p. 33, *Illust.*, L. DIMIER: Les Peintres français du XVII siècle, 1928, p. 30, No. 7; R. H. WILENSKI: French Painting, 1931, p. 99, *Illust.*

WATTEAU, JEAN ANTOINE

FRENCH, 1684-1721

408 *Figure of a Nude Woman.*

Panel: 6 x 6⅞ inches.

LENT BY MR. SAMUEL H. KRESS, NEW YORK.

COLLECTION: Prince Alexis Orloff.
EXHIBITION: Knoedler Galleries, New York, 1939.
BIBLIOGRAPHY: ANON: Classics of the Nude Exhibition, Knoedler Galleries, N. Y., 1939, No. 14.

WATTEAU, JEAN ANTOINE

FRENCH, 1684-1721

09 *The Musician.*

Canvas, oval: 9 x 7¼ inches.

LENT BY MRS. I. D. LEVY, NEW YORK.

COLLECTIONS: Camille Groult, Paris; Mrs. Benjamin Stern, New York; Wildenstein Galleries, New York.

EXHIBITION: California Palace of the Legion of Honor, San Francisco, 1934.

BIBLIOGRAPHY: w. HEIL: Exhbn. of French Painting, Cal. Palace of Legion of Honor, 1934, No. 59; ANON: *In* Connoisseur, April, 1934, p. 275, *Illust.*, ANON: *In* Art News, March 31, 1934, pp. 3-4, *Illust.*

WEYDEN, ROGER VAN DER

FLEMISH, C. 1400-1464

Roger van der Weyden, or de la Pasture, was born at Tournai, the son of a sculptor. In 1429 he married Isabella Goffaerts. He subsequently settled in Brussels. In 1436 he was appointed state-painter. In 1449-1450 he visited Rome and Ferrara. His influence was considerable in Germany as well as in the Netherlands, where Dirk Bouts and Memling were his direct followers. He was the leading painter in the Southern Netherlands during the first part of the XV c., whose art is closely connected with Burgundian sculpture and painting.

0 *Portrait of a Lady of High Rank.*

48 Painted about 1425-30. Inscribed PERSICA SIBYLLA Ia. Possibly a portrait of Isabella of Portugal, third wife of Philip the Good, Duke of Burgundy. At her wedding in 1430 the Order of the Golden Fleece was founded. Evidently one of a series of portraits of courtly ladies, each personating one of the ten legendary sibyls—the Persian sibyl being a favorite with Flemish women of the Middle Ages.

Panel: 18½ x 15 inches.

LENT BY MR. AND MRS. JOHN D. ROCKEFELLER, JR., NEW YORK.

COLLECTIONS: Charles J. Nieuwenhuys; Prince Licio Odescalchi; Baron Adolph de Rothschild; Baron Maurice de Rothschild.

EXHIBITIONS: Royal Academy, London, 1927; Kleinberger Galleries, New York, 1929; Cleveland Museum of Art, 1936.

BIBLIOGRAPHY: ANON: Tableaux anciens et moderns, 1883, Colln. C. J. Nieuwenhuys, No. 4, *Illust.*, s. REINACH: Répertoire, Vol. IV, 1910, p. 242, *Illust.*, M. J. FRIEDLÄNDER: Von Eyck bis Bruegel, 1916, p. 185; s. DE RICCI: *In* Burl. Mag., April 1922, p. 166, *Illust.*, w. BÜRGER: Roger v. d. Weyden, 1923, No. 50b, *Illust.*, M. J. FRIEDLÄNDER: Rogier v. d. Weyden, 1924, pp. 41, 95, No. 13, *Illust.*, w. STEIN: *In* Berlin Jahrb., Vol. XLVII, 1926, pp. 10 *et seq*; T. BORENIUS: Flemish Belgian Art, Royal Academy, London, 1927, No. 29, *Illust. in color*; P. JAMOT: *In* Gaz. des B.-Arts, Nov. 1928, p. 276, *Illust.*, M. J. FRIEDLÄNDER: Flemish Primitives, Kleinberger Loan Exhibition, 1929, pp. 15, 40, No. 7, *Illust.*, J. DESTREE: Roger de la Pasture-vd d. Weyden, 1930, p. 181, *Illust.*, E. G. TROCHE: Niederl. Malerei, 1935, p. 32, *Illust.*, H. S. FRANCIS: Great Lakes Expos. Catalogue, Cleveland Mus. of Art, 1936, p. 86, No. 212, *Illust.*

WEYDEN, ROGER VAN DER

FLEMISH, C. 1400-1464

411 *Madonna and Child.*

PI. 50 Late work of the artist, painted about 1455-60. Memling, in his Madonna in Lady Wernher's collection in London, was influenced by the present composition. Characteristic of the late style of the artist is the complicated turning of the body of the Child, and the intimate feeling between Mother and Child.

Panel: 12⅜ x 8⅞ inches.

LENT BY MR. PERCY S. STRAUS, NEW YORK.

COLLECTIONS: A Hungarian collection; Paul Cassirer; Paul Hess.

BIBLIOGRAPHY: M. J. FRIEDLÄNDER: Rogier van der Weyden, 1924, p. 102, No. 35, *Illust.*, J. DESTREE: Roger de la Pasture, Van der Weyden, Vol. I, 1930, p. 119, *Illust.*

YSENBRANDT, ADRIAEN

FLEMISH, C. 1510-1551

Adriaen Ysenbrandt, or Isenbrandt, was a native of Haarlem, and settled in Bruges before 1510, and became a pupil of Gerard David. His name appears in the registers of the Bruges Guild from 1510 to 1537, becoming governor in 1526. He acquired a reputation for skill in painting the nude and the human countenance, although no document has as yet been discovered connecting his name with any particular picture; careful execution and sweetness of expression are characteristics attributed to his works by old writers.

412 *The Holy Virgin Among the Virgins.*

Painted during the early period of the master, under the influence of Gerard David. The Saints are, right—Catherine, Barbara; left—Dorothea, Margaret, Agnes.

Panel: 31 x 23½ inches.

LENT FROM THE WILLIAM GOLDMAN COLLECTION, NEW YORK.

COLLECTION: Count Arco-Valley, Munich.

EXHIBITION: Bruges, 1902.

BIBLIOGRAPHY: W. H. J. WEALE: Exposition des Primitifs flamands, Bruges, 1902, pp. 61-62, No. 145; G. H. DE LOO: Catalogue critique, Exposition de Tableaux flamands, Bruges, 1902, p. 37, No. 145; M. J. FRIEDLÄNDER: Adriaen Ysenbrandt, 1933, p. 136, No. 184a.

YSENBRANDT, ADRIAEN

FLEMISH, C. 1510-1551

413 *Portrait of a Lady.*

Attributed to Ysenbrandt by Friedländer. Exhibited at Burlington Fine Arts Club, 1892, as Jacob Cornelisz.

Panel: 14¼ x 10¼ inches.

COLLECTIONS: Charles T. D. Crews, London; Alfred Spero, London; Arnold Seligmann, Rey Galleries, New York.

EXHIBITIONS: Burlington Fine Arts Club, London, 1892; New Gallery, London, 1899-1900; Dallas Museum of Fine Arts, Texas, 1936.

BIBLIOGRAPHY: SIR WALTER ARMSTRONG: Masters of the Early Netherlandish Schools, Burl. F. A. Club, 1892, p. 14, No. 26; H. F. HOWARD: Catalogue of the Texas Centennial Exhn., Dallas Museum, 1936; ANON: In Art Digest, June 1, 1936, p. 11.

CATALOGUE OF SCULPTURES

CATALOGUE OF SCULPTURES

BENEDETTO DA MAIANO
FLORENTINE, 1442-1497

Follower of Donatello and Antonio Rossellino; influenced by his elder brother, Giuliano da Maiano, an architect. He worked especially in marble and terracotta; he also carved in wood and possibly executed intarsia work. A considerable number of his original terracotta models are preserved. He was one of the great sculptors of Florence during the second half of the fifteenth century.

4 *The Madonna and Child.*

Terracotta polycrome group: 41½ inches high.

LENT BY MRS. LEON SCHINASI, NEW YORK.

COLLECTIONS: Judge Elbert H. Gary, New York; Lord Duveen of Millbank.
EXHIBITION: Detroit Institute of Arts, 1927.
BIBLIOGRAPHY: L. DUSSLER: Benedetto da Majano, ein Florentiner Bildhauer des späten Quattrocento, 1924, p. 82, No. 37, *Illust.*

FALCONET, ETIENNE MAURICE
FRENCH, 1716-1791

Born in Paris. First apprenticed to a cabinet-maker, but interested himself in modelling during his leisure hours, through which he came under the notice of the sculptor Lemoine, who made him his pupil. At the invitation of Catherine II he went in 1766 to St. Petersburg, where he executed a colossal statue of Peter the Great. In 1788 he became director of the French Academy. He is celebrated for his beautiful figurines in marble.

5 *The Dancer with Castanets.*

Made about 1765.

Marble statuette: 14 inches high.

LENT BY MRS. F. F. PRENTISS, CLEVELAND, OHIO.

COLLECTIONS: Marquis de Juigné, French Ambassador to Russia (1775); M. Goetz, Paris; M. Perdreau, Paris; M. de Jonghe (?); Edward M. Hodgkins.
EXHIBITION: Palais de la Présidence du Corps legislatif (Alsaciens-Lorrains), Paris, 1874.
BIBLIOGRAPHY: ANON: La Danseuse aux Castanettes, by Etienne-Maurice Falconet (Monograph) n.d.; L. REAU: Etienne-Maurice Falconet, Vol. II, 1922, p. 507.

FRENCH SCHOOL

ILE DE FRANCE, LATE THIRTEENTH CENTURY

416 *The Madonna and an Angel.*

Two Statues representing 'The Annunciation'.

Stone: The Madonna, 48½ inches high; The Angel, 46½ inches high.

LENT BY THE WILLIAM RANDOLPH HEARST COLLECTION, NEW YORK.

FRENCH SCHOOL

ILE DE FRANCE, FOURTEENTH CENTURY

417 *Madonna and Child.*

Boxwood statuette: 17 inches high.

LENT BY MRS. FELIX M. WARBURG, NEW YORK.

FRENCH SCHOOL

BURGUNDIAN, FIFTEENTH CENTURY

418 *Two Statues of Mourning Monks.*

Known as 'Les Pleureuses'. Formerly attributed to the Atelier of Jean de Cambrai.

Stone: Each 17 inches high.

LENT BY DR. PRESTON POPE SATTERWHITE, NEW YORK.

COLLECTION: French and Co., New York.

FRENCH SCHOOL OF TROYES

EARLY SIXTEENTH CENTURY

419 *St. Barbara, holding a Chalice with the Host.*

Marble Statuette: 47½ inches high.

LENT BY THE WILLIAM RANDOLPH HEARST COLLECTION, NEW YORK.

GRAECO-ROMAN

SECOND CENTURY, A.D. C. 170-200

420 *Sculptured Sarcophagus.*

The subject of the relief on the front represents three episodes in the story of

Achilles and Hector, taken from the *Iliad*, Book XXII. From left to right, Hector makes a stand against Achilles, who slays him; Achilles strips off Hector's armor, fastens his feet to a chariot, and drags him past the walls of Troy. Hecuba and Priam, beholding this insult to their son, utter lamentations, and Andromache also mourns her husband's fate. The back of the sarcophagus represents three 'Erotes attempting to subdue the lions' (*cf.* Euripides, Hipp. 1277). At the right end two youths, probably Zethos and Amphion, place a lyre on a pedestal. At the left end the scene appears closely related to that on the back panel, and is possibly a continuation of the battle with the lions, by the Erotes. The lid is of gabled form.

Marble: Height, 41½ ins.; length, 89 ins.; width, 39 ins.

LENT BY THE RHODE ISLAND MUSEUM OF ART, PROVIDENCE.

COLLECTION: Said to have been found in Rome; acquired by the Museum in 1920.

BIBLIOGRAPHY: J. D. YOUNG: *In* Art Bulletin, Vol. XIII, 1931, pp. 139-159, *Illust.*

HOUDON, JEAN ANTOINE
FRENCH, 1741-1828

Born at Versailles. He studied under Slootz and won the *Prix de Rome* as a sculptor at nineteen, and remained in Italy ten years. In 1771 he exhibited in the Salon, and soon after made his celebrated 'Flayed Man', copies of which are known in all drawing schools. About 1777-78 he executed the celebrated marble statue of 'Diana the Huntress' for Catherine II of Russia, of which the terra-cotta version is in the Frick Collection, New York, and the bronze in the Huntington Collection, San Marino, California. In 1781 he produced the statue of Voltaire. He visited America with Benjamin Franklin in 1785, and resided with Washington, whose statue he made. He returned to France in 1786, and during the Revolution was denounced by the Convention for having the statue of a saint in his studio. He was a member of the Institute from 1796. In 1809 he was decorated for his portraits of Napoleon I. He was one of the most famous representatives of the French School of Sculpture.

421 *Bust of Comte de Guibert.*

Signed and dated, *Houdon f.* 1791. A posthumous work, made to the order of Comtesse de Guibert. Count Jacques Antoine Hippolyte Guibert, born at Montauban in 1743, was a celebrated French military tactician, Field Marshal, and writer. He received the rank of Colonel in 1767. In 1770 he published *Essai général de tactique*. He went into semi-retirement in 1777. On the eve of the Revolution he was recalled to the War Office, but having been involved in the fall of Count St. Germain several years before, he did not receive the command he expected, and died, practically of disappointment, May 6, 1790.

Marble: 32½ inches high.

210

COLLECTIONS: Alexandrine-Louise Boutinon de Courcelles, Comtesse de Guibert (1765-1826); Lord Duveen of Millbank; Mrs. Alexander Hamilton Rice.
BIBLIOGRAPHY: H. BAUDOIN: Catalogue vente Houdon, 1828 (*Refers to Plaster cast of this bust*); G. GIACOMMETTI: Le Statuaire Jean-Antoine Houdon, Vol. III, 1919, pp. 187-189; IDEM: La Vie et l'Oeuvre de Houdon, Vol. II, 1929, pp. 63-64, *Illust.*

LEINBERGER, HANS

GERMAN, C. 1510-1630

The name of this sculptor was discovered only in recent years from the monogram used on some of his works—"H. L." He worked particularly at Landshut about 1510 to 1530, and in the neighboring towns, like Moosburg, where he created his most important altar; a tomb at Landshut is dated 1524. He may be regarded as the strongest exponent of the late Gothic sculpture in Bavaria, representing in figures of extraordinary movement, flowing garments and sharp silhouettes, the restlessness of the period before the Renaissance. His work reflects the temperamental and dramatic style in early Bavarian sculpture.

422 *St. John the Evangelist.*

Formed originally, with the companion figure of the 'Mourning Madonna' in the collection of Mrs. Ralph H. Booth, part of a Crucifixion Group, the central part of which, the Crucifixion itself, has been lost.

Wood Statuette: 53 inches high.

LENT BY THE DETROIT INSTITUTE OF ARTS.
COLLECTIONS: Purchased in Florence; Ralph H. Booth, Detroit.
BIBLIOGRAPHY: W. R. VALENTINER: *In* Detroit Institute Bulletin, March 1926, pp. 68-69, *Illust*

PISANO, NINO

PISAN, ACTIVE, C. 1350-1368

Nino Pisano, son of Andrea Pisano, after whose death (1348) he became chief architect of the Cathedral at Orvieto. Active in Pisa from c. 1350-1368. Received orders for goldsmith work from the city of Pisa in 1357 and 1358, and for the tomb of Bishop Scherlatti (d. 1362). He was the last great sculptor of the Pisan School of the XIV c. influenced strongly by French Gothic art.

423 *Madonna and Child.*

One of the finest of Italian Gothic sculptures, combining the grace of French Gothic art with the solidity and individuality of the Italian style. The statue is in composition, technique, colour and back view, closely related to the Madonna in the Cathedral of Orvieto, dated about 1347.

Marble: Height, 30 inches.

LENT BY THE DETROIT INSTITUTE OF ARTS.
COLLECTION: A private collection, Paris.
EXHIBITION: Detroit Institute of Arts, 1938.
BIBLIOGRAPHY: w. heil: Jn Detroit Inst. Bulletin, Mar. 1927, p. 61, Jllust., w. r. valen-
tiner: Jn Art in Amer., Vol. XV, 1927, pp. 195-216, Jllust., idem: Italian Sculpture, 1250-1500,
Detroit Inst., 1938, No. 16, Jllust.

RIEMENSCHNEIDER, HANS TILMANN
GERMAN, 1468-1531

Born in Osterode. Like his contemporaries, Veit Stoss and Michael Pacher, he was
partial to wood as a material, although he also worked considerably in marble and
stone. He settled early in Würzburg and became one of its notable citizens in 1495.
He was admitted into the Guild of Carvers in 1483, elected member of the lower
council in 1504, and of the upper council in 1518; became Burgomaster in 1521-24.
He was an adherent to the Reformation, lost his offices in 1525 and died in retirement.

24 The Madonna and Child.

Wood Statuette: 52½ inches high.

LENT BY MRS. FELIX M. WARBURG, NEW YORK.

ROBBIA, LUCA DELLA
FLORENTINE, 1399?-1482

Born in Florence in 1399 or 1400. Probably pupil of a goldsmith. Influenced by
Ghiberti. Worked (almost entirely in Florence) in marble, bronze and enamelled
terracotta. His great technical innovation, the glazed terracotta relief, for which he
became famous, must have been made about 1440. In his glazing he used mainly
white and blue, with touches of violet, green, and brown. Luca is, next to Ghiberti
and Donatello, the leading sculptor of Florence in the first half of the fifteenth century. His clear and simplified composition have a classic symmetry and balance;
with a great sense of beauty he combines a deep religious sentiment.

25 Madonna and Child ('The Genoese Madonna').

This enchanting composition belongs to Luca's middle period (c. 1455-60) and is in
style closely related to the Madonnas in the Pieve of Impruneta (near Florence).
It exists in four versions: 1. Benda Collection, Vienna, which comes from a street
tabernacle in Genoa (for this reason the present composition is called the Genoese
Madonna); 2. Berlin Museum; 3. Museo Nazionale, Florence; 4. The present one,
which Dr. Bode claimed to be the finest of the four. The glaze is of the purest quality and the original gilding of the hair and ornaments, missing in the other versions,
is well preserved.

Glazed Terra-Cotta: 40 x 29½ inches.

LENT BY THE DETROIT INSTITUTE OF ARTS.

COLLECTIONS: Dr. Eduard Simon.

EXHIBITIONS: Kaiser Friedrich Museums Verein, Berlin, 1914; Detroit Institute of Arts, 1938.

BIBLIOGRAPHY: w. von bode: In Münchener Jahrbuch, 1906, pp. 28-32, *Jllust.*, a. marquand: Della Robbias in America, 1912, No. 2, p. 8, *Jllust.*, idem: Luca della Robbia, 1914, p. 153, No. 39, *Jllust.*, e. f. bange: *Jn* Die Sammlung Dr. Eduard Simon, Berlin, 1929, p. 86, No. 33, *Jllust.*, j. walther: *Jn* Bulletin of the Detroit Inst. of Arts, Dec. 1929, pp. 33-35, *Jllust.*, w. r. valentiner: Italian Gothic and Early Renaissance Sculptures, Detroit Institute of Arts, 1938, No. 33.

ROBBIA, LUCA DELLA

FLORENTINE, 1399?-1482

426 *Madonna and Child* ('The Rovezzano Madonna').

The composition belongs to Luca's middle period (c. 1455-60), and represents the Madonna of Humility (the Virgin sitting on the ground). It is called the *Rovezzano Madonna*, as the same composition in a less successful example exists still in the original place, in S. Andrea at Rovezzano (near Florence). Other original versions, all differing in detail, are in the Widener Collection, Philadelphia; the Liechtenstein Gallery, Vienna; Q. Shaw Collection, Boston Museum (the latter with the addition of three angels).

Glazed Terra-Cotta: 17½ x 14¼ inches.

LENT BY MRS. LOUIS F. HYDE, GLENS FALLS, NEW YORK.

COLLECTIONS: Dr. Eduard Simon.

EXHIBITIONS: Kaiser Friedrich Museums Verein, Berlin, 1914; A. S. Drey Galleries, New York, 1935; Detroit Institute of Arts, 1938.

BIBLIOGRAPHY: a. marquand: Luca della Robbia, 1914, p. 264, No. 113, *Jllust.*, w. von bode: Illustrierter Katalog, Kaiser Friedrich Museums Verein, Berlin, 1914, No. 208; idem: Florentiner Bildhauer der Renaissance, 1921, p. 159; e. f. bange: *Jn* Die Sammlung Dr. Eduard Simon, Berlin, 1929, p. 88, No. 34, *Jllust.*, w. r. valentiner: Catalogue of Italian Gothic and Early Renaissance Sculptures, Detroit Institute of Arts, 1938, No. 32, *Jllust.*

SIENESE MASTER

FIRST HALF OF THE XV CENTURY

427 *Madonna and Child*, Statuette.

This delicate figure is in the style closely related to the reliefs on the façade of the Cathedral at Orvieto, which were executed by a Sienese master; probably by Lorenzo Maitani.

Polychrome wood: Height, 24 inches.

LENT ANONYMOUSLY.

SLUTER, CLAUS

ATELIER OF, BURGUNDIAN, EARLY XV CENTURY

Claus Sluter came from Holland and studied in Brussels. He worked mostly in Dijon, the capital of Burgundy, which at that time did not belong to France politically. Although belonging almost entirely to the fourteenth century (he died in 1406), he clearly reveals in his copious, naturally falling draperies, in his heavy bodies with their individualized features, the realistic tendencies of the coming new era, and erected a widespread influence upon the sculpture of nearly all the northern countries; Burgundy of his time had usurped artistic leadership, and its influence was felt throughout France for the greater part of the fifteenth century.

8 *St. John the Baptist.*

Stone statuette: 24 inches high.

LENT BY MRS. FELIX M. WARBURG, NEW YORK.

EXHIBITION: Detroit Institute of Arts, 1938.

BIBLIOGRAPHY: w. r. valentiner: French Gothic Art, XIII-XIV c., Detroit Inst., 1928, No. 40, Illust., r. kahn: In Art News, Nov. 24, 1928, p. 3, Illust.

STOSS, VEIT

GERMAN, 1447?-1533

Probably born in Nuremberg. In 1477 he went to Cracow, where he was active until 1496, during which time he carved the high altar for the Marienkirche; in 1492 he carved the tomb of Kasimir IV for the Cathedral, and soon afterwards the Stanislaus altar for the Marienkirche. He returned to Nuremberg in 1496, and became a citizen. Stoss was a craftsman of a wide range of capability—a sculptor, woodcarver, painter, and engraver, and one of the most prominent artists of Upper Germany during the XV and XVI centuries.

9 *Two Angels supporting Candelabra.*

Made about 1500. Attributed to Stoss by Dr. Feulner, Director of the Museum of Applied Art, Cologne.

Wood: Each 36 inches high.

LENT BY MR. F. GUTMANN, HAARLEM, HOLLAND.

COLLECTIONS: Benoit Oppenheim, Berlin; Arnold Seligmann and Rey Galleries.

TINO DI CAMAINO

SIENESE, 1280?-1337

Tino di Camaino, the leading Sienese sculptor of the Trecento, was born in Siena, and went to Pisa (1300-1315) where he became a pupil of Giovanni Pisano. He was again in Siena from 1315-1320; he was in Florence from 1321-1323, and

Naples from 1323-1337, where he died. His most important works were the tombs of Henry VII at Pisa, Riccardo Petroni at Siena, Antonio degli Orsi at Florence, and of the Anjou family at Naples.

430 *The Madonna and Child.*

This is the only known Madonna statue of small size of Tino's last Neapolitan period, and one of the most perfect examples of his art; it was possibly executed for Queen Sanzia, wife of Robert the Wise, for one of her private chapels.

Marble Statuette: Height 19¼ inches.

LENT BY THE DETROIT INSTITUTE OF ARTS.

COLLECTION: Count Alessandro Contini-Bonacossi, Rome.
EXHIBITION: Detroit Institute of Arts, 1938.
BIBLIOGRAPHY: w. r. valentiner: *In* Art in America, Vol. XI, 1922-23, p. 306; idem: *In* Detroit Inst. of Arts Bulletin, Dec. 1925, p. 26; idem: Tino di Camaino, A Sienese sculptor, 1935, p. 119, No. 58, *Illust.*, idem: Italian Gothic and Early Ren. Sculptures, Detroit Inst. of Arts, 1938, No. 11, *Illust.*

VERROCCHIO, ANDREA DEL

FLORENTINE, 1438-1488

Born in Florence. Pupil of the goldsmith Giuliano dei Verrocchio; influenced by Donatello and Luca della Robbia. The studio of Andrea was the most famous training ground in Florence for young artists; among his pupils were Leonardo da Vinci, Lorenzo di Credi, Domenico Ghirlandajo, Perugino, Fiorenzo di Lorenzo, and sculptors like Francesco di Simone and Agnolo di Polo. Next to Antonio Pollaiuolo, Verrocchio was the most important bronze sculptor in Florence in the second half of the fifteenth century.

431 *Profile of Alexander the Great.*

One of the few authentic marble reliefs by Verrocchio, of great importance for the knowledge of the later development of the artist (about 1475-80), during the period when Leonardo da Vinci worked in his studio. Very likely identical with the relief mentioned by Vasari representing Alexander the Great, which was ordered from Verrocchio by Lorenzo Medici.

Marble: 22½ x 14½ inches.

LENT BY MRS. HERBERT N. STRAUS, NEW YORK.

COLLECTION: Formerly in private possession in Hungary.
EXHIBITION: Detroit Institute of Arts, 1938.
BIBLIOGRAPHY: w. bode: Leonardostudien, 1921, p. 30; a. venturi: Storia dell'Arte Italiana, Vol. X, i, 1930, p. 30; e. möller: *In* Raccolta Vinciana, Vol. XIV, 1930-34, pp. 1-38; e. maclagan and m. h. longhurst: Catalogue of Ital. Sculpture, 1932, p. 60; l. planiscig: *In* Vienna Jahrbuch, 1933, pp. 89-96, *Illust.*, s. de ricci: *In* Gazette des B.-Arts, April 1934, p. 244, *Illust.*, w. r. valentiner: Italian Gothic and Early Ren. Sculptures, Detroit Inst., 1938, No. 54, *Illust.*, f. f. sherman: *In* Art in America, April 1939, p. 76, *Illust.*

VERROCCHIO, ANDREA DEL

FLORENTINE, 1435 - 1488

2 *The Madonna and Child.*

Another less well-preserved stucco after the same composition is in the possession of Mr. G. B. Diblee at Oxford. Both have been cast after a lost marble relief by Verrocchio or after the glazed terracotta relief in the sacristy of S. Croce, Florence (the latter probably modelled in the Verrocchio workshop and glazed in the della Robbia atelier). The Diblee stucco has been attributed to Leonardo da Vinci (A. Venturi, and T. A. Cook), but without convincing reasons (E. Maclagan). The original composition may be dated in the seventies of the fifteenth century.

Stucco relief: 33¼ x 23½ inches.

LENT ANONYMOUSLY.

COLLECTION: Formerly in private possession in Florence.

EXHIBITION: Detroit Institute of Arts, 1938.

BIBLIOGRAPHY: E. MACLAGAN: In Burl. Mag., August 1923, pp. 67-69, Diblee stucco Illust., T. A. COOK: Leonardo da Vinci, Sculptor, 1923; A. VENTURI: Storia dell'Arte Ital., Vol. X, 1, 1930, p. 3; W. R. VALENTINER: In Art Bulletin, March 1930, pp. 43 et seq, No. 37, Illust., M. MORSELL: In Art News, Nov. 30, 1935, pp. 3-4, Illust., W. R. VALENTINER: Italian Gothic and Early Renaisance. Sculptures, Detroit Inst., 1938, No. 55, Illust.

129. TADDEO GADDI   MADONNA

Mr. Maitland F. Griggs

72. B. DADDI   CRUCIFIXION

Estate of Dan Fellows Platt

PLATE 1

240. Maso di Banco   St. Anthony
Mr. Maitland F. Griggs

237. S. Martini   St. John
Mr. Maitland F. Griggs

PLATE 2

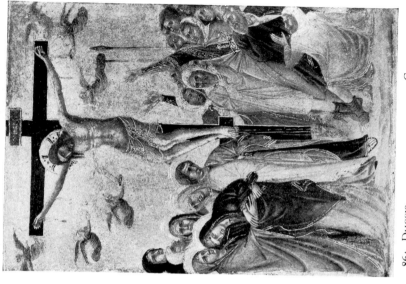

86. Duccio   Mr. Robert Lehman   Madonna and Angels

86a. Duccio   Mr. Robert Lehman   Crucifixion

Plate 3

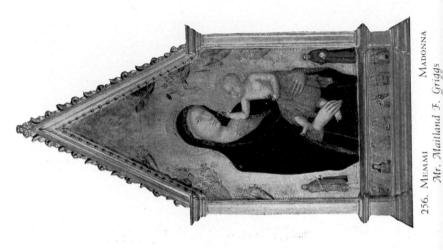

256. MEMMI   MADONNA
Mr. Maitland F. Griggs

220. A. LORENZETTI   CRUCIFIXION

PLATE 4

221. P. Lorenzetti

Mrs. Felix M. Warburg

Madonna, SS. Catherine and Magdalen

Plate 5

265. NEROCCIO   MADONNA AND CHILD
Dr. G. H. A. Clowes

394. VANNI   MADONNA AND CHILD
The Edwin D. Levinson Collection

PLATE 6

347. SASSETTA ST. ANTHONY DISTRIBUTES HIS MONEY
The Estate of Dan Fellows Platt

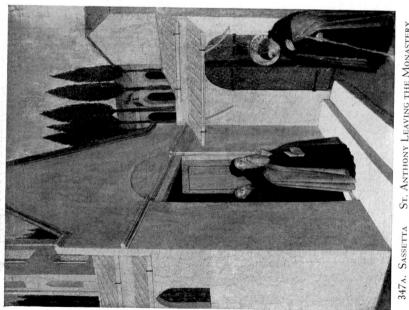

347A. SASSETTA ST. ANTHONY LEAVING THE MONASTERY

PLATE 7

148. GIOVANNI DI PAOLO   MIRACLE OF ST. CLARE

Mr. Percy S. Straus

149. GIOVANNI DI PAOLO   DEATH OF LUCRETIA

Lent Anonymously

PLATE 8

249. MATTEO DI GIOVANNI   THE VISITATION
The John G. Johnson Collection

248. MATTEO DI GIOVANNI   MARRIAGE OF THE VIRGIN
The John G. Johnson Collection

PLATE 9

1. ALBERTI   THE MADONNA AND ST. MAURILIUS
                              Mrs. Arthur Lehman

PLATE 10

3. FRA ANGELICO

THE ANNUNCIATION

Mr. and Mrs. Edsel B. Ford

PLATE 11

4. FRA ANGELICO   TEMPTATION OF ST. ANTHONY

Mr. Percy S. Straus

20. BOTTICELLI   THE ANNUNCIATION

Mr. Robert Lehman

PLATE 12

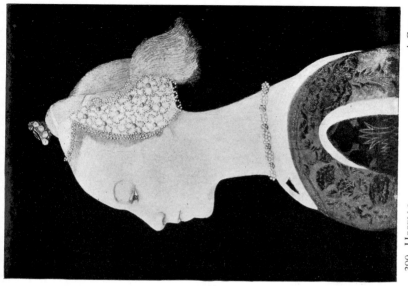

390. Uccello   A Girl

The Bache Collection

391. Uccello   Michèle Olivieri

Mr. and Mrs. J. D. Rockefeller, Jr.

Plate 13

157. Gozzoli   Madonna and Child

Mr. and Mrs. Edsel B. Ford

Plate 14

219. FRA FILIPPO LIPPI   MADONNA AND CHILD

Mrs. Leon Schinasi

PLATE 15

280. PESELLINO   MADONNA AND CHILD

Mr. and Mrs. Harold J. Pratt

PLATE 16

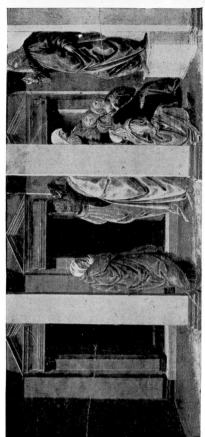

19. BOTTICELLI LEGEND OF THE MAGDALEN
The John G. Johnson Collection

19. BOTTICELLI LEGEND OF THE MAGDALEN
The John G. Johnson Collection

PLATE 17

21. BOTTICELLI   MADONNA AND CHILD

Lent Anonymously

PLATE 18

141. GHIRLANDAJO   FRANCESCO SASSETTI AND SON

The Bache Collection

PLATE 19

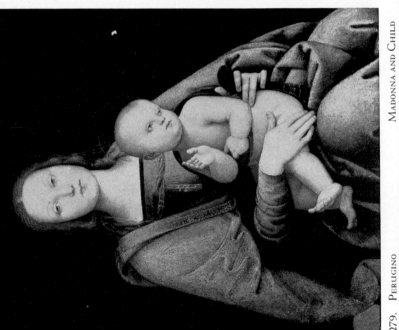

279. PERUGINO   MADONNA AND CHILD   64. CRIVELLI   MADONNA AND CHILD

PLATE 20

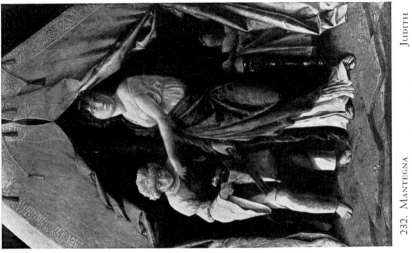

232. MANTEGNA JUDITH

Mr. Joseph E. Widener

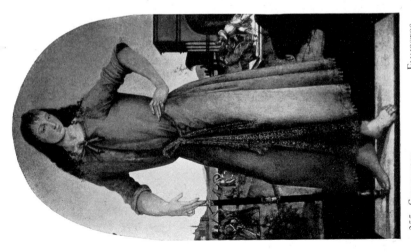

355. SIGNORELLI EUNOSTOS

Lent Anonymously

PLATE 21

403. Antonio Vivarini   Madonna and Child

Mr. Percy S. Straus

Plate 22

9. GIOVANNI BELLINI   MADONNA AND CHILD
Mrs. Van Wie Willys

8. GIOVANNI BELLINI   MADONNA AND CHILD
The Ralph H. Booth Collection

PLATE 23

214. Leonardo da Vinci   Madonna and Child

Mr. and Mrs. Robert W. Reford

Plate 24

289. De' Predis   Gian Galeazzo Sforza
Lent Anonymously

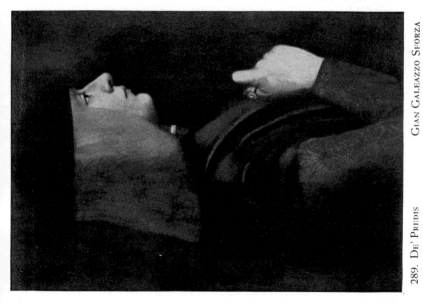

14. Boltraffio   A Youth
The Ralph H. Booth Collection

Plate 25

2. ANDREA DEL SARTO   LUCREZIA DEL FEDI

Mr. William H. Thompson

294. RAPHAEL   GIULIANO DE' MEDICI

The Bache Collection

PLATE 26

284. Piero di Cosimo   The Visitation

Mr. Samuel H. Kress

Plate 27

287. Pontormo   The Halberdier
Mr. Chauncey D. Stillman

7. Bartolommeo Veneto   Duke of Milan
Mr. Samuel H. Kress

Plate 28

144. GIORGIONE
THE HOLY FAMILY
Lent Anonymously

PLATE 29

381. TITIAN   VENETIAN NOBLEMAN   382. TITIAN   GIORGIO CORNARO

The Bache Collection   Lent Anonymously

PLATE 30

388. TITIAN JUDITH

The Detroit Institute of Arts

PLATE 31

82. Dosso Dossi   CIRCE

Lent Anonymously

83. Dosso Dossi   THE ARGONAUTS

Mr. Samuel H. Kress

PLATE 32

Mr. Arthur Sachs

377. TINTORETTO

PLATE 33

PLATE 34

274. PAOLO VERONESE   REBECCA AT THE WELL

Lent Anonymously

271. PAOLO VERONESE   MYSTIC MARRIAGE OF S. CATHERINE

Mr. and Mrs. Charles V. Hickox

PLATE 35

370. TIEPOLO   THE MADONNA AND CHILD
                        The Detroit Institute of Arts

PLATE 36

45. CLAUDE LORRAIN   CLASSICAL LANDSCAPE

Mr. and Mrs. Ernest Kanzler

168. GUARDI   MESTRE, NEAR VENICE

Mr. and Mrs. E. B. Whitcomb

PLATE 37

167. Guardi   Campo San Zanipolo

Mr. Samuel H. Kress

Plate 38

PLATE 39

140. GERMAN SCHOOL.   TWO LOVERS
Cleveland Museum of Art

138. COLOGNE SCHOOL.   BISHOP ANNO AND ST. GEORGE
The William Goldman Collection

PLATE 40

59. CRANACH   NYMPH OF THE SPRING

Mr. and Mrs. C. Y. Palitz

56. CRANACH   FEAST OF HEROD

The Wadsworth Atheneum

PLATE 41

90. DÜRER   *The Paul J. Sachs Collection*   DRAWING

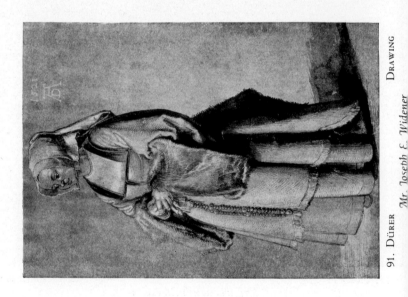

91. DÜRER   *Mr. Joseph E. Widener*   DRAWING

PLATE 42

ANNO·1532· ÆTATIS SVÆ·29

197. HOLBEIN HERMANN WEDIGH

Mr. Edward S. Harkness

PLATE 43

199. HOLBEIN   A HANSEATIC MERCHANT

Dr. A. Hamilton Rice

198. HOLBEIN   DIRK BERCK

The Bache Collection

PLATE 44

DA MAN·1517·ZALT·SEBASTI^{AN}
WAS ICH·48·IAR ALT·ANNDOR FEER

231. Hans Maler zu Schwaz   Seb. Andorffer
Mrs. Charles R. Henschel

364. Strigel   A Lady
The Ralph H. Booth Collection

PLATE 45

113. Van Eyck   The "Ince Hall" Madonna

National Gallery, Melbourne

Plate 46

114. Van Eyck and P. Christus   St. Jerome
                  Detroit Institute of Arts

Plate 47

243. MASTER OF FLÉMALLE   A NOBLEWOMAN
Dumbarton Oaks Collection

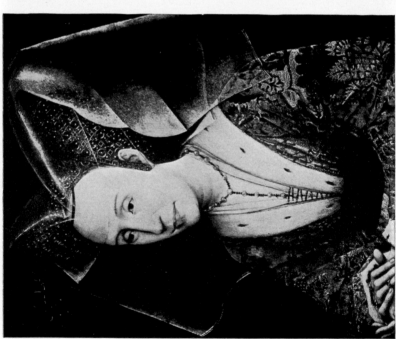

410. VAN DER WEYDEN   ISABELLA OF PORTUGAL
The and Mrs. John D. Rockefeller, Jr.

PLATE 48

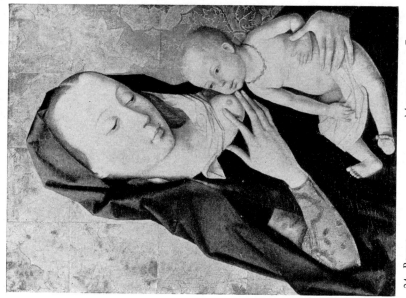

PLATE 49

25. BOUTS   THE BURNING BUSH

The John G. Johnson Collection

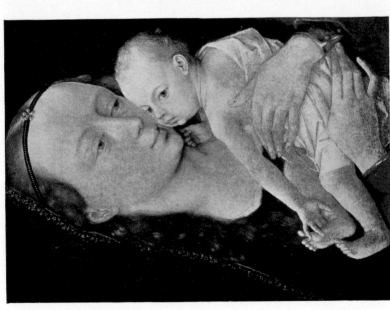

411. VAN DER WEYDEN   MADONNA AND CHILD

Mr. Percy S. Straus

PLATE 50

29. BRUGES MASTER OF 1473

MADONNA AND CHILD WITH DONORS

Mr. and Mrs. Solomon R. Guggenheim

PLATE 51

254. MEMLING · MAN WITH A PINK
The J. Pierpont Morgan Collection

255. MEMLING · A YOUTH
Mrs Van Wie Willys

PLATE 52

77. GERARD DAVID   MADONNA AND CHILD
The Bache Collection

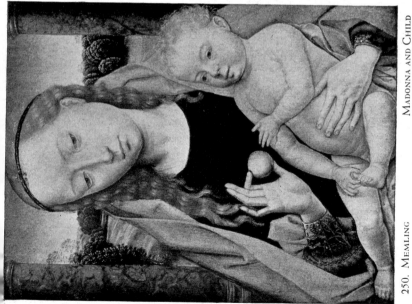

250. MEMLING   MADONNA AND CHILD
The Bache Collection

PLATE 53

18. BOSCH
BETRAYAL OF
CHRIST
*Fine Arts Gallery,
San Diego*

16. BOSCH   MOCKING OF CHRIST

The John G. Johnson Collection

PLATE 54

241. Master Michiel. Young Man in Red Cap
Mrs. Lillian Henkel Haass

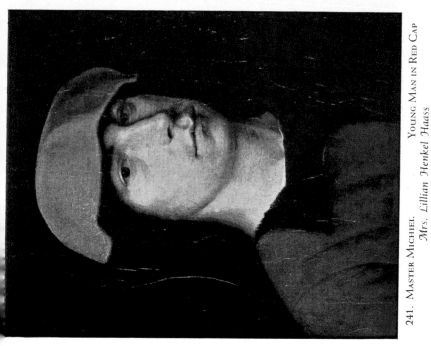

268. Van Orley. A Young Man
The Detroit Institute of Arts

Plate 55

226. MABUSE   COUNT OF NASSAU

Mr. and Mrs. Charles V. Hickox

PLATE 56

47. Van Cleeve   Portrait of a Man

The William Goldman Collection

Plate 57

224. LUCAS VAN LEYDEN ST. PAUL
Lent Anonymously

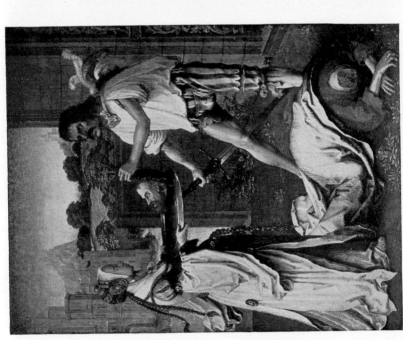

223. LUCAS VAN LEYDEN BEHEADING OF ST. JOHN
The John G. Johnson Collection

PLATE 58

PLATE 59

321. RUBENS   PHILIPPE RUBENS
The Detroit Institute of Arts

320. RUBENS   DUKE OF MANTUA
Mrs. Henry Goldman

PLATE 60

324. Rubens   Meleager and Atalanta

Mrs. Henry Goldman

Plate 61

110. VAN DYCK   COUNT OF NASSAU-SIEGEN
                              The Cincinnati Art Museum

PLATE 62

103. VAN DYCK

MADONNA AND ST. CATHERINE

Mr. and Mrs. W. R. Timken

100. VAN DYCK

MADONNA AND CHILD

Mrs. Henry Goldman

PLATE 63

107. Van Dyck   Viscount Grandison

Mrs. Harry Payne Whitney

Plate 64

181. HALS   AN OFFICER

Mrs. Henry Goldman

185. HALS   A YOUTH

Mr. and Mrs. Edsel B. Ford

PLATE 65

180. HALS   THE BEER-KEG

Mr. Henry Reichbold

177. HALS   TWO FISHER BOYS

Lent Anonymously

PLATE 66

183. HALS   HENDRIK SWALMIUS

Mr. H. E. ten Cate

188. HALS   SELF-PORTRAIT

Dr. G. H. A. Clowes

PLATE 67

302. Rembrandt   Christ and the Woman of Samaria

Mrs. William R. Timken

Plate 68

309. REMBRANDT   PRAYING PILGRIM

Mrs. Van Wie Willys

308. REMBRANDT   CHRIST WITH FOLDED ARMS

Mrs. Louis F. Hyde

PLATE 69

115. Fabritius   Portrait of Rembrandt
          Dr. C. J. K. Van Aalst

305. Rembrandt   Titus
Mrs. Charles S. Payson

Plate 70

398. Vermeer   The Milk Maid

Rijksmuseum, Amsterdam

Plate 71

399. VERMEER   A LADY WRITING

The J. Pierpont Morgan Collection

PLATE 72

PLATE 73

367. TERBORCH   CURIOSITY   358. STEEN   THE DOCTOR'S VISIT

The Bache Collection   *The John G. Johnson Collection*

PLATE 74

202. De Hooch   The Linen Cupboard

Rijksmuseum, Amsterdam

Plate 75

341. Van Ruisdael
Windmill
Mr. and Mrs. Edgar B. Whitcomb

191. Hobbema

The Watermill

Mr. H. E. ten Cate

Plate 76

67. Cuyp   Fishing Boats on the Maas

The John G. Johnson Collection

66. Cuyp   The Flight into Egypt

Mr. and Mrs. Charles J. Fisher

PLATE 77

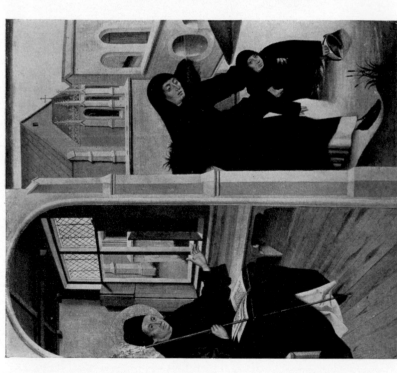

127. Sch. of Provence St. Robertus
Mrs. Lillian H. Haass

236a. Marmion St. Benedict

Lent Anonymously

Plate 78

288. POUSSIN

Musée du Louvre, Paris

FUNERAL OF PHOCION

PLATE 79

211. A. LE NAIN   THE VILLAGE PIPER

The Detroit Institute of Arts

212. L. LE NAIN   PEASANTS IN A LANDSCAPE

The Wadsworth Atheneum

PLATE 80

The Jules Bache Collection

406. WATTEAU

PLATE 81

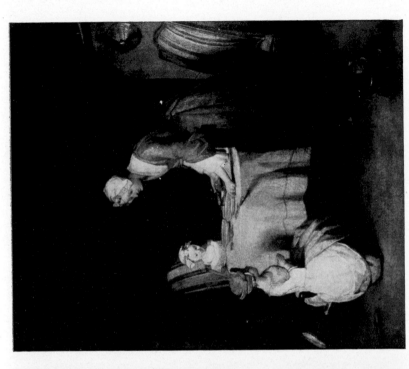

37. CHARDIN   GRACE BEFORE MEALS
Musée du Louvre, Paris

38. CHARDIN   SOAP BUBBLES
Mrs. John W. Simpson

PLATE 82

120. FRAGONARD   L'INVOCATION DE L'AMOUR

Mr. John Mortimer Schiff

118. FRAGONARD   L'ETUDE

Musée du Louvre, Paris

PLATE 83

80. J. L. DAVID   MME. DE RICHEMOND
Miss Julia Berwind

79. J. L. DAVID   MARQUISE D'ORVILLIERS
Musée du Louvre, Paris

PLATE 84

159. EL GRECO
THE DEPOSITION
Comtesse de la Beraudière

PLATE 85

163. EL GRECO   CHRIST IN THE HOUSE OF SIMON
The Hon. Oscar B. Cintas

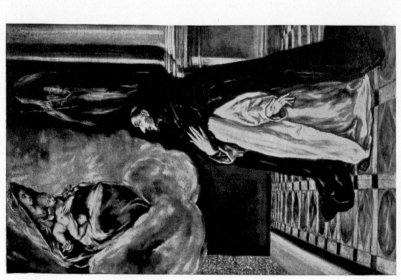

162. EL GRECO   ST. DOMINIC
Rochester Art Gallery

PLATE 86

brece en Santidad Gil Del nouena   Vifitale fray Gil el pecho lleno   Teme entrar, y al fin Entra al clauftro pleno, Q admira do ʒ el Pontifice aquedado,
rgorio por hablarle. Vu apere∫a.   De ʒeruor ʒ obediencia Afectuo∫a.   Siendo ʃu amor, y ʃe tan milagro∫a,   E n exta∫is Diuino arrebatado.

260. MURILLO   ST. GILES BEFORE POPE GREGORY IX

Lent Anonymously

PLATE 87

397. Velazquez

Mrs. Van Wie Willys

The Sibyl

Plate 88

259. MURILLO   GIRL LIFTING VEIL

Mr. Jakob Goldschmidt

396. VELAZQUEZ   INFANTA MARIA THERESA

The Bache Collection

PLATE 89

154. GOYA   ST. PETER REPENTANT
         The Phillips Memorial Gallery, Washington

151. GOYA   GOSSIPING WOMEN
                  Wadsworth Atheneum, Hartford

PLATE 90

150. Goya   Don Manuel Orsoris

The Bache Collection

PLATE 91

195. HOGARTH

THE GRAHAM CHILDRE

The National Gallery, London

PLATE 92

315. Reynolds   Countess of Harrington and Children

Mrs. William H. Moore

Plate 93

134. Gainsborough

The Market Cart

Mr. and Mrs. Charles J. Fisher

Plate 94

208. LAWRENCE   COUNTESS OF DERBY

Mr. Edward S. Harkness

PLATE 95

291. RAEBURN   THE DRUMMOND CHILDREN

Mr. Edward S. Harkness

PLATE 96

14224